1 Building Structure and Services

London: Her Majesty's Stationery Office

ISBN 0 11 671358 5
Printed in the U.K. for HMSO
Dd 736563 C15 12/83 37009

An Introduction

In 1931, Notes from the Information Bureau of the Building Research Station written in the form of questions and answers, were published as a supplement to the RIBA Journal. The Notes continued until 1938 when they took the form of discussions on selected topics. These ran until the autumn of 1939. The next comparable series was published between 1944 and 1946 under the title *Repair of damaged buildings* but the pre-war monthly series was resumed in December 1948 under the new title of BRS Digests (now BRE). This series has continued, every month, to the present day.

Topics range across the field of design, construction and repair of buildings; subjects are introduced when a need becomes apparent (indicated, for example, by enquiries received by the Building Research Advisory Service) or when BRE has gained sufficient information on a topic for it to be included in the series. A digest's function is to extract from the mass of research data on how the work was done and the conclusions reached, the matter directly applicable to the work of the designer and builder. The series is under constant review for technical relevance; new versions of old digests are introduced from time to time when there is a significant amount of additional or revised information available. About 150 titles are still current.

Concise and precise, current digests form a manual of up-to-date authoritative building know-how. They are presented here in convenient bound form in four volumes. Some digests appear in more than one volume (for example, *Sound insulation of party floors* can be found in Vol 1 under *Floors and flooring* and in Vol 3 under *Sound, acoustic requirements*. This has been done to keep each volume self-contained.

Digests have become recognised as defining the state of the art in the area of building they cover; they may be purchased by annual subscription or singly from any supplier of HMSO publications or direct from:

HMSO
Publications Centre
PO Box 276
London SW8 5DY

The volumes include the following digests

Volume 1	Volume 2	Volume 3	Volume 4
8	35	41	12
18	45	42	53
33	46	54	69
54	69	108	73
63	83	110	75
64	89	119	89
67	98	127	98
73	109	128	109
77	121	129	139
79	137	140	144
81	157	141	152
83	160	143	166
95	161	145	167
104	164	158	172
140	165	162	176
144	175	163	179
145	177	173	198
151	178	180	200
161	194	185	202
170	196	186	211
180	197	187	212
205	198	190	217
206	199	191	223
208	200	192	234
210	201	193	238
217	209	203	247
218	211	204	251
220	212	208	259
221	213	214	263
223	216	215	264
230	224	218	265
232	237	220	268
235	239	225	271
236	244	226	
240	250	227	
241	258	228	
242	261	229	
245	263	230	
246	264	232	
248	265	233	
249	269	236	
252	273	245	
253		252	
254		256	
256		260	
257		266	
262		270	
266		272	
270			
272			
274			
275			
276			

Contents, this volume

Contents, other volumes

Fill

Part 1: Classification and load carrying characteristics

This digest is published in two parts: this first part discusses different causes of settlement of fill and gives guidance on the likely magnitude of settlement in different situations. A simple classification of fill materials is suggested. Part 2 of the digest – No 275 – describes techniques of improving the load carrying characteristics of fills, and foundation design. The digests give guidance only of a general nature and it must be recognised that the services of a civil or a structural engineer will usually be needed. A third digest – No 276 – discusses hardcore.

Definitions

Fill and *made ground* are tems used interchangeably to denote a large quantity of material which has been deposited over a considerable area to raise the level of a site. The limited amount of material put down (usually within a single building unit) as infill within foundations or beneath an oversite concrete slab is termed *hardcore* – see Digest 276.
Granular soils are coarse-grained soils of high permeability, eg sand, gravel.
Cohesive soils are fine-grained soils of low permeability, eg clay, silt.
Bearing capacity of the ground is the pressure that the foundation soil can safely carry.
Loose, unsaturated fills may undergo a reduction in volume upon wetting; this is called *collapse compression* or *settlement*.

It is important at the outset to make a distinction between sites where filling has yet to take place and control over the type of fill material and method of placement can be exercised (*new fill*) and sites where filling, which may have been uncontrolled, has already taken place (*existing fill*).

Serious problems can arise where construction takes place on filled sites; CP 2004; 1972 warns that 'All made ground should be treated as suspect, because of the likelihood of extreme variability'. Nevertheless, the scarcity of good building land and the desirability of redeveloping inner city areas and reclaiming industrial waste lands have increasingly led to the development of filled sites. Two aspects may need to be assessed: whether the fill is able to support the building without excessive settlement and whether the fill contains materials which are hazardous to health or harmful to the environment or building. Only the first of these aspects is considered in this digest.

New fill

When new fill is to be placed, careful selection of the material and controlled placement can ensure that the fill forms an adequate foundation material. Some general information about placing fills is given in the Code of practice for earthworks (BS 6031:1981). Care

should be taken in selecting fill materials that are not contaminated in such a way as to present an environmental or health hazard.

Fill should be placed in layers and compacted. A useful guide to layer thickness and typical compaction requirements for different types of soil is given in the Department of Transport's *Specification for Road and Bridge Works*[1] but it should not be assumed that all the types of soil listed in this specification are necessarily suitable for use as a fill which is to support buildings. Wherever possible granular soils should be used, such as rockfill, gravels and coarse sands, since these materials drain readily and consolidate quickly. The smaller the predominant particle size, the longer may be the time required for consolidation to take place under the self-weight of the fill. Where a fill containing a large proportion of fine grained cohesive material (eg clay) is used, the moisture content should be controlled close to optimum (BS 1377:1975, Test 12) and filling during wet weather should be avoided whenever possible. When various types of material are used as fill they should be disposed in horizontal layers across the site. If there is only a limited amount of good granular material, it will be best to use the granular material in layers interspersed between layers of poorer cohesive fill; this will assist drainage and thus reduce the time required for the cohesive materials to consolidate.

If the natural ground on which the fill rests is soft and compressible (eg layers of peat or soft clay) the surface of the fill may settle appreciably and unevenly as a result of the weight of the fill consolidating the soft layers below. This settlement will, of course, be additional to that resulting from the compression of the fill itself. Penetration of the fill into a soft sub-soil can occur but can be avoided by leaving vegetation intact or by placing a layer of fabric over the sub-soil. Wherever possible surface water should be removed from ponds or depressions before filling begins. The consolidation of a cohesive fill on relatively impermeable ground will be much slower than if the underlying ground were free draining; an adequate drainage layer at the bottom of the fill will speed up the process. On sloping sites, the stability of the existing slope should be checked and the possibility of a landslip being caused by the filling should be considered.

Where conditions are such that filling cannot be carried out in a controlled manner, with placement in thin layers and with adequate compaction, eg if an old dock has to be backfilled by end tipping through water, a situation arises similar to that where construction has to take place on an existing filled site where uncontrolled filling has taken place and similar procedures should be followed.

Existing fill

A wide variety of human activity has left many sites covered by fill materials. Large areas of ground have been covered with deposits of industrial, mining and domestic wastes, sometimes to a considerable depth. Opencast mining generally leaves large depths of uncompacted fills. In urban areas there are frequently relatively shallow fills where marshy land has been reclaimed by raising the ground level and where new buildings have been errected on the rubble of older demolished buildings. Disused docks, claypits and quarries have often been infilled with little control or supervision.

Fill may have been placed above original ground level or as a backfill for an excavation; it may have been compacted or loosely tipped, placed dry or tipped through water. The fill may consist of local soil or imported soil or waste materials.

Especially hazardous types of fill are those that contain large voids or materials liable to decay or decompose. For example, refuse dumps may contain metal containers which rust and leave large voids, and plastics containers which compress but do not decompose. Decomposition of organic matter can cause large settlements and may result in potentially hazardous concentrations of methane or carbon dioxide while the presence of some chemicals may present potential hazards to human health or inhibit plant growth. A large proportion of combustible material present in a fill into which air can penetrate involves a risk of underground fires of which there may be no sign on the surface. The support afforded where such fires have taken place is likely to be varied and sites of this nature are best avoided for building purposes. If they must be used the foundations should be piled down to natural ground with provision made in their design for possible down-drag by the fill as a consequence of natural consolidation.

The development of these various types of filled sites can, therefore, present a wide variety of problems which can include chemical attack on foundations, the risk of explosion or fire within a waste deposit, hazards to health or the environment from contaminated land. This digest is concerned only with the evaluation of the load carrying characteristics of the filled ground.

Settlement of fill

Where fill has been placed above natural ground level, the stability of the slopes at the edge of the fill and the stability of the underlying natural ground may need to be examined. If structures are built on piles which pass through the fill into underlying natural strata, negative skin friction caused by the fill settling under its own weight around the piles may be a major consideration in the foundation design.

Compression due to self-weight Where the fill is deep, self-weight will often be the principal cause of long-term settlement. With granular fills and poorly compacted unsaturated fills of all types, the major compression occurs almost immediately a load is applied (primary compression) and as a consequence most of the settlement due to self-weight occurs as the fill is placed. Nevertheless, some significant further movements do occur under conditions of constant effective stress and moisture content and can be termed 'creep' settlement. With many fills it is found that the rate of creep compression decreases fairly rapidly with time and shows an approximately linear relationship when plotted against the logarithm of the time that has elapsed since the deposit was formed: see Fig 1. A parameter, α, can be defind as the percentage vertical compression of the fill that occurs during a $\log_{10}$ cycle of time, say between one year and ten years after the fill was placed. Some typical values of α are given in Table 1. The magnitude of α can depend on the depth of the deposit as well as on the nature and degree of compaction of the fill. It should be remembered that the

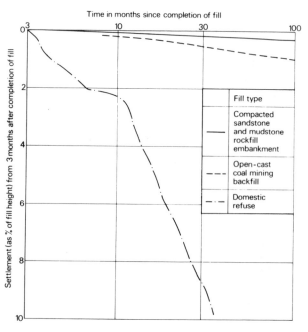

Fig 1 Settlement rates of different types of fill (vertical compression plotted against $\log_{10}$ time)

use of an α parameter to predict the settlement of a fill can only be valid where conditions in the fill remain unaltered. An increase in stress due to a change in the applied load or a change in moisture content could cause much greater movements.

Compression due to the loads of buildings constructed on the fill The fill will be compressed by the loads applied to it by the building constructed on it. The compressibility of fill materials shows wide variation depending on the nature of the fill, its particle size distribution, compactness, the existing stress level, the stress increment and the moisture content. Assuming that the stress increments due to the building loads do not bring the fill to condition close to a bearing capacity failure, the settlements can be most simply calculated using a compressibility parameter related to one-dimensional compression. If in one-dimensional compression an increment of vertical stress $\triangle\sigma_v$ produced an increase in vertical strain $\triangle\varepsilon_v$, the constrained modulus is defined as $\frac{\triangle\sigma_v}{\triangle\varepsilon_v}$ Some typical values of constrained modulus for a number of different fill types are quoted in Table 2. They are applicable to small increments in vertical stress, say $\triangle\sigma_v = 100$ kN/m^2, where the initial vertical stress was about 30 kN/m^2. The modulus of the uncompacted stiff clay fill quoted in Table 2 might seem relatively high compared with the other types of poorly compacted fill. It should be recognised that such a fill may be particularly prone to collapse settlement on wetting.

Table 1 Creep compression rate parameter

Fill type	Typical values of α per cent
Well compacted sandstone rockfill	0.2
Uncompacted opencast mining backfill	0.5–1
Domestic refuse	2–10

With the exception of fine-graded saturated fills, most of the compression of a fill due to the imposition of a structural load will occur almost immediately the load is applied (as in the case of settlement due to self-weight). However, movements that occur during construction of a building are likely to be much less of a problem than those which occur after completion of the structure. Consequently the long-term creep component of the settlement is of particular significance. Values of the parameter α have been listed in Table 1 for creep

Table 2 Compressibility of fills

Fill type	Compressibility	Typical value of constrained modulus kN/m^2
Dense well-graded sand and gravel	very low	40 000
Dense well-graded sandstone rockfill	low	15 000
Loose well-graded sand and gravel	medium	4 000
Old urban fill	medium	4 000
Uncompacted stiff clay fill above water table	medium	4 000
Loose well-graded sandstone rockfill	high	2 000
Poorly compacted colliery spoil	high	2 000
Old domestic refuse	high	1 000–2 000
Recent domestic refuse	very high	

settlement under self-weight in various fills. In general these values are equally applicable to settlement produced by the loads applied to the building, although zero time now corresponds to the application of the load, not the placement of the fill. However, the α values for domestic refuse are different under the two different loading situations. The values of α for domestic refuse quoted in Table 1 are largely governed by the decay and decomposition of organic matter. Clearly, when old domestic refuse is loaded by the weight of a building the creep rate due to the increase in stress will not be principally a function of this organic decay; a value of one per cent would probably be more appropriate.

Compression due to inundation Loose unsaturated fill materials are usually liable to collapse settlement on inundation with water. If inundation occurs after construction on the fill, a serious settlement problem may arise. It is believed that this is often a major factor where settlement problems have occurred in building development on restored opencast mining sites. Problems can also be caused by water penetrating into the fill from the surface through deep trench excavations for drains associated with the building development. The percentage compressions caused by the inundation of two opencast mining backfills are given in Table 3.

Table 3 Field measurements of collapse compression in uncompacted opencast mining backfills[2][3]

Fill type	Maximum measured compression per cent
Sandstone and mudstone fragments	2
Stiff clay lumps	6

Consolidation. Most of the discussion of the causes of settlement has been related principally to loose uncompacted fills formed by tipping. When fine material is placed under water, as in a tailings lagoon, a soft cohesive fill is formed which is characterised by low permeability. Consequently, settlement due both to self-weight and to applied loads is controlled by a consolidation process in which excess porewater pressures dissipate slowly as water is squeezed out of the voids of the fill. Both the magnitude and the rate of settlement can be estimated from one-dimensional consolidation theory using values of compressibility measured in laboratory tests and field measurements of permeability. This type of fill could be susceptible to liquefaction. A firm crust may form over the surface of the lagoon deposit but this may be thin and overlie very soft material.

Differential settlement. It must be remembered that it is differential settlement rather than total settlement that leads to distortion and damage to buildings. However, the poorer types of fill, which contain organic matter or were placed without control, are not only liable to large total settlements but, because of their variability, are also liable to large differential movements. Differential movements should also be expected at the edges of filled areas and in places where the depth of fill changes rapidly.

Classification of fills

Fill materials show quite as wide a range of engineering properties as do natural soils and rocks. Properly engineered fills, such as those typically used in highway embankment construction, may have excellent engineering properties. Recently-placed domestic refuse would be at the opposite end of the range. It is important, therefore, to classify the fill material initially into this wide range of behaviour. The investigation that has been carried out should make it possible to classify the fill in a qualitative manner under the headings listed in Table 4.

From a classification of this type important deductions can be made about the causes and possible magnitude of settlement of the fill subsequent to construction on it. Whenever possible, field loading tests should be carried out to enable quantitative estimates of settlement to be made with more confidence. It is useful then to distinguish between three different situations on the basis of these estimated movements.

(a) Small movements (vertical compression of the fill subsequent to construction everywhere smaller than 0.5 per cent). This is likely to be the case with a granular fill that has been placed under controlled conditions and received adequate compaction. Such a material forms a good foundation material and there should be few problems.

(b) Significant movements (vertical compression of the fill subsequent to building estimated to have a maximum value between 0.5 per cent and two per cent). A granular fill that has been placed without compaction, but has little organic matter within it and which has already been in place for some years, could come into this category. In this situation special attention needs to be given to foundation design. If piling is considered to be uneconomic, the basic alternatives are either to use some ground treatment technique to improve the load carrying properties of the fill and effectively produce a category (a) situation or to design the foundations to withstand the differential movements caused by settlement of the fill. Reinforced concrete rafts with edge beams have often been used for two-storey dwellings. It should be realised, however, that where large differential settlements can occur very substantial foundations may be needed and building units should be kept small and simple in plan.

(c) Very large movements (vertical compression of the fill subsequent to building estimated to exceed two per cent). This might include both recently placed domestic refuse with high organic content liable to decay and decomposition, and fine-grained materials which have been transported in suspension and discharged into lagoons forming highly compressible cohesive fill which might be liable to liquefaction. Problems due to settlement will be very severe and ground improvement techniques may be quite limited in what they can achieve. With recently placed domestic refuse methane emission may be a major problem and such sites may be prohibitively expensive to develop.

Table 4 Qualitative classification of fills

Classification	Description
Nature of material	Chemical composition. Organic content. Combustibility. Homogeneity.
Particle size distribution	Coarse soils, less than 35 per cent finer than 0.06 mm; fine soils, more than 35 per cent finer than 0.06 mm (BS 5930:1981)
Degree of compaction	Largely a function of method of placement: thin layers and heavy compaction – high relative density; high lifts and no compaction – low relative density; end tipped into water – particularly loose condition; Fine grained material transported in suspension and left to settle out produces fill with high moisture content and low undrained shear strength, eg silted up abandoned dock or tailings lagoon.
Depth	Boundary of filled area. Changes in depth.
Age	Time that has elapsed since placement; If a fill contains domestic refuse, the age of the tipped material may be particularly significant, since the content of domestic refuse has changed considerably over the years. During the last 40 years the ash content has decreased whilst the paper and rag content has increased. The proportion of metal and glass in domestic refuse has also increased during this period. It may be that more recent refuse will be a much poorer foundation material than older refuse not only because there has been a shorter time for settlement to occur, but also because the content of material which can corrode or decompose is greater.
Water table	Does one exist within the fill? Do fluctuations in level occur? After opencast mining a water table may slowly re-establish itself in the fill.

References and further reading

(1) Specification for road and bridge works: Department of Transport, HMSO, London 1976.
(2) CHARLES, J A; NAISMITH, W A; and BURFORD, D. Settlement of backfill at Horsley restored opencast coal mining site. BRE Current Paper CP 46/77
(3) CHARLES, J A; EARLE, E W; and BURFORD, D. Treatment and subsequent performance of cohesive fill left by opencast ironstone mining at Snatchill experimental housing site, Corby. BRE Current Paper CP 79/78.

British Standards Institution
BS 1377:1975 Methods of test for soil for civil engineering purposes.
BS 5930:1981 Code of practice for site investigations.
BS 6031:1981 Code of practice for earthworks.
CP 2004:1972 Foundations.

Other BRE Digests
63 Soils and foundations: Part 1
64 Soils and foundations: Part 2
67 Soils and foundations: Part 3
95 Choosing a type of pile
251 Assessment of damage in low-rise buildings.
275 Fill: Part 2 Site investigation, ground improvement and foundation design
276 Hardcore.

Fill
Part 2: Site investigation, ground improvement and foundation design

Construction on existing filled areas should be preceded by careful investigation of the site. The investigation of a filled site to assess its suitability for development generally should include two complementary approaches: an historical review and an investigation of the ground. This digest discusses these two approaches and describes how ground improvement techniques can be used to increase the density of a fill. The design of foundations on filled ground is discussed.

Site investigation

Reference should be made to the *Code of practice for site investigations* (BS 5930:1981); this document is complemented by the CIRIA/PSA *Site investigation manual*.

Historical review

A thorough review should be undertaken of all the available historical evidence relating to previous use of the site and in particular the placement of the fill[1]. This could include oral testimony, business records, old plans and maps and air photographs. Sources of information might include previous occupiers of the site, local authorities and libraries.

Ground investigation

A ground investigation should be carried out and should generally include trial pits and boreholes. Trial pits are particularly useful as they enable large quantities of the fill to be inspected and reveal the nature of the fill, its composition and variability. The boundary of the filled area should be established. Standpipe piezometers can be sealed into boreholes; they provide valuable information about water levels within the fill. With a variable fill material, small-scale laboratory tests may be of limited use whereas a programme of field tests may yield much important information. The most useful field test on deep fills may be simply to monitor the current rate of settlement of the fill by precise levelling. The levelling stations need not be elaborate. Stable datums (bench marks) need to be established away from the filled ground. It is useful to have a number of levelling stations close to each other so that differential movements likely to occur over the area of a building can be estimated. Simple field loading tests can prove very useful in some situations since they provide direct evidence of performance. Lightweight structures with strip footings stress the ground significantly only to depths of 1.5 to 2.5 metres. Consequently, it is relatively simple to test-load the fill to reproduce the actual stress level and distribution with depth, using for example a weighted rubbish skip: see Fig 1 and ref (2). Tests should be carried out over a period of at least one month. Settlements can be plotted against the logarithm of time and extrapolated to predict the likely settlement during the life of the structure: Fig 2. However such tests reflect the properties of the fill near ground surface only and this limitation should be kept in mind. In some fills (for example, fine grained soils without any large, hard fragments), the resistance to penetration of a probing tool or cone can give an indication of the condition of the fill at depth. In-situ measurements of the density and moisture content of the fill may be useful.

Non-geotechnical considerations

It is clearly desirable, both in the review of historical evidence and in the ground investigation, that the geotechnical aspects should be integrated with the investigation of any other relevant factors which could, in some situations, include chemical attack, gas generation, combustibility and toxicity. On some sites, special precautions may be necessary to ensure the safety of personnel carrying out the investigation. The British Standards Institution is currently preparing a code of practice for identification and investigation of contaminated sites. This will complement the existing Code of practice for site investigations (BS 5930: 1981).

Health or environmental hazards

Care should be taken in selecting fill materials that they are not contaminated in such a way as to present an environmental or health hazard.

Hazards may arise for construction workers through direct contact; subsequent occupants of the site through direct contact or indirectly through uptake by food crops; or to a wider population through wind blown dust, or pollution of water courses or aquifers. Attention should also be paid to the possibility of the material being toxic to plant growth (phytotoxicity). Radioactivity may also be a problem. Materials from a

Fig 1 Simple field loading test using a skip filled with sand

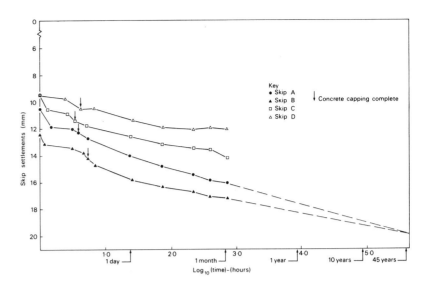

Fig 2 Settlement records of field loading tests on 2 m depth of urban fill (settlement plotted against $\log_{10}$ time)

wide range of industrial sites may be contaminated but the chemicals of most concern are the metals cadmium, chromium, mercury, lead, zinc, copper, beryllium, arsenic and nickel, or their salts, together with fluorides, cyanides, phenols, oils and certain other organic chemicals. The fill materials in which such chemicals are most likely to occur are the non-ferrous slags, tailings from metalliferous mining, and soil subjected to repeated deposition of sewage sludge. Some materials, while not acutally containing aggressive chemicals, may contain substances which in the long term produce offensive odours which can permeate into the building.

Similar problems can occur with existing fill on old industrial sites (particular care should be taken on the sites of former gasworks, oil storage areas and former scrap yards) or when building over domestic refuse dumps. There is also the possibility of natural ground being contaminated if liquid industrial waste has been tipped over many years. If it is necessary to build on such sites precautions which may have to be taken include the provision of an appropriate type and depth of cover (which may for example include an impermeable barrier) and choice of the type of foundation. For example, piles may provide pathways for the escape of gases or the penetration of pollutants into underlying aquifers.

Some contaminated fill materials may be subject to control under the Control of Pollution Act 1974. No firm guide lines exist at present on the level of contamination that can be accepted in fill materials where development is to take place; advice can be obtained on this and on protective measures from the Central Directorate on Environmental Pollution of the Department of the Environment.

Chemical attack

Care must be taken to ensure that the fill material does not contain chemicals at concentrations which could damage any concrete[3], the mortar in brickwork or metals with which they may come in contact. Classification of the levels of soluble sulphates in natural soils and precautions to be taken to protect concrete against attack are described in Digest 250. For a fill material, the limits pertaining to a 2:1 water extract are suitable to classify the material and to indicate the concrete quality required. An extract giving less than 1g/l of SO_3 may be taken as falling in Class 1 of Table 1 of Digest 250. If any sulphate is found or suspected, a water barrier such as a polythene sheet should be placed beneath any concrete floor slab as an additional precaution.

Precautions for the protection of brickwork mortar against sulphates are given in Digest 89. Any sulphate attack is dependent on the presence of water and much can be done to minimise the risk by provision of adequate drainage. Information on the effect of contaminants in water on the durability of metals is given in Digest 98. Fill materials taken from industrial sites may be appreciably acid and could therefore cause damage to concrete and corrosion of metals.

Certain organic chemicals can attack plastics used, for example in pipes, protective coatings to metals, or O-rings in other pipe systems. Some chemicals may penetrate plastics pipes without damaging them but tainting the water within them.

Ground improvement techniques

Where buildings are to be founded on fill and the site investigation has indicated that significant differential movement may occur over the area of a building, improving the load carrying characteristics of the fill by the use of a ground improvement technique prior to development of the site may be an attractive solution. Many treatment techniques are essentially methods of increasing the density of the fill. (Other methods such as grouting may be applicable in some situations.) This should make the fill less compressible and consequently movements in the fill subsequent to construction will be reduced.

Refilling in thin layers with compaction When the main problem with a fill is its loose uncompacted state, the simplest solution may be to excavate the fill and replace it in thin layers with adequte compaction. The Department of Transport *Specification for Road and Bridge Works* (1976)[4] gives a good guide to the layer thickness and type of compaction suitable for different fill types. With this approach it is possible to examine all the fill and remove any unsuitable material. Where the fill is very deep it may not be practicable or economic to excavate the full depth of fill and a decision has to be made about the minimum depth of fill that should be recompacted. This is unlikely to be less than 4 to 5 metres and in some situations it could be much deeper.

Pre-loading with a surcharge Another ground treatment method involving bulk earth moving is the pre-loading of filled ground with a surcharge of fill. As a loose fill will compress immediately under loads, the surcharge need not be left in position for an extended period. On a large site a small area can be surcharged and the surcharge fill moved around the site in a continuous earth-moving operation. Usually the

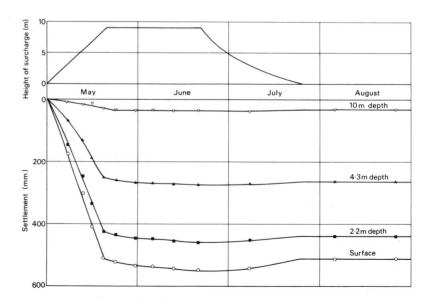

Fig 3 Settlement at different depths within a 24 m deep openscast ironstone mining backfill due to pre-loading with 9 m high surcharge.

surcharge will be designed so that it applies stresses to the filled ground greater than any that will be applied during the subsequent development of the site, but other factors may also need to be considered. Figure 3 shows that the settlement produced by a 9 m high surcharge of fill on an uncompacted 24 m deep cohesive fill left by opencast ironstone mining occured mainly as the surcharge was being placed with little subsequent movement[5]. The compression of this cohesive fill can be attributed to reduction of air voids between the lumps in the fill rather than the squeezing out of water from the clay lumps themselves. This is an important consideration as surcharging is sometimes rejected as a ground treatment method because it is thought to be a lengthy process and this is not the case for uncompacted fill materials.

Dynamic consolidation In this ground treatment technique, deep compaction of soils is attempted by repeated impacts of a heavy weight on to the ground surface. In the UK, the Menard system of dynamic consolidation has typically involved dropping a 15 tonne weight from heights of up to 20 metres. Usually, the initial tamping consists of repeated impacts at a number of points on a fairly widely spaced grid and the final stage consists of a general tamping of the whole area with a reduced fall of the weight. Figure 4 shows the enforced settlement measured at different depths within two fills treated by dynamic consolidation. It is seen that the ground treatment technique (in which there was an average energy input of 2800 kN.m/m^2 at site A and 2600 kN.m/m^2 at site B) effectively compacted the fills to depths of about 5 metres.

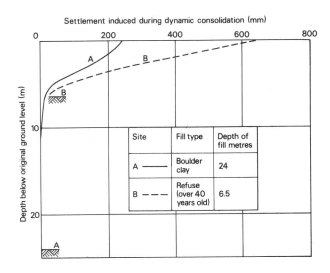

Fig 4 Dynamic consolidation of two fills — effectiveness at depth

Vibro methods This type of process was developed in Germany in the early 1930's to compact loose, naturally occurring sands. The basic tool is a cylindrical poker which contains in its bottom section an eccentric weight. Rotation of the weight results in vibrations in a horizontal plane being transmitted to the soil and the poker penetrates the ground. This leads to the densification of a granular soil. In a cohesive soil little compaction is achieved, but the long cylindrical hole produced by the poker vibrator can be backfilled with granular fill. The cohesive soil is consequently stiffened by stone columns. The method can be used in fill materials in a similar way to its use in natural soils.

When considering which ground improvement techniques to use in a particular situation both the effectiveness of the different methods and their costs need to be examined. Where the fill is deep, the costs of all the methods will be closely related to the depth to which the fill is to be treated. Refilling and pre-loading with a surcharge are purely earth-moving operations and it should be a simple matter to estimate costs. The mobilisation costs of dynamic consolidation are high as a very large crane is needed to lift the weight to the required height. This means that this method is more likely to be economic on large sites; vibro methods may be cheaper on smaller sites. In built-up areas dynamic consolidation may be prohibited by the possibility of damage being caused to existing buildings by vibrations produced by impacts: 30 metres has been suggested as a safe distance from the point of impact to a building. Vibro methods can be used much closer to existing structures.

Any ground improvement technique that is considered for use on a filled site should be examined both for its effects in compacting the fill and in the light of other problems existing at the site. There are situations in which a particular improvement method may be beneficial in more than one respect. For example, compaction of a colliery spoil will not only improve its load carrying characteristics but may also eliminate the risk of combustion within the fill. In other situations, the various problems associated with a waste fill may lead to conflicting requirements, eg where gases are being generated during organic decay, solutions involving either piling or vibro techniques could lead to the formation of paths through which methane gas could enter into the foundations of a building. Also, although excavation and refilling with adequate compaction might improve the load carrying properties of a waste fill, it could also lead to mixing and reactivation of chemicals with associated ground movements.

Foundation design

Where a relatively large structure is to be built on shallow fill, poor load carrying characteristics of the fill can be circumvented by using piled foundations and a suspended floor. The piles should be designed for negative skin friction caused by settlement of the fill. The skin friction can be calculated in terms of effective stress:

$$\tau = (\gamma.d - \gamma_w h_w). K \tan \delta$$

where τ = shaft friction at depth d below ground level,

γ = bulk density of fill,

γ_w = density of water,

h_w = depth below water table

K = earth pressure coefficient = $(1 - \sin \phi')$ approximately

ϕ' = angle of shearing resistance

δ = angle of friction of the fill on the pile surface.

For a loose granular fill a value of $K \tan \delta = 0.2$ might be appropriate. In some situations it may be considered that negative skin friction is taking too large a proportion of the allowable bearing capacity of the pile. The use of a slip coating can greatly reduce its effect. Special attention is needed in the design of services which span from the filled ground into buildings founded on piles. In a fill in which methane gas is being generated by the decay and decomposition of organic matter, piles could form paths for the escape of the gas.

Where small structures have to be built on deep fill, piling through the fill to an underlying firm stratum is not likely to be an economic solution and the structure may have to be founded directly on the fill. Reinforced concrete rafts with edge beams have been used, but it should be realised that where large differential movements may occur, very substantial foundations may be required. In Digest 274, under *Classification of fills*, three different situations are distinguished on the basis of the percentage vertical compression that can occur in the fill. In the foundation design it is also important to distinguish between settlement due to the weight of the building and settlement due to other causes, such as self-weight of the fill. With small structures on deep fills, almost invariably the latter will predominate and so 'bearing capacity' can be a misleading concept. Foundation design should be based on an assessment of the magnitude of movements of the fill subsequent to construction on it. Where large movements could occur, the use of a ground improvement technique prior to construction on the fill should be considered.

The problems associated with low-rise buildings on filled ground can be minimised by avoiding building across the edges of filled areas where the structure would be partly founded on fill and partly on undisturbed ground. Construction should be restricted to small units and long terraces of houses should not be built on existing filled ground. The relative movements between the building and services entering it and between various sections of the piping merit careful consideration. If the movements are not likely to be large, the use of short lengths of pipes with flexible connections may be sufficient. In more severe cases it may be necessary to use flexible pipes or carry services on piles bearing on a firm stratum beneath the fill. Generous falls should be given to drains to reduce the risk of backfalls.

References and further reading

(1) DUMBLETON, M J. Historical investigation of site use; Proc. Conf. on Reclamation of contaminated land, Eastbourne 1979, Society of Chemical Industry.

(2) CHARLES, J A; and DRISCOLL, R M C. A simple in-situ load test for shallow fill. Ground Engineering, 14 (1), pp 31, 32, 34, 36.

(3) GUTT, W H; and HARRISON, W H. Chemical resistance of concrete; BRE Current Paper CP23/77.

(4) Specification for road and bridge works: Department of Transport, HMSO, London 1976.

(5) CHARLES, J A, EARLE, E W; and BURFORD, D. Treatment and subsequent performance of cohesive fill left by opencast ironstone mining at Snatchill experimental housing site, Corby. BRE Current Paper CP 79/78.

British Standards Institution
BS 5930: 1981 Code of practice for site investigations

Other BRE Digests
63 Soils and foundations: Part 1
64 Soils and foundations: Part 2
67 Soils and foundations: Part 3
89 Sulphate attack on brickwork
95 Choosing a type of pile
98 Durability of metals in natural waters
250 Concrete in sulphate-bearing soils and groundwaters.
251 Assessment of damage in low-rise buildings.
274 Fill: Part 1 Classification and load carrying characteristics
276 Hardcore

CIRIA/PSA
WELTMAN, AJ; and HEAD, JM. Site investigation manual; CIRIA special publication 25/PSA Civil Engineering Technical Guide 35.

Hardcore

The principal uses of hardcore are as a make-up material to provide a level base on which to cast a ground floor slab, to raise levels, and to provide a dry, firm base on which work can proceed or to carry construction traffic.

A variety of materials have been used satisfactorily but difficulties can occur and there are a number of factors that need to be taken into account in the selection of materials for use as hardcore. Ideally, they should be granular and drain and consolidate readily; they should be chemically inert and not affected by water. However, few of the materials available at reasonable cost satisfy these requirements completely. The main hazards to be avoided are chemical attack by hardcore materials on concrete and brickwork mortar, settlement due to poor compaction and swelling or consolidation due to changes in moisture content or chemical instability.

This digest discusses some problems related to the use of hardcore and considers the suitability of some materials in common use.

Fig 1 Distortion and cracking of thin floor slab caused by sulphate attack

Definition

Hardcore is the limited amount of material put down as infill within foundations or beneath an oversite concrete slab. In some parts, particularly in Scotland, the term 'bottoming' is also used.

Water soluble sulphates

Concrete ground floor slabs are particularly vulnerable to attack by water soluble sulphates in hardcore and there have been many failures. The use of colliery shale has been particularly notorious but other materials containing sulphates have also been responsible: there are cases where demolition rubble has contained substantial quantities of gypsum plaster and others where industrial waste has been used. Eventually, in damp conditions, sulphates in such hardcores can migrate into the underside of the slab and react with constituents of the Portland cement. This is the chemical reaction normally referred to as sulphate attack. It produces a gradual breakdown of the concrete and causes it to expand and lift.

The effects of the expansion are usually the first to be noticed. It causes distortion and cracking of the relatively thin floor slab (see Fig 1) and consequent disturbance and movement of any partition built off it and can, in some circumstances, exert sufficient pressure on the enclosing walls to cause them to move outwards. The movements are quite slow and are not usually noticed for five years or longer.

In general, hardcore materials containing water soluble sulphates should be avoided; alternatively, a concrete quality should be chosen that will resist the effects of the sulphates. The use of a 2:1 water extract method as described in Digest 250 is recommended to classify the levels of soluble salts present in hardcore materials and the quality of the concrete used should be in accordance with the recommendations in Digest 250*. If any sulphate is found or suspected in the hardcore, a moisture barrier (such as a polythene sheet at least 0·2 mm thick) should be placed between the hardcore and the concrete floor slab. Chemical attack will, however, take place only when water is available to the material and much can be done to mitigate the effects of sulphates by providing good drainage. Many waste materials are inhomogeneous and it may be difficult to take a representative sample for sulphate analysis. If there is any doubt about the adequacy of sampling (for example, from a tip) precautions against sulphate attack should be taken, in particular the use of a moisture barrier.

---

* Some hardcore materials, eg blastfurnace slag, can contain sulphur compounds locked in fused granules and inaccessible for solution in groundwaters. Total SO_3 determination would, therefore, be misleading and the 2:1 water extract method is recommended. For the same reason, the degree of size reduction of the sample for the extraction is also relevant and so special attention should be paid to sampling and preparing the sample for the water extract. This should still be representative of the original sample and contain the correct proportion of any original fine material. A method of sample preparation for the determination of water soluble sulphate in blastfurnace slags is given in BS 1047.

Swelling due to chemical and volume changes in the material

Hardcore materials can swell from the following causes, (a) to (d), but the number of cases where movement in buildings has been caused by hardcore materials swelling is quite small. Although swelling may have been suspected initially, the movement has usually been proved subsequently to be due to sulphate attack and consequent volume change of concrete in contact with the hardcore.

Possible causes of swelling are:

(a) Unhydrated lime or magnesia in steel slags will produce volume expansion in the presence of moisture.

(b) Materials which contain broken concrete or old, partially vitrified slags from old slag dumps may expand when exposed to sulphate solutions originated in either the groundwater or other components of the hardcore. Modern, air-cooled blastfurnace slags are not susceptible to attack by sulphates.

(c) Materials which contain a significant proportion of clay, eg some colliery spoil, can swell if they are placed in a dry condition but subsequently become wet. These should be placed at a moisture content close to optimum: see Test 12 in BS 1377.

(d) Sulphides in the form of pyrites can oxidise to form soluble sulphate in the presence of air, moisture and, possibly, bacterial action. They can therefore contribute to problems of sulphate attack on concrete. In addition, if pyrites are present together with calcite there is danger of expansion due to the growth of gypsum crystals formed by reaction between calcite and sulphuric acid from the oxidation of pyrites. Failures due to swelling by this mechanism have been found in the Teesside area, where a natural Whitbian shale, quarried for the purpose, was used as a hardcore and in Glasgow where such a shale formed the natural bedrock beneath a building. The methods of recognising potentially troublesome shales are discussed in ref (1). The observable indications that such an action is taking place are similar to those associated with sulphate attack: cracking, lifting and hogging of floors, movement and cracking of internal partitions and outward movement of external walls.

Consolidation of hardcore

Hardcore may consolidate after building operations are complete if it has been inadequately compacted, if the depth is too great or if materials which can degrade in wet conditions have been used. When consolidation occurs, the ground floor slab loses its support over part or all of its area, gaps appear between the floor and skirting board, the slab can crack and any partitions or features built off it can be disrupted (see Fig 2). There have been many cases

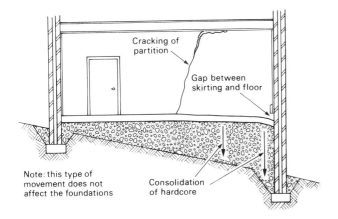

Fig 2 "... the slab can crack and any partitions off it can be disrupted"

where this has occurred to some extent. Sites where a considerable depth of hardcore is needed are particularly vulnerable. At one time, the National House Building Council found that settlement of ground floor slabs was the most frequent structural defect in new houses where solid floor construction had been used; they now require that a suspended floor be used where the depth of filling material needed is more than 600 mm at any point. Even on sites where the average depth of hardcore over the site is relatively small, difficulties can still be experienced at the edges if deep trenches have been formed to facilitate the construction of the foundations (Fig 3).

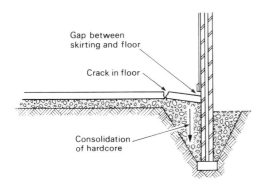

Fig 3 "... difficulties if deep trenches have been formed to facilitate construction of the foundations"

Materials used for hardcore

Gravel and crushed hard rock Suitably-graded gravel and crushed hard rock are good hardcore materials but are usually expensive. Coarse ungraded gravel and rock may be obtainable more cheaply and can be used as a base layer covered by a layer of well-graded material.

Quarry waste The material is clean, hard and safe to use; it may be unevenly graded and therefore difficult to consolidate to give a good working surface. Many quarry owners can often offer crusher-run stone and similar products which should be economical near to the quarry.

Chalk Widely and successfully used in some areas, chalk has been known to cause problems of frost heave in floors of buildings when a prolonged frost has occurred during construction. Movements occur due to the build-up of ice layers in the hardcore and can exert considerable pressures with consequent disruption. If it is used during winter building, it should be protected (by heat if necessary) from frost during long, cold spells. Experience suggests that a few days of continuously freezing conditions are needed before difficulties are likely to be encountered. Normal occupied buildings are unlikely to be affected but unheated buildings and cold stores may merit special consideration.

Concrete rubble If clean and suitably graded, this is a good hardcore material. Care should be taken with rubble from general building demolition which may contain mixtures of materials. In particular, there may be lumps of gypsum plaster which could cause sulphate attack if put in close proximity to concrete or brickwork in wet conditions.

Brick or tile rubble When taken from old buildings, this can be a very useful source of hardcore. Unless the bricks are soft and crumble easily, there may be a lack of fine material and it might, therefore, be difficult to compact. Since many clay bricks contain sulphate, the use of a water barrier between the fill and a concrete floor would be a wise precaution, particularly if new bricks, or old bricks with adhering gypsum plaster, are used. Also, there have been a number of outbreaks of dry rot in new buildings where the infection has arisen from the use of hardcore containing pieces of timber taken from demolished buildings where an outbreak of dry rot was already established. Care should be taken to avoid the use of refractory bricks such as those from chimneys and furnaces, as some types can expand when exposed to moisture.

Blastfurnace slag Slag from the making of iron is a hard, strong material which is often used as a fill or hardcore. The slags may contain sulphates, but these are predominantly calcium sulphate which has a limited solubility in water. Moreover, slags are free-draining materials which will not retain water in contact with the concrete or brickwork. The use of the water extract method as proposed in Digest 250 is recommended to classify the sulphate content of the slag and an extract giving less than 1 g/l of SO_3 may be taken as falling in Class 1 in Table 1 of Digest 250. This criterion is more relevant than a requirement that the slag should comply with the sulphate requirements of BS 1047.

It is however, inadvisable to place large volumes of slag in wet stagnant conditions as there have occasionally been problems of water pollution by sulphur species leached from slags. Slags from old 'slag banks' should not be used unless thoroughly sampled and tested as they may be mixed with slag wastes other than blastfurnace slag and other industrial wastes. Moreoever, old, partially vitrified slags may swell owing to attack by sulphate solutions arising either from the groundwater or other components of the fill.

Slags from steelmaking are *not recommended* for use as hardcore because they may contain phases which cause expansion on wetting, eg free lime, free magnesia or broken refractory bricks.

Colliery spoil Both unburnt spoil (known commercially as 'minestone') and burnt (or partly burnt) spoil are available. Burnt spoil ('red shale') is the result of the combustion of the residual coal and carbonaceous matter in old, poorly consolidated tips. Burnt colliery spoils have been the cause of many failures of ground floor slabs by sulphate attack when used as hardcore on wet sites. Well-burnt spoil provides a useful free-draining hardcore material but it can be variable in its properties because of incomplete combustion and it tends to have a higher soluble sulphate content than unburnt spoil because of oxidation of sulphides (mainly pyrites) during burning.

For most purposes the use of the unburnt colliery spoil is preferred. Its sulphate content is generally lower and good compaction is easier to achieve. When well-compacted, access of oxygen is prevented and it has been shown that combustion will not take place. There is no convincing evidence that colliery spoils have caused failures by swelling. Further information can be obtained from the NCB Minestone Executive, Hobart House, Grosvenor Place, London SW7X 7AE.

Oil shale residue The spent shale from the extraction of oil from oil shale is available in the Lothians area of Scotland. It is a tough material which resists disintegration by weather and has been extensively used for fill and hardcore. Its soluble sulphate content can however be appreciable and variable; on wet sites precautions against sulphate attack on concrete or mortar should be taken.

Pulverised fuel ash PFA or flyash, the fine waste material from the precipitators of coal burning power stations, can be used as hardcore. When conditioned with water, it produces a lightweight material which has self-hardening properties. It is generally low in sulphate but when it is obtained from a power station mixed with furnace bottom ash (the other major waste from the burning process), the total sulphate content may be increased; it should be checked by a water extract method. Further information can be obtained from the CEGB Ash Marketing, Walden House, 24 Cathedral Place, London EC4P 4EB

Reference and further reading
1. NIXON, PJ. Floor heave in buildings due to the use of pyritic shales as fill material. Chemistry and Industry; 4 March 1978; pp 160–164.

British Standards Institution

CP 2004: 1972 Foundations
BS 1047: Part 2: 1974 Air-cooled blastfurnace slag coarse aggregate for concrete
BS 1377: 1975 Methods of test for civil engineering purposes

BRE Digests

 63 Soils and foundations: Part 1
 64 Soils and foundations: Part 2
 67 Soils and foundations: Part 3
 89 Sulphate attack on brickwork
 98 Durability of metals in natural waters
250 Concrete in sulphate-bearing soils and groundwaters
251 Assessment of damage in low-rise buildings
274 Fill: Part 1 Classification and load carrying characteristics
275 Fill: Part 2 Site investigation, ground improvement and foundation design.

Soils and foundations : 1

This Digest and the next show how soil conditions on site affect the design of foundations and the subsequent behaviour of buildings.

In the past the choice of foundation type has been little influenced by soil conditions but the increasing use of sites with difficult soils has more serious implications for foundation design and calls for a better appreciation of the way soil reacts to applied loads and natural forces.

This Digest therefore considers the principles of soil behaviour and examines the movements which result from the construction of foundations or which can be induced by other factors such as the weather, vegetation and subsidence.

Digest 64 deals with the choice of building sites and the investigations necessary to determine soil conditions. Digest 67 considers the types of foundation most appropriate to these conditions.

Interaction between superstructure, foundation and soil

A building, its foundation and the supporting soil interact with one another in a complex manner, the behaviour of one depending upon, and influencing, that of the others. Foundation design must therefore take into account not only the type of structure to be supported, its function and the constructional materials to be used, but also the soil conditions on site. The basic properties of soils are outlined below.

Soil properties

Soil structure

Most soils consist of solid particles of varying shapes and sizes, with water and, to a lesser extent, air filling the spaces between them. Large particles (sands) are held together mainly by their weight and when loose have very little strength. In fact, strength is related to the closeness of the packing and to the size of external forces; the influence of additional water on strength is only marginal unless it is flowing rapidly (*see* page 6). On the other hand, the amount of water that can be held by fine particles (clays) is very much larger, the water films between the particles being responsible for the characteristic stickiness which binds them together. The strength of clays therefore depends on how much water they contain. The strength increases as the film thickness is reduced, e.g. by the drying action of tree roots.

Shrinkage and swelling

When water is removed from a soil the solid particles tend to move closer together. Such movement is very limited in sands because of the negligible amounts of water held between the particles, but in clays the proportions of solid matter and water are more nearly equal and particle movements can be appreciable. Clays therefore shrink when they are dried, the shrinkage being accompanied by an increase in strength.

Conversely, when clays absorb water the water films thicken and the clays swell and lose strength. In sands the volume changes are almost negligible. Soils of intermediate particle size, such as silts, have properties intermediate between those of sand and clay.

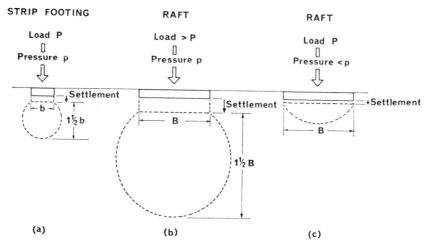

Fig. 1 Stress envelopes and settlements

Consolidation

Increased external pressure on a soil, e.g. that applied by a foundation load, increases both water and soil pressures. Water is squeezed from between the solid particles and driven to areas where the water pressure is less, while the soil particles are forced into closer contact with each other. As the ground is compressed so the foundation settles. This process of consolidation continues until the water pressure has fallen to its original value and the forces between the particles have increased by an amount equal to the newly applied load. If the soil particles and consequently the pore spaces are large, as in sands, the water movements are rapid. Foundations on sands therefore settle quickly once the load is applied and settlement after construction is completed is unlikely to be of any significance.

With clays the story is different; they offer considerable resistance to the expulsion of water and settlement caused by consolidation can continue for years after construction.

If the load on a soil is reduced, e.g. by excavation, the process just described is reversed: water tends to move towards the unloaded areas and swelling of the soil occurs.

Shrinkage (including consolidation) and swelling are thus fundamental to an understanding of soil behaviour. Often they operate simultaneously, as, for example, when the weight of clay removed by excavation approximates to the new structural load. Then long-term swelling may have settlement superimposed upon it.

Movements caused by loading

The extent to which solids deform under pressure depends on properties such as hardness, and the size of the imposed load. Soils behave similarly and a load applied through a foundation always causes settlement. However, not even uniform ground uniformly loaded settles evenly and the complex properties of soil make it difficult to assess the settlement of individual foundations or to predict the distortion of buildings as a whole.

Settlement of shallow foundations

Under normal loading shallow foundations consisting of strip and pad footings and rafts increase the pressure in a uniform soil significantly to a depth and breadth roughly equal to one-and-a-half times the breadth of the foundation. The resulting settlement depends on the increase in pressure and the soil properties in an imaginary envelope bounded by these dimensions (Fig. 1(a)).

For the same bearing *pressure* the settlement of a broad foundation or raft will be greater than for a narrow one (Fig. 1(b)), but the total load carried by the raft will be greater.

It the *load* is the same the pressure on the raft will of course be less than that on the narrow foundation, and the depth to which pressures in the soil are of any importance will be much less than one-and-a-half times the breadth of the foundation (Fig. 1(c)). The settlement of a raft is thus less than that of a strip footing carrying the same load.

In practice this simple appraisal needs modification when firmer or weaker strata pass through the stressed zones as, for example, when sand overlies soft clay.

Settlement of deep foundations

Pile foundations are supported by frictional forces acting at the surface of each shaft and by bearing forces acting at the point or base. Only small movements are necessary for frictional forces to be developed and in clay soils these can be much greater than the bearing forces at the base. In sand or gravel most of the resistance to a pile is provided at its base irrespective of whether this is pointed or flat. The settlement of a single pile under working conditions is related to its breadth or diameter, and is usually very small. In fact, in stiff soils the compression of the pile itself may be comparable to the settlement necessary for the development of supporting forces.

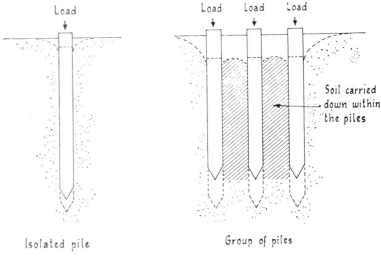

Isolated pile   Group of piles

Fig. 2 Pile settlements

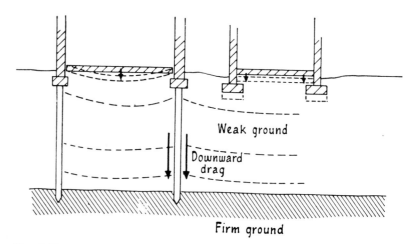

Fig. 3 Weak ground consolidating
and increasing pile load

Piles in a closely spaced group tend to carry the soil within the peri-meter of the group down with them as they settle and this soil may be less effective in providing support than the soil outside the group. Thus the strength of a pile group in clay is frequently less than the sum of the strengths of the individual piles. In sand the increased compaction of the soil during pile-driving can often more than com-pensate for this loss. A closely spaced group behaves very much as a single foundation and the settlement at the design load is likely to be related more to the size of the whole group than to that of a single pile (Fig. 2).

Piles are frequently used to carry loads through soft soils containing a lot of water to a firm layer in which the points are founded. In these circumstances the soft soils may consolidate under the weight of floor slabs or adjacent buildings and exert a downward drag on a pile instead of supporting it; this tends to increase the load which must be carried by the point (Fig. 3).

Basements with a raft floor and retaining walls are a useful form of deep foundation which is less common now than it deserves to be. By excavating for the basement a weight of soil roughly equal to that of the building, the net increase in pressure on the soil—and hence the probable settlement—can be kept very small.

Soil movements from causes other than loading

These movements, which are not necessarily vertical or evenly distri-buted, are caused, for example, by seasonal weather changes, the growth or removal of vegetation, by earth flows and subsidence and, less frequently, by the particular use of the structure in question. The problems raised by these movements are usually most acute with soils composed of fine particles.

The behaviour of clay soils
Clays which shrink on drying and swell again when wetted are com-monly responsible for the movement of shallow foundations. If such clays are firm enough to support buildings of a few storeys they are known as firm shrinkable clays.

(i) *Shrinkage and swelling caused by vegetation and climate.* The roots of plants penetrate soil to considerable depths and dry it when rainfall is low in summer. Beneath large trees and shrubs permanent drying has been detected in the United Kingdom at depths of 5 m or more, and shrinkage of the order of 100 mm has been measured at the ground surface. Beneath grasses shrinkage occurs to depths of about 2 m, but drying to these shallow depths is less likely to be permanent, the water transpired by the grasses in summer usually being replaced by rainfall the following winter. Even so, vertical movements of more than 25 mm have been measured at the surface between April and September. A building on shallow foundations close to vegetation is therefore liable to seasonal movements or long-term settlement, depending on the root growth. To some extent the building protects the clay beneath it from seasonal drying and wetting, and movement is more likely under the outer walls and corners. Shrinkage of clays occurs horizontally as well as vertically and so there is a tendency for walls to be drawn outwards in addition to settling and for cracks to open between the clay and the sides of the foundations. These cracks allow water to enter during the following winter and to soften the clay against or beneath the foundations (Fig. 4).

Fig. 4 also shows typical cracking of the building. During the winter these cracks partially close but, because of the relative displacement of parts of the building and the accumulation of debris within the cracks, closure is seldom complete and the cracks go on widening each dry summer.

To reduce the risk of damage as far as possible it is advisable, *as a rough guide,* not to erect buildings on shallow foundations closer to single trees than their height at maturity. The roots of groups or rows of trees competing for water over a limited area can be much more extensive, and, again *as a rough guide,* one-and-a-half times the mature height of the trees is suggested as the limiting distance. It is of course equally important that young trees should not be planted closer to buildings than these distances.

(ii) *Swelling caused by tree removal.* When trees are felled to clear a site for building, considerable time should be allowed for the clay (which was previously dried by tree roots) to regain water. Otherwise there is a serious risk that as the clay swells it will lift the building.

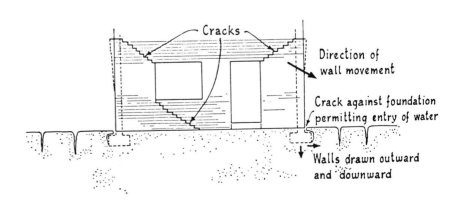

Fig. 4 Cracking associated with shallow foundations on shrinkable clay

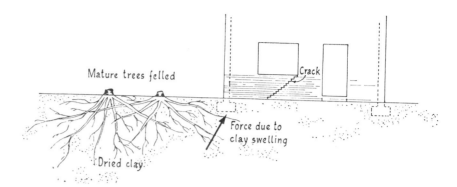

Fig. 5 Consequences of tree felling

And because the swelling is most marked close to the sites of the trees which have been removed, damage is likely from relative movements (Fig. 5). The pressures that dried clays develop when reabsorbing water are often greater than those applied by shallow foundations, and the resulting upward movements can continue for several years. For example, regular measurements made by the Building Research Station on an office block built in 1959 on a site cleared of trees a year previously show an upward movement of about 6 mm per year since construction was completed. Observations suggest that these movements may continue for up to ten years.

(iii) *Shrinkage caused by artificial drying.* Boilers and furnaces inadequately insulated from the clay beneath have been known to dry and shrink the clay, and so cause cracking of the concrete foundation slab through lack of support. Heating appliances not normally provided with adequate air ventilation or water channels between the furnace and the base should have such cooling systems installed as part of the foundation.

The behaviour of sandy soils

Water can move much faster through sands than through fine-grained soils; some foundation problems are directly attributable to this property.

(i) *Loss of ground.* Dense beds of sand are normally excellent foundation soils but occasionally water washes out the finer particles, leaving the coarser material in a less stable condition. This happens, for example, when fine sands and silts are affected by water flowing underground from high ground nearby; these exhibit a 'quick-sand' condition, particularly if an excavation is made, and much of their bearing capacity can be lost. Such situations must be dewatered or avoided completely for building purposes.

(ii) *Frost heave.* During severe winters in the United Kingdom frost may penetrate the soil to a depth of 600 mm or so. If the water table is close to the ground surface and the spaces between the soil particles are of a particular range of sizes—as they are with fine sands, silts and chalk—water can move into the frozen zone and form ice lenses of increasing thickness. As a result the ground surface is lifted in what is known as 'frost heave'. For this reason these materials should not be used as filling under floor slabs. Well-heated buildings are unlikely to be affected because of heat loss to the ground, but not so the outer walls of poorly heated houses, nor houses under construction—the concrete ground floor slabs of the latter are particularly vulnerable until glazing is complete. The slabs tend to heave more than the external walls, and service connections and wall to floor connections can be damaged. Unheated garages and outhouses, often built on concrete slabs and footings shallower than those of adjoining houses, are likely to be similarly affected.

Organic soils and made-up ground

Peats and other soils containing a lot of organic matter in the form of decaying vegetation vary greatly in volume as their water content changes. They are also very compressible and settle readily even under their own weight. Made-up ground behaves in much the same way and settles for many years unless it is good material, carefully placed, and compacted in thin layers. The bearing capacities of sites filled by end-tipping are often poor and variable; these sites should never be built upon unless deep foundations passing through the fill can be provided. Poorly compacted fill is unsuitable for foundations no matter how long it consolidates under its own weight.

Large-scale movements

Some foundation movements result from deep-seated instability in what would otherwise be good foundation soil. They can be caused by natural or geological phenomena, artificial agencies or by a combination of both.

(i) *Slopes and landslips.* Clay soils on sloping sites are likely to move downhill, albeit slowly, if the angle of slope exceeds about 1 in 10. Larger landslips occur intermittently above cliffs, river valleys and deep cuttings.

(ii) *Swallow holes.* In chalk and limestone areas cavities in the bedrock can form by the action of underground streams or water courses dissolving the rock away. If the overburden collapses into a cavity, as is common where the overburden is sandy, a 'swallow hole' is formed at the surface with consequential damage to buildings above or nearby. Because water movement is essential to swallow hole formation, soakaways should always be placed at a safe distance from buildings in these areas.

(iii) *Mining subsidence.* Large settlements must be expected in mining areas as the ground subsides over workings. Usually the ground surface 'stretches' as the front of a subsidence approaches and buildings start to tilt towards it. The tilt eventually decreases but the settlement increases as the ground beneath is affected. If structural damage is of a minor character buildings slowly return to a more or less plumb position at a lower level. To withstand the horizontal and vertical forces acting on a building during subsidence the construction should be either rigid, using a heavily reinforced concrete raft, or extremely flexible; movements can then be accommodated without serious damage to structure or finishes. Usually, small brick houses on quite thin rafts reinforced to resist the horizontal forces can survive moderate movements without undue damage.

Movement and damage

The effect of a differential vertical movement h between any two points A and B on a building depends on their distance apart. It is therefore more useful to measure differential movement as 'angular distortion', defined as h/AB (Fig. 6). Brickwork and plaster quickly show the effects of differential movement and from the limited data available the onset of cracking can be associated with an angular distortion of about 1/300. This is equivalent to a differential movement of 10 mm over a span of 3 m. Warehouse and factory buildings of framed construction can usually tolerate larger angular distortions but at about 1/150 structural damage may be expected unless the joints have been specially designed to tolerate movements.

Fig. 6 Angular distortion

Soils and foundations : 2

This Digest outlines the soil and other investigations necessary in assessing the suitability of sites for new buildings. Digest 63 deals with the movements resulting from interactions between soils and foundations; foundation design is discussed in Digest 67.

The need for site investigation

An investigation of the site is needed when any building work is envisaged that is likely to be affected by conditions below ground level. This applies equally to alterations and extensions of existing work and to new schemes. It is of particular importance at the present time, when the possible use of sites that have been avoided as building land in the past is being considered. This may seem to be stating the obvious, but in fact it is known that schemes have been prepared, and in some cases work actually started, before any consideration has been given to below-ground conditions at the site and whether they are suitable for the project in hand. The extent of the investigation will depend largely on the situation, size and type of the proposed work.

This Digest is intended to emphasise the need for an early appraisal of the site so that any special measures that may be required to deal with difficult conditions can be planned at the outset. Many other aspects which bear on the intended use of the site, and which will need to be considered, such as leases, wayleaves, limitations on use and so on, are outside the scope of the Digest.

Outlined below are the main stages that can be undertaken in an investigation. A comprehensive study of the procedure is contained in the British Standard Code of Practice CP 2001 : 1957, *Site investigations.*

Stage 1. Information available off site

The local authority should be regarded as a main source of information at this stage. Its intimate knowledge of the soil and general conditions in the area, particular difficulties that can arise and local building practice can be invaluable.

Older editions of the Ordnance Survey maps, ancient maps and records from other local sources can also provide useful clues to the positions of features that might cause difficulty, such as infilled ponds, ditches and streams, disused pipes, sites of old buildings and services. Current maps, plans and records that might also be studied to advantage are set out in the Appendix.

Stage 2. Site reconnaissance

Useful information can be obtained from a surface exploration of the site and its surroundings. Nearby buildings should be looked at to see if they show any signs of distress or damage, and if possible the depth and types of foundations used should be established. The information gathered in this stage can be grouped under the following headings:

Topography

In walking over the site, nearby quarries, cuttings, ditches and slopes should be examined. These should show whether the soil conditions vary. Topographical features such as a step in the line of a valley may indicate a geological fault or a zone where shattered rock has been more rapidly eroded than the surrounding rock. Broken and terraced ground on hill slopes, especially when steep, may be caused by landslips. While gentle slopes usually make good building sites because of the drainage they promote, slopes greater than about 1 in 10 should be examined for soil creep. Slowly moving clay slopes are often responsible for the tilt of walls, fences and trees.

Low-lying flat areas in hilly country may have been the sites of lakes and suggest the possible presence of soft silty soils and peats. On the other hand, mounds and hummocks in more or less flat regions frequently indicate former glacial conditions and the possibility of boulder clay and glacial gravel overlying solid strata.

In limestone or chalk country, craters or gentle depressions usually indicate swallow holes formed by the collapse of sandy or loamy soils into the fissured rock below. Examples may be seen in the Mendips, in parts of Pembrokeshire and Monmouthshire, on the edge of

Fig 1 Damage caused by trees on clay

the London basin, and wherever chalk or limestone occur. Local farmers will be familiar with them because they are potential cattle traps—to be fenced off or kept filled in.

Unstable conditions can also occur where springs issue from fine sand and silt strata on grassy slopes. The sand frequently erodes when turf is removed for building purposes, and ground of this nature is best avoided.

Where a polygonal pattern of cracks about 25 mm wide is seen in the ground surface during a dry summer, the surface soil is shrinkable. Shallow depressions round mature trees in open ground, broken kerb-stones and frequent repairs to paved surfaces close to trees in developed areas are further indications of shrinkage due to drying (Fig. 1). Larger cracks, more or less parallel to each other, are frequently indicative of deeper-seated movements such as are caused by mining, brine pumping, or landslips.

Flooding

Sites along river valleys and coasts may be liable to flooding from time to time, and the highest recorded flood levels should be established. Dry inland valleys may also be flooded as a result of heavy rain or melting snow, particularly when the soil beneath the snow is frozen.

Groundwater

The water levels in nearby ponds, streams and rivers noted in a site reconnaissance may not be a good guide to the level of the water in the adjoining country; near coasts and estuaries the groundwater level may fluctuate with the tide. The groundwater conditions in each of the underlying strata should be determined, as excavation below water level, particularly in fine sands, is difficult and costly. A layer of clay at foundation level may also confine a lower bed of sand with a high water pressure which could cause uplift during excavation.

Because of constructional difficulties, foundations on sands and gravel should, where possible, be kept above the groundwater level. Where basements are to be constructed, precautions should be taken to ensure that they do not 'float' if the water level rises during construction. For purposes of basement design it should be assumed that the water level in clay soils extends to the ground surface.

Some soils contain sulphates; under certain conditions these may cause corrosion of buried concrete, iron and steel. If the presence of sulphates is suspected, the groundwater should be analysed, care being taken to avoid contamination of the samples by surface water.

Vegetation

The kinds of vegetation growing on a site can provide further useful pointers to the level of the water table in the ground for at least part of the year. For example, naturally occurring reeds, rushes, cotton-grass, poplars and willows indicate a high water table, whereas bracken and gorse usually indicate a well drained soil. The presence of stunted specimens of heather and gorse often means that the water table is occasionally too high for the good health of these plants. However, many plants tolerate a wide range of soil types and climatic conditions, so that the conclusions drawn from such inspections should preferably be checked with other evidence.

A change in the vegetation over quite a small area may indicate an important change in the subsoil or rock formation, and show where more detailed soil investigations should be made. Unless it cannot be avoided, individual buildings should not be founded in varying soils because of the probability of differential settlements.

The existence of peats and swamps will usually be obvious. Such sites should be avoided unless deep and extensive foundations are justified. The shrinkage of clays caused by plant roots is discussed in Digest 63. Most of the damage is caused by large trees and, in the London area, poplars have been particularly troublesome because they grow rapidly and are often planted closely spaced to form screens. If trouble from this source is anticipated, buildings close to the site and particularly near trees should be examined carefully.

The absence of vegetation typical in surrounding areas may suggest made-up ground, and a fairly superficial examination may reveal brick, wood, rubble and other kinds of mineral or chemical matter.

Stage 3.   Site history

Previous uses of a site may suggest acceptable types of foundation for the proposed new works or in extreme cases make it clear that the site is unsuitable for new building. In areas where there have been underground workings, such as worked-out ballast pits, quarries, old brickworks, coal mines, mineral workings and brine pumping, enquiries should be made to establish their exact location. Reports of damage to structures, services and drainage systems should be investigated.

Sites previously cleared of orchards or woodland may be of dried clay and this must be allowed to re-absorb moisture and swell before construction is started—unless specially designed deep foundations are to be provided (see Digest 241).

A good deal of site history will of course be apparent from site reconnaissance and the study of maps and local records. The latter should be searched for evidence of landslips, floods, bomb craters, disused drainage systems and so on. In urban areas, the positions of sewers, drains and services should be verified to avoid risk of damage by new foundations later.

Stage 4.   Soil investigations

The previous Digest showed that foundation movements are of two kinds: those caused by the foundation load acting on the soil, and those caused by soil movements generated by other factors. The objects of soil investigations are to determine the strength and deformation characteristics of the soil under load and to identify the conditions in which soils are otherwise susceptible to movement. Some guidance on both will have been obtained by visual examination of the exposed surface of the site, while other simple tests, not involving detailed measurement, can yield useful results.

Scope of the investigations

In plan
For buildings of up to four storeys, sufficient inspection pits should be dug near the boundaries of the site to establish the soil profile. On a sloping site, or one with rock near the surface, other pits may have to be dug nearer the centre so that any variations in profile may be noted.

In depth
In the last Digest the depths were given to which soils are stressed by different types of foundation. Soil investigations should therefore be made to these depths at least.

If the inspection pits or the information obtained from other sources mentioned above suggest that piled foundations will be necessary then the investigation must be made to greater depths and a specialist firm should be consulted. In investigations for raft and piled founda-

Table 1 Soil identification

Soil type	Field identification	Field assessment of structure and strength	Possible foundation difficulties
Gravels	Retained on No. 7 BS sieve and up to 76·2 mm Some dry strength indicates presence of clay	Loose—easily removed by shovel 50 mm stakes can be driven well in	Loss of fine particles in water-bearing ground
Sands	Pass No. 7 and retained on No. 200 BS sieve Clean sands break down completely when dry. Individual particles visible to the naked eye and gritty to fingers	Compact—requires pick for excavation. Stakes will penetrate only a little way	Frost heave, especially on fine sands Excavation below water table causes runs and local collapse, especially in fine sands
Silts	Pass No. 200 BS sieve. Particles not normally distinguishable with naked eye Slightly gritty; moist lumps can be moulded with the fingers but not rolled into threads Shaking a small moist lump in the hand brings water to the surface Silts dry rapidly; fairly easily powdered	Soft—easily moulded with the fingers Firm—can be moulded with strong finger pressure	As for fine sands
Clays	Smooth, plastic to the touch. Sticky when moist. Hold together when dry. Wet lumps immersed in water soften without disintegrating Soft clays either uniform or show horizontal laminations Harder clays frequently fissured, the fissures opening slightly when the overburden is removed or a vertical surface is revealed by a trial pit	Very soft—exudes between fingers when squeezed Soft—easily moulded with the fingers Firm—can be moulded with strong finger pressure Stiff—cannot be moulded with fingers Hard—brittle or tough	Shrinkage and swelling caused by vegetation Long-term settlement by consolidation Sulphate-bearing clays may attack concrete and corrode pipes Poor drainage Movement down slopes; most soft clays lose strength when disturbed
Peat	Fibrous, black or brown Often smelly Very compressible and water retentive	Soft—very compressible and spongy Firm—compact	Very low bearing capacity; large settlement caused by high compressibility Shrinkage and swelling—foundations should be on firm strata below
Chalk	White—readily identified	Plastic—shattered, damp and slightly compressible or crumbly Solid—needing a pick for removal	Frost heave Floor slabs on chalk fill particularly vulnerable during construction in cold weather Swallow holes
Fill	Miscellaneous material, e.g. rubble, mineral, waste, decaying wood		To be avoided unless carefully compacted in thin layers and well consolidated May ignite or contain injurious chemicals

tions, samples for soil testing should normally be obtained from boreholes; these are a more economic and practical proposition than deep inspection pits. Shrinkage of clays is to be expected to depths of about 2 m and they should invariably be examined to these depths. Where trees are growing on clays, boreholes to about 5 m may be needed (*see* Digest 241).

Information required

Information is required on the following soil characteristics and the depths at which they are observed:

soil type
soil uniformity
whether deformable or breakable in the fingers
whether gritty, smooth, plastic, sticky
whether homogeneous, fissured or shattered
presence of organic or foreign matter
colour, smell
depth of water table.

Soil identification

In this Digest it is possible only to discuss the qualitative aspects of soil identification. Table 1 classifies soil types as they are indentifiable in the field and indicates their suitability for various foundations.

Quantitative tests in the field and the laboratory will, however, be necessary where a comprehensive account of soil conditions is required, and reference should be made to CP 2001 : 1957 and BS 1377 : 1975, *Methods of testing soils for civil engineering purposes.*

Sampling

Equipment for sampling depends on whether inspection pits or boreholes are taken out and this, as suggested above, depends upon the depth of investigation necessary. For boreholes the simplest tool is the post-hole auger; with this two men can easily reach 7–8 m in soft or firm clays. It is important that the samples are extracted in as undisturbed a form as possible and that they are immediately protected from drying, because otherwise wrong conclusions may be drawn about the soil conditions. Inspection pits are of course more accessible than boreholes and allow removal of clay from the walls with a spade or knife. In sands and gravels, casing tubes prevent collapse of the borehole and percussive tools are necessary, and the services of specialist firms should be used.

Appendix—Sources of information
British Ordnance Survey Maps

The most useful are likely to be the large and medium scale maps and plans, ranging from 1/1250 to 1/25 000. Six-inch (1/10 000) maps cover the whole of Great Britain and 25-in. plans (1/2500) cover all areas except waste and mountainous districts. These maps and plans may be purchased from the Main Agents:

Cook, Hammond & Keli Ltd
22-24 Caxton Street   } for England and Wales
London SW1

Thomas Nelson & Sons Ltd
18 Dalkeith Road   } for Scotland
Edinburgh EH16 5BS

Further information is available from The Director General, Ordnance Survey, PO Box 32, Romsey Road, Maybush, Southampton SO9 7BR

Air photographs

Air photographs covering England and Wales at scales of 1/10000 and 1/20000, and enlargements of these, can be obtained from the Air Photographs Officer, Department of the Environment, 2 Marsham Street, London SW1. In Scotland enquiries should be addressed to the Department of the Environment, Directorate of Scottish Services, Argylle House, 3 Lady Lawson Street, Edinburgh EH3 9SD. Details of the area and grid references should be quoted.

Geological Survey Maps

The geology of much of Great Britain has been recorded on 1 in. (1/50000) scale maps and that of many coal-mining areas and the County of London on 6 in. (1/10000) maps. Manuscript 6 in. (1/10000) maps of other areas may be inspected at the Institute of Geological Sciences Library in London, and at the appropriate Geological Survey Offices in Leeds, Edinburgh and Belfast. Much additional information is available as memoirs, reports and handbooks. Requests for lists of maps, currently available, and other enquiries should be addressed to The Director, Institute of Geological Sciences, Exhibition Road, South Kensington, London, S.W.7.

Meteorological Office publications

These are available as daily, monthly and annual records of the climate in Britain and are generally obtainable from H M Stationery Office. Enquiries should be addressed to the appropriate office of the Meteorological Office.*

Admiralty charts and publications

The charts show high and low water marks for Home waters and the levels of the sea and river beds with reference to a low-water datum. The Authority for chart information is the Hydrographer of the Navy, Ministry of Defence, Old War Office Building, Whitehall, London S.W.1.

Mining records

In coal-mining areas the Divisional Offices of the National Coal Board should be consulted for details of active and prospective workings and for records of abandoned workings. Records of abandoned mines of other than coal and oil-shale are held by the Department of Trade and Industry.

*Advisory offices of the Meteorological Office:

Meteorological Office	Meteorological Office	Meteorological Office
Met 0.3	Tyrone House	26 Palmerston Place
London Road	Ormeau Avenue	Edinburgh
Bracknell	Belfast	EH12 5AN
RG12 2SZ	BT2 8HH	

References

British Standard Code of Practice, CP 2001 (1957), 'Site investigations'.
British Standard BS 1377 : 1975, 'Methods of testing soils for civil engineering purposes'.
Digest 63   Soils and foundations: 1
Digest 67   Soils and foundations: 3
Digest 95   Choosing a type of pile.
Digest 174   Concrete in sulphate-bearing soils and groundwaters.
Digest 240   Low-rise buildings on shrinkable clay soils: 1
Digest 241   Low-rise buildings on shrinkable clay soils: 2
Digest 242   Low-rise buildings on shrinkable clay soils: 3

Soils and foundations : 3

This Digest considers the factors governing the choice of foundations for buildings and shows in what circumstances the choice is dependent upon soil conditions and other site characteristics such as vegetation and nearby buildings. The Digest should be read in conjunction with Digests 63 and 64, which deal with soil and foundation behaviour and site investigations.

Construction types

Both the type of construction and the subsequent use of the building are important determinants of foundation design. Strip footings are usually chosen for buildings in which the load is carried mainly on walls. Pad footings, piles or pile groups are more appropriate when the structural loads are carried by columns. If differential settlements must be controlled to within fine limits, shallow strip or pad footings (except on rock or dense sand) will probably be inadequate and surface rafts may have to be considered as an alternative.

Foundation loading

The forces carried at ground level by each load-bearing wall or column of a building should be calculated, taking account of how roofs and floors are supported. Superimposed loadings are specified in the Building Regulations 1972, and BS CP 3, Chapter V; Part 1 : 1967, *Dead and imposed loads,* and BS 648 : 1964, *Schedule of weights of building materials,* enables calculation of dead load forces.

A typical two-storey semi-detached house of about 85 m² area, in cavity brickwork, with lightweight concrete or clay block partitions, timber floors and a tiled roof, has a mass of 100 tonnes (approx. 1000 kN) excluding the weight of the foundations. The loads at ground level are, in kN/m, approximately : party wall 50, gable end wall 40, front and back walls 25 and internal partitions less than 15. While the use of modern materials tends to reduce the *total* loads, some forms of construction, e.g. the cross-walled type, may exert higher foundation loads on *individual* walls than is the case with more traditional forms.

When the foundations have been designed, their weight must be added to the loadings already calculated so as to obtain the total bearing pressures on the soil beneath.

Soil data

Inspection pits, samples from boreholes and simple field tests suggested in Table 1 of *Digest 64* should provide data enabling near-surface soils to be identified and their strengths estimated. Geological maps and local records will often indicate whether the soils beneath pits and boreholes are likely to influence foundation design.

Adjacent buildings

New construction must not put the stability of existing properties at risk. If new foundations are placed close to those of an existing building, the envelopes of stressed soil will overlap and the loads on the soil will increase. As a result, clays may consolidate further and cause cracking of both buildings by differential settlement.

When an excavation is made, the stability of adjacent buildings may be threatened unless the excavation is adequately supported. This is particularly important with sands and gravels which derive their support from lateral restraint. Water draining towards excavations below the water table can also disturb the ground beneath adjacent buildings by increasing the effective weight of the soil and by carrying fine particles away.

When piles are to be driven the effects of vibration on surrounding soils must be considered.

Vegetation

Clays which have supported mature trees for many years will be in a dried state and likely to swell when the trees are felled (*see Digest 63*). Buildings erected before swelling is completed will therefore be subject to uplift. Unless the resulting differential movements can be accommodated by the structure or eliminated by the foundations, it will be necessary to defer

Table 1. Choice of foundation

Soil type and site condition	Foundation	Details	Remarks
Rock, solid chalk, sands and gravels or sands and gravels with only small proportions of clay, dense silty sands	Shallow strip or pad footings as appropriate to the load-bearing members of the building	Breadth of strip footings to be related to soil density and loading (see Table 2). Pad footings should be designed for bearing pressures tabled in CP 101 : 1972. For higher pressures the depth should be increased and CP 2004 : 1972 'Foundations' consulted	Keep above water wherever possible. Slopes on sand liable to erosion. Foundations 0·5 m deep should be adequate on ground susceptible to frost heave although in cold areas or in unheated buildings the depth may have to be increased. Beware of swallow holes in chalk
Uniform, firm and stiff clays: (1) Where vegetation is insignificant	Bored piles and ground beams, or strip foundations at least 1 m deep	Deep strip footings of the narrow widths shown in Table 2 can conveniently be formed of concrete up to the ground surface	
(2) Where trees and shrubs are growing or to be planted close to the site	Bored piles and ground beams	Bored piles dimensions as in Table 3	Downhill creep may occur on slopes greater than 1 in 10. Unreinforced piles have been broken by slowly moving slopes
(3) Where trees are felled to clear the site and construction is due to start soon afterward	Reinforced bored piles of sufficient length with the top 3 m sleeved from the surrounding ground and with **suspended floors** or basement rafts		
Soft clays, soft silty clays	Strip footings up to 1 m wide if bearing capacity is sufficient, or rafts	See Table 2 and CP 101 : 1972	Settlement of strips or rafts must be expected. Services entering building must be sufficiently flexible. In soft soils of variable thickness it is better to pile to firmer strata (See Peat and Fill below)
Peat, fill	Bored piles with temporary steel lining or precast or in situ piles driven to firm strata below	Design with large safety factor on end resistance of piles only as peat or fill consolidating may cause a downward load on pile (see Digest 63) Field tests for bearing capacity of deep strata or pile loading tests will be required	If fill is sound, carefully placed and compacted in thin layers, strip footings are adequate. Fills containing combustible or chemical wastes should be avoided
Mining and other subsidence areas	Thin reinforced rafts for individual houses with load-bearing walls and for flexible buildings	Rafts must be designed to resist tensile forces as the ground surface stretches in front of a subsidence. A layer of granular material should be placed between the ground surface and the raft to permit relative horizontal movement	Building dimensions at right angles to the front of long-wall mining should be as small as possible

construction until swelling is complete, which can mean a delay of many years.

To avoid this delay the following alternative methods should be considered:

(i) Anchoring the building by reinforced bored piles sleeved from the ground over their top 3 m, and providing suspended floors. Beams spanning between the piles must be well clear of the ground surface.

(ii) Using flexible framed construction without brickwork or plastering.

(iii) Making the building rigid by either constructing a basement or reinforcing the foundations and brickwork.

Buildings erected close to standing trees should be supported on piles of sufficient depth, and for small structures bored piles are likely to be the most economical. Where nearby vegetation is insignificant, strip footings 1 m deep are usually adequate.

Choice of foundation type

Subject to the factors already considered, Table 1 gives the most appropriate foundations for buildings of not more than four storeys for a variety of typical soil conditions.

Economic and constructional factors

The availability of builders' plant can influence the relative costs of foundation types, particularly for small works. Large works may require specialist equipment; if so, the foundation design chosen should make the fullest use of it.

Experience has shown that, in shrinkable clay areas, short piles bored with mechanical augers are competitive in cost with traditional strip footings of the required depth, even for quite small contracts. For single house contracts bored piles are usually slightly more costly than strip footings, but the extra cost is justified by the additional safety obtained.

In any case, simple costing on a labour-plus-materials basis may be misleading. Construction of bored piles can often continue through the winter months when the trenches for strip foundations would be waterlogged or damaged by exposure to frost. On large sites, once all vegetation has been cleared, piles can sometimes be placed in one operation in summer, leaving above-ground construction to continue through the following winter. In addition to use on clay sites, bored-pile foundations with pre-cast ground beams should be useful for low-rise industrialized systems; in cross-wall house construction more than 10 piles are rarely necessary.

Constructional problems must also be considered. Elimination of water from excavations other than by pumping from drainage sumps can be expensive. Foundations on sands and gravels should be kept above the water-table whenever possible; if not, water should be drained or pumped away from the excavation rather than towards it so as to reduce the risk of erosion at its face. If the sides of excavations in coarse-grained soils are not sufficiently shallow to prevent collapse, support by timbers or sheet piles is necessary. Cuts in firm clay and chalk normally stand unsupported for short periods at steeper slopes than in granular soils, although some very soft clays lose much of their strength when disturbed. Clay and chalk surfaces deteriorate when exposed to water and frost and should be protected by concreting. Ground which has softened must be removed. Filling often has to be placed within the foundations of a building to bring the ground level up to that necessary for pouring concrete floor slabs. This cannot be compacted with mechanical plant, particularly if the fill level is higher than that of the ground outside, without risk of damaging the brickwork. The fill should therefore be chosen for its ability to bed well under light compaction. Alternatively, the fill should be placed and compacted before the foundations are laid.

Table 2. Minimum width for strip foundations

Soil type	Field assessment of structure and strength	Minimum width (mm) for total load (kN/m) of not more than:						
		16	24	32	40	48	56	64
Gravels and sands	Loose	300	450	600				
	Compact	225	225	300	375	450	525	600
Silts	Soft	450	675	900	Silts are frequently combined with sands or clays. Values for composite types are given in the Building Regulations			
	Firm	300	450.	600				
Clays	Very soft	450	675	900				
	Soft	360	525	675				
	Firm	260	325	375	450	560	675	750
	Stiff or hard	225	225	300	375	450	525	600
Peat	Soft	Footings should be in firm ground beneath the peat. Rarely does investigation show that the peat itself will support foundations						
	Firm							
Chalk	Plastic	Assess as clay above						
	Solid	Equal to the width of the wall						
Fill		To be determined after investigation						

Table 3. Load-carrying capacity of bored piles (in kN)

Strength classification	Diameter of pile (mm)	Length of pile (m)				
		2·5	3	3·5	4	4·5
Stiff	250	40	48	56	64	72
(Undrained shear strength	300	50	60	70	80	90
more than 70 kN/m²)	350	65	77	90	102	115
Hard	250	55	65	75	85	95
Undrained shear strength	300	70	82	94	106	118
more than 140 kN/m²)	350	95	108	120	132	145

Note: The figures are for clay which increases in strength with depth to the 'stiff' and 'hard' classifications near the bottom of the piles. The figures should not be applied to piles in other situations.

Design
Strip footings
The recommendations for strip footings in Table 2 are in SI units which correspond approximately to the provisions of the Building Regulations (1972) and BS CP 101 : 1972, *Foundations and substructures for non-industrial buildings of not more than four storeys*. The table gives minimum values for the width of strip foundations in soil types identified in Table 1 of *Digest 64*.

Pad footing and rafts
Pad footings and surface rafts should be designed using the bearing capacities tabled in CP 101 : 1972. They should be proportioned wherever possible so that the centre of area of the foundation is vertically beneath the centre of pressure of the imposed loads, and the thickness and reinforcement should be calculated to resist all shear and bending forces. An angle of spread of load of 45° to the vertical may be assumed.

The bearing pressure on soil beneath deep rafts or basements is reduced because of the amount of soil excavated. Further, because of the associated walls, deep rafts possess considerable rigidity. These two advantages may be somewhat offset, however, by the greater expense of deep rafts compared with piles and ground beams.

Note: The design of raft foundations requires considerable knowledge and care, and expert advice should be taken.

Short bored piles
Table 3 gives load-carrying capacities for bored piles in shrinkable clay soils. A simple method of design not requiring laboratory measurements of clay strength is referenced (Ward and Green) below. It is most important that an adequate thickness of compressible material such as loose ash is placed between the ground beams and the clay surface to

allow for relative movement. Concrete floor slabs, if used, should be isolated from the beams and main walls. Suspended floors are preferable when swelling is expected.

Other foundations
Except for major works, when expert advice must be taken, the foundations of all extensions, garages and bay windows should be of the same form and at the same depth as the foundations of the main building.

Further reading
Digests
63 Soils and foundations : 1
64 Soils and foundations : 2
142 Fill and hardcore
240 Low-rise buildings on shrinkable clay soils : Part 1
241 Low-rise buildings on shrinkable clay soils : Part 2
242 Low-rise buildings on shrinkable clay soils : Part 3

Papers
Green H Building on shrinkable clays—some applications of short concrete piles *JRIBA* 1952, **59** (April) pp. 212–213

Green H Long-term loading of short-bored piles. *Geotech.*, 1961, **11** (1) (March) pp. 47–53.

Lacey W D and Swain H T Construction theory : design for mining subsidence *Archit. J.*, 1957, **126** (October 10), pp. 557–570.

Ward W H House foundations, *JRIBA* 1947, **54** (February), pp. 226–235

Ward W H and Green H House foundations : the short-bored pile. Public Works and Municipal Services Congress 1952

Tomlinson M J, Driscoll R, Burland J B Foundations for low-rise buildings. *The Structural Engineer* Part A 1978 56A (6) 161-173. BRE Current Paper CP 61/78.

Low-rise buildings on shrinkable clay soils: Part 1

The need for additional guidance on building on clay soils was established by the concern at the high incidence of subsidence damage during the 1975-76 drought. This digest supplements Nos 63, 64 and 67 - Soils and foundations - and is based on work done by BRE following the drought.

The digest is published in three parts: Part 1 describes the shrinking and swelling behaviour of these soils and shows the general location within the UK of the more common shrinkable clays. It also gives guidance on identifying such clay and assessing its shrinking or swelling potential. Part 2 discusses designs which should provide stable foundations in the most adverse circumstances and Part 3 describes the design of bored pile and beam foundations.

Nature of clay soils

Soils which contain a large proportion of very small mineral particles (defined as having a diameter less than 0.002 mm and which are invisible to the naked eye) are called 'clays'. Clays are characteristically plastic, and smooth and greasy to the touch. The more clay in the soil, relative to any silt or other coarser-grained material, then the more pronounced are these characteristics.

In the wet state, clays are soft and sticky and require scrubbing to remove them from boots. When dried out, clays shrink and crack and intact lumps become very hard to break. When a clod of firm, shrinkable clay is immersed in water it will soften only slowly, without disintegrating. If the clod disintegrates quickly, it contains silt and other coarser-grained materials. In the field, firm shrinkable clays can be identified by their highly fissured nature, by the high polish left by digging tools and by the extensive crazing that occurs as the clay dries on the sunny side of a trench.

While clays are recognised by the small size of their constituent particles, it is as much the type of mineral in these particles as their size that contributes to the behaviour of the clay. For example, the very 'clayey' minerals hold water within their molecular structure, much as jelly does, whereas some soils, such as rock flours containing clay-sized particles, only hold water between particles and do not exhibit clay-like behaviour; in particular, their dry strength is low. The clays which contain the very 'clayey' minerals are called 'fat' clays and in nature they always hold more water than the 'lean' clays which contain fewer of the 'clayey' minerals.

Engineers use simple, standardised, mechanical index tests (BS 1377) to identify the clay-nature and plasticity of soils. In the first test, water is progressively added and thoroughly mixed into the soil to form a smooth paste. Each successive mix becomes weaker until the consistency may be described as 'liquid' when measured by a mechanical device. The amount of water (expressed as a percentage of the dry weight) in the clay at this 'liquid' consistency is called the Liquid Limit; the higher the Liquid Limit, the more 'clayey' the behaviour.

The Liquid Limit defines the amount of water required to bring the clay to a very weak, plastic consistency. At the other extreme is the Plastic Limit, which is the amount of water in a clay soil below which it is no longer plastic and pasty, but breaks up when worked in the hands. Below the Plastic Limit there is insufficient water to fill the spaces between the solid particles and increasingly the voids become filled with air as the water content reduces. A simple, standard test to determine the Plastic Limit is described in BS 1377. The range of water contents over which the soil behaves plastically therefore lies between the Plastic and Liquid Limits. Within this range the soil is saturated with water which lubricates and separates the solid particles. At these water contents the soil shrinks as it dries and the volume change is in direct proportion to the amount of water removed (see Fig 1). However, when soil at water contents near the Plastic Limit is dried, air enters the soil and the volume shrinkage becomes less than the amount of water removed.

Occurence and identification of shrinkable clays in the UK

Firm, shrinkable clays, capable of supporting buildings of up to three or four storeys on shallow foundations, occur widely in the SE of England, as shown on the map in Fig 2. Examples of these clays are London, Gault, Weald, Kimmeridge, Oxford, Woolwich and Reading, Lias, Barton and the glacial drift clays, for example the chalky boulder clays of E Anglia, that are derived from the above-mentioned clays by glaciation. When originally laid down under water, these clays existed with moisture contents above the Liquid Limit. In the ensuing millions of years, the clays slowly consolidated as the imposed loads of soil overburden and glaciation squeezed the water out of the soil.

Many of the clays encoutered in SE England are termed 'overconsolidated' because great thicknesses of soil have been eroded with time leaving soils which have been consolidated by loads far greater than they now experience in the ground. In consequence, these clays often exist normally in the fully saturated condition, at moisture contents close to the Plastic Limit, ie typically 25 to 30 per cent for London Clay. However, close to the ground surface, in the top 1 - 1.5 m, fluctuations in moisture content from as little as 15 per cent in dry summer weather to 40 per cent in wet winters frequently occur.

Some shrinkable clays occur further north than the areas indicated in Fig 2; for example, those derived from the weathering and glaciation of Carboniferous shales around Sunderland and north of Shrewsbury. However, in the North the surface clays are generally sandy and their potential shrinkage is, therefore, smaller. In addition to the firm clays, there are soft, alluvial clays found in, and adjacent to, estuaries, lakes and river courses. Examples of these are the Fens, the Somerset levels, the Kent and Essex marshes along-side the Thames, and the clays of the Firths of Forth and Clyde. All these clays have a firm, shrunken crust which is drier than the body of the clay beneath. The foundation problems in these areas are not only of clay shrinkage, but also of avoiding excessive settlement due to loading the underlying softer clay and peat. Figure 2 gives only a general indication of the location of shrinkable clays; more detailed information on the location and identification of clay soils should be obtained from the Geological Survey maps and accompanying memoirs.

Shrinkage and swelling of clay soils

As the water content of a clay soil is reduced below its 'natural state' the soil will shrink. As the soil dries and shrinks, the soil moisture exerts more and more suction. If water is then brought into contact with the soil, it is absorbed as the soil swells. The concept of soil moisture suction in relation to moisture content is important when considering the influence of trees and other large vegetation on shrinkable clays.

The only way in which clay volume change can occur, other than as a result of load change, is through change in its moisture content. This can be brought about in two ways: one is through moisture movement near the ground surface where moisture evaporates in dry weather and is replenished by rainfall and by upward migration from the water table. The other way is by transpiration of soil moisture from greater depths than the first process, through the action of the roots of vegetation. In general the larger the vegetation, the greater will be its demand for moisture in dry weather.

Research at BRE has shown that, with the exception of the ground around large trees, and possibly hedges and large shrubs, the seasonal volume changes due to the presence of vegetation extend only about 1 - 1.5 m

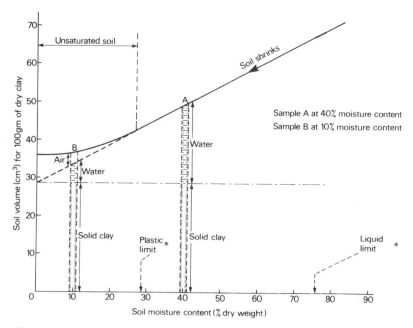

Fig 1 Clay soil shrinkage
*Typical values for a clay with potential very high shrinkage

Sample A at 40% moisture content
Sample B at 10% moisture content

into the clay ground. Significant clay shrinkage and swelling is confined to the top 1m or so.

However, large trees can create deep zones of dried and shrunken clay beneath them. In a dry summer, the zones will extend and when the wet weather returns the slow rate of penetration of water into the more impermeable dry clay will be insufficient to replenish the soil before the next summer arrives. Thus the larger dry zone becomes permanent.

For practical purposes then, serious drying of clay soils in the UK, to depths in excess of 1 to 1.5 m is almost always associated with the removal of moisture by tree roots. The amount of shrinkage or swelling that a clay will undergo is not easy to determine. The change in volume will depend on the localised clay properties (clay content and mineralogy) and the soil moisture changes that occur. The most useful way of assessing soil volume changes is to measure ground movements on site but, since the moisture changes are brought about by seasonal climatic changes, a considerable period of time is required. This approach is clearly impractical.

A practical alternative is to measure the shrinking and swelling of a sample taken from the site. In the case of shrinkage this approach is simple. A block of clay is removed, trimmed to have smooth sides and allowed to dry slowly at room temperature for two to three weeks. Comparison of linear measurements before and after drying give an estimate of the in-situ shrinkage. The block will probably dry out to a greater extent than will the clay on site so that the prediction will be an over-estimate. The measurement of sample swelling is not normally available as a practical test and because of its relative complexity remains a research tool.

Another approach to predicting shrinkage and swelling is the indirect method of determining the *potential* to shrink or swell. This involves examining properties of the clay that can be obtained from simple, standard classification tests. These properties are the Plasticity Index and the percentage clay content or clay fraction* of the soil. The Plasticity Index is obtained by substracting the Plastic Limit from the Liquid Limit.

Tests to determine these properties are specified in BS 1377 and are readily available from a competent soil testing laboratory at little cost.

In Table 1, Plasticity Index and clay fraction have been used to indicate the potential of a soil to shrink or swell. The figures have been obtained from many different sources and frequently overlap. Since a set of soil properties will often not fit neatly into one category, the determination of shrinkage potential requires some judgement.

---

* Percentage of the soil with particle size less than 0.002 mm.

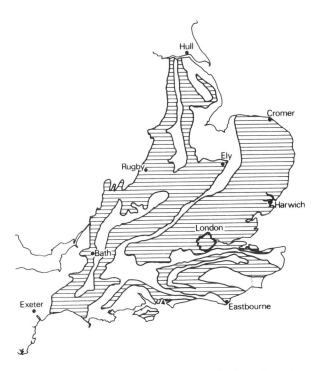

Fig 2 General distribution of firm shrinkable clays - based on BRE records and Institute of Geological Sciences maps

Table 1 Clay shrinkage potential

Plasticity Index %	Clay fraction %	Shrinkage potential
> 35	> 95	Very high
22 - 48	60 - 95	High
12 - 32	30 - 60	Medium
< 18	< 30	Low

To give an indication of how Table 1 may be used, the shrinkage potential of some clays commonly found in the UK is given in Table 2. It should be remembered that the properties of a clay can vary considerably from site to site.

Table 2 Shrinkage potential of some common clays

Clay type	Plasticity Index %	Clay fraction %	Shrinkage potential
London	28	65	Medium/high
London	52	60	High
Weald	43	62	High
Kimmeridge	53	67	High/very high
Boulder	32	-	Medium
Oxford	41	56	High
Reading	72	-	Very high
Gault	60	59	Very high
Gault	68	69	Very high
Lower Lias	31	-	Medium
Clay silt	11	19	Low

Foundation design and performance in shrinkable clays

The design of foundations for low-rise buildings must take account of the shrinkage and swelling behaviour of clays, as the moisture content varies according to climatic and vegetation conditions. In practice, two courses of action are open: firstly, to estimate the potential to swell or shrink and then to try to avoid events which cause changes in moisture content; or secondly, to accept that swelling or shrinkage will occur and to take account of this in design. The foundations can be designed to resist resulting ground movements, or the superstructure designed to accommodate movement without damage.

Work carried out by the Building Research Establishment indicated a minimum foundation depth requirement of 0.9 m, below which seasonal wetting and drying and the influence of minor vegetation produce no significant ground movement. This depth has now become the accepted minimum for foundations on all clay soils. The research further identified the influence that roots of large trees may have in removing moisture from clay beneath foundations. This may cause subsidence leading to structural damage in dry weather conditions. The design of foundations suitable to withstand the larger movements sometimes induced by root action is discussed in Part 2 of this digest.

Further reading

BRE Digests
63 Soils and foundations: Part 1
64 Soils and foundations: Part 2
67 Soils and foundations: Part 3

British Standards
BS 1377:1975 Methods of test for soil for civil engineering
purposes
BS 5837:1980 Trees in relation to construction

Low-rise buildings on shrinkable clay soils: Part 2

Foundations for firm shrinkable clays

Volume changes in clay soils brought about by seasonal changes in soil moisture content, and by the removal of soil moisture by deeply rooted vegetation, have caused widespread damage to low-rise buildings, especially following periods of low rainfall. Whether or not substantial shrinkage will occur on any given site is difficult to predict since it depends not only on the soil type, but also on many other factors. Of these the local groundwater condition, which can vary enormously over short distances, is probably the most important. There are considerable differences in the performance of buildings with similar foundations on shrinkable clays. These differences depend largely on whether buildings are sited on open ground, away from the influence of deeper-rooted vegetation (trees, hedges and large bushes), or whether they are sited within the zones affected by growth of such vegetation. Accordingly, these two aspects are discussed separately.

Building on 'open' ground

For more than 25 years the Building Research Establishment has recommended a minimum foundation depth of 0.9 m in order to eliminate significant seasonal ground movements. The value of 0.9 m was selected to cater for movement in the worst types of clay soil during severe droughts. Even during the most severe drought of 1976 there appear to have been very few proven cases of damage to buildings founded at this depth in open ground.

The traditional strip foundation, which is the most common foundation in the UK, may not be economic when placed at depths of 0.9 m or more, and so the narrow strip (trench fill) foundation has gained general acceptance for the 'open' shrinkable clay site.

As protection against the possibility that trees subsequently planted close to new buildings may eventually produce damaging ground movements, or where local ground conditions dictate foundation depths in excess of 0.9 m, the bored pile foundation described later will be most suitable. Pile lengths of up to about 4.5 m are generally satisfactory depending on soil conditions and structural loadings. For large developments, and given favourable ground conditions, these foundations can be as economic as narrow strip foundations. Unless ground beams are cast in exceptionally dry conditions there is no need to allow for large uplift forces on the beams, and floors need not be suspended.

Buildings sited near major vegetation

The problem of volume changes in clay soil due to the drying action of tree roots is still not appreciated by many builders, engineers, planners and landscape architects. The Building Research Establishment has long warned of the possibility of damage occurring to buildings with foundations which have not been designed to withstand the effects of the roots of nearby large vegetation. Numerous case studies have indicated that there is a risk of some damage once the height of a tree exceeds its distance from a building. The risk appears to be greater when the trees are in groups or rows. Studies have also shown that damage can be caused by most of the common species of tree founded in the UK and also that large shrubs adjacent to buildings can occasionally cause damage. It is difficult to predict with certainty whether damage will occur in any given situation since so many factors are involved which relate both to the building and the ground conditions. Any site investigation for buildings on shrinkable clay with trees present should determine the spread of roots by examination in trial pits.

An assessment of the potential shrinkage of the clay and of the local hydrological conditions should help to identify sites where tree roots may present problems to buildings on shallow foundations.

Buildings can be safely sited close to trees, and vice versa, on clay soil of very high shrinkage potential provided adequate foundations are used. It is necessary to take the foundations below the existing or probable zone of desiccation, or root growth as determined by investigation. Since for large trees of high moisture consumption, especially in periods of very dry weather, these zones can extend to depths of as much as 5 m, the best technical solution appears to be the bored pile foundation.

There has recently been an increasing tendency among builders to construct very deep narrow strip foundations when building close to trees: strip foundation depths of 3 m and more are not uncommon. Three factors make this trend undesirable: the deep strip will, except in small schemes, almost certainly be more expensive than the bored pile solution; instability of the trench sides can lead to serious construction difficulties; there is a danger of horizontal foundation movement when large vertical areas of concrete are subjected to differential lateral pressures resulting from either shrinking or swelling of clay. Piled foundations should not be susceptible to any such lateral pressures.

An additional potentially damaging situation is where trees or hedges have been cut down prior to building. The subsequent long-term swelling of the zone of clay, desiccated by the roots, as moisture slowly returns to the ground, can be substantial. The rate at which the ground recovers is very difficult to predict and if there is any doubt that recovery is complete then bored pile foundations and suspended floors should be used.

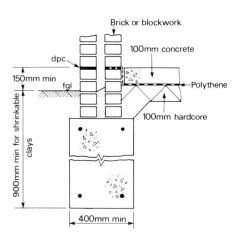

Fig 1   Narrow strip foundation for shrinkable clays

Foundations on the 'open' clay site

The use of the narrow strip (or 'trench fill') foundation for houses on clay sites was first proposed in 1947. At that time the need was accepted to take foundations to a depth of 0.9 m in order to avoid excessive movements by the seasonal swelling and shrinkage of clays. It was appreciated that the minimum width of about 500 mm required for laying bricks in the 0.9 m deep trench resulted in bearing pressures which were uneconomically low for stiff clays. By adopting a narrow trench, say 400 mm wide, which could be cut by a mechanical excavator and filled with mass concrete (Fig 1), a bearing pressure of about 125 kN/m² would result. This pressure would not be excessive for stiff clays and the trench could be cut to a depth of 0.9 m or more without support. The narrow strip foundation considerably reduced the volume of excavation and while there was a 50 per cent increase in the quantity of concrete for a strip 0.9 m deep, this was cheaper in 1 : 9 concrete than the brickwork it replaced. There were also useful savings in unskilled labour in trimming the trench sides and bottom and in the skilled labour for foundation brickwork.

In order to achieve the economies inherent in this design, the narrow strip foundation requires a standard of accuracy in setting out and construction somewhat higher than that needed for the traditional strip. Accuracy in line is required to avoid the brick footing courses projecting over the edge of the narrow concrete strip, and accuracy in level is needed since there are usually no more than four or five courses of brickwork between the top of the foundation and the dpc. Three of these courses must be built true to line and level to achieve the required architectural appearance of the external brickwork. Care is also needed in positioning the services which pass through the footings, since their location cannot be easily adjusted once they are cast into the foundation concrete. In the case of traditional strip foundations, the services are located within the footing brickwork.

Nominal reinforcement may readily be inserted in narrow strip foundations. Modern buildings are frequently brittle because of the use of strong mortars and such reinforcement will provide added assurance against the possibility of foundation movement causing minor damage. This is particularly relevant where there is some local variability in soil composition and strength that might cause differential settlement within a foundation.

Cases have been reported of damage to narrow strip foundation in desiccated clay following a period of low rainfall during construction. Heavy rain falling before the superstructure loads had been applied to the foundations caused the clay to swell and heave, lifting and cracking the foundations. Swift construction of the superstructure is desirable in these circumstances.

Pile foundations for clay sites with trees

In cohesive soils above the water table, piles can be bored by mechanical auger. Reinforced ground beams supporting the load-bearing walls are usually cast in situ in trenches cut below ground level to avoid formwork. The resulting foundation (Fig 2) should cost less than strip footings taken to the required depth. Where ground conditions are unfavourable to mechanical auger boring, (such as in glacial clays containing boulders and clays containing hard, claystone layers or pockets of dense sand) cased percussion drilling or driven and cast-in-situ piling is necessary, with substantially increased costs.

Small diameter, driven precast, shell piles, as shown in Fig 3, can also be used on level sites of uniform clay soil. However, light piling rigs for small, driven piles are not widely available and bringing larger and heavier plant to site adds to the overall cost of piling work. On speculative housing sites where the builder does not want to commit himself to constructing all the foundations in advance of selling the houses, several visits by the specialist piling contractor may be necessary.

For buildings on sites where large trees and hedges have been removed, the upper part of the pile shaft should be sleeved in polythene sheeting, or pvc or cardboard tubes, to reduce uplift forces from the swelling clay. Tension reinforcement over the full length of the pile is necessary to deal with any residual uplift forces (see Fig 4). The pile shaft below the sleeved zone should be of sufficient length to provide the required frictional resistance to any residual uplift force. As an alternative to sleeving the upper part of the pile, the pile may be lengthened to provide the necessary frictional resistance against uplift. Adequate tensile reinforcement must, of course, be included to resist the full uplift force.

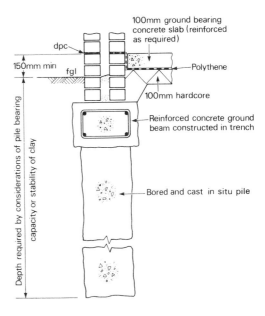

Fig 2 Design of bored pile foundation for houses sited on loose fill, soft compressible soils and open heavy clay

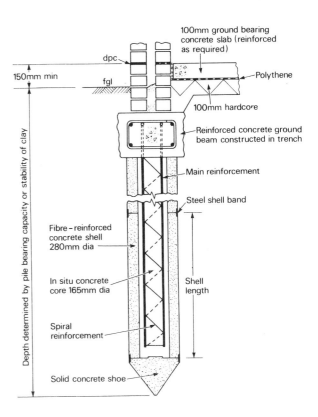

Fig 3 Design of driven, mini-shell pile foundation for houses sited on loose fill, soft compressible soils and shrinkable clays
(Courtesy of West's Piling and Construction Co Ltd)

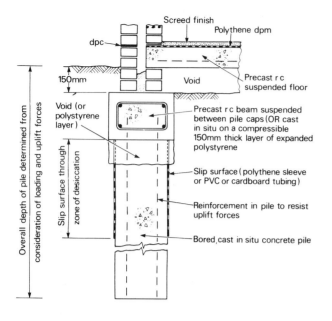

Fig 4 Design of bored pile foundation to resist uplift in swelling clay condition

In order to accommodate swelling pressures on the underside of the capping beams they may be cast in situ on to a layer of compressible material eg polystyrene. Alternatively, pre-cast, suspended, beams may be used, in which case the void beneath the beam accommodates any vertical ground swell. Ground floor slabs should also be suspended. Either pre-cast concrete units or timber floors, with void ventilation, are suitable. A recently developed, alternative method of providing a void beneath in-situ ground beams is to cast directly on to a honeycomb fibre board of sufficient compressive strength when dry to support the weight of concrete and steel. The fibre board is designed to deteriorate structurally as it moistens, producing a moist layer of degraded board which can compress when ground heave occurs so that upward forces are not transmitted to the beams.

Whilst most piling for low-rise foundations is carried out by piling contractors, some builders have successfully developed their own light, mobile lorry or tractor-mounted auger rigs. In favourable conditions some 80 piles per day can be drilled with these machines (ie the foundations for approximately four to eight houses, depending on type). However, the installation of piled foundations requires considerable care and experienced supervision since defective workmanship in piles or ground beams can result in severe damage to the superstructure.

A comparison of foundation costs

The construction of terraced houses in a new town in Essex was costed to compare two types of foundation in firm/stiff shrinkable clay, on an 'open' site, well away from the influence of major vegetation. The average cost of narrow strip foundations for 25 houses was compared with the average for 25 houses with bored-pile and beam foundations. The strip foundations were taken to a depth of 1 m, while the piling was to a depth of about 4 m. Reinforced ground beams between piles were cast in situ on a layer of building paper over ash. In the table, the costs of these foundations per house are shown relative to the costs of piled foundations (100), to remove the effects of inflation.

It was not possible to construct traditional strip foundations on this site but, for comparison, the cost of a 1 m deep, traditional strip foundation has been included, based on labour productivity and material costs for the site.

	Estimated foundation costs *(Average of 25 terraced houses)*		
	Narrow strip (trench fill)	**Bored pile and beam**	**Deep traditional strip**
Total relative foundation costs	102	100	127

In all cases, costs included site stripping, setting out, excavation and spoil removal, concrete, reinforcement, hardcore, concrete slabs and brickwork to dpc level. An additional cost was included for design and supervision of the piling. Overhead costs and profit were not included.

The excavation plant consisted of a trenching machine with a 0.38 m bucket and a 0.3 m dia mechanical auger mounted on a tractor.

The main factors, apart from the designer's specification, which affect relative costs are:

(a) Properties of the soil.

(b) Design of foundations and shape of the building. Pile and beam foundations are particularly advantageous when lightweight superstructure materials are used, the smaller loads permitting fewer or smaller piles and cheaper beams. When buildings have large window openings on the ground floor, piling is particularly suitable as loads between openings can be carried on single piles whereas the dimensions of continuous footings are normally not varied around a building.

(c) Method of construction and size of contract.

(d) Local prices of materials.

Low-rise buildings
on shrinkable clay soils: Part 3

Pile layout and loading

In typical designs for pairs or terraces of two-storey houses of 280 mm cavity wall construction, with tiled roofs and timber first floors spanning between party walls, end gable walls and internal load-bearing walls, the average load taken by the foundations is about 34 kN/m (1 ton per foot).

Approximate values of individual wall loadings are given in the table below.

	Party	End gable	Front and back	Internal*
Load (kN/m)	50	40	25	15

(*Excluding any heavy chimney)

Foundation loads can be reduced to almost half the values for 280 mm cavity brick walls by using light-weight concrete blocks in weak mortar. Several types of prefabricated construction cause similar reductions in load but high wall-loadings must be presumed for foundation design where large stiff panels are weakly-connected and joint movements need to be small. To support the walls most economically, piles should be placed at the corners of buildings, at appropriate intermediate positions along the walls and adjacent to openings for doors and large windows. Ground beams should span between piles beneath all loadbearing walls. Typical pile layouts are illustrated in Figs 1 and 2.

From the wall loadings, the loads carried on each beam can be calculated and the reactions of the piles can be estimated. Adjustments can then be made to the positions and number of piles to equalise the loading as far as possible and to reduce pile loads to the desired level.

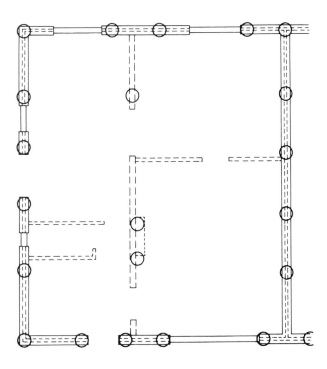

Fig 1 Arrangement of piles to suit a semi-detached house

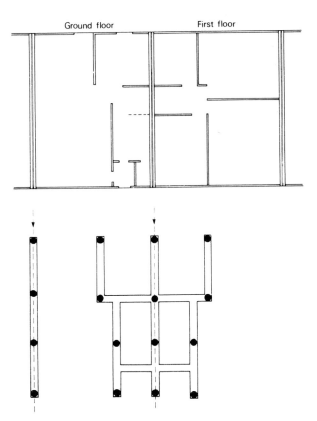

Fig 2 Simple layout of piles and beams for two-storey terraced house of cross-wall construction

Calculation of allowable pile load

The ultimate resistance of a pile to external loading is given by two components: the base resistance and the shaft frictional resistance. The allowable load is then determined by dividing the ultimate resistances by suitable factors of safety and summing them. Figure 3 shows values of allowable base load for various pile diameters and values of the undrained shear strength (Cu) of the clay at the base of the pile. These values have been calculated using a factor of safety on ultimate base resistance of 2. Figure 4 shows values of allowable shaft resistance, per metre of pile, for various pile diameters and values of shaft adhesion. Shaft adhesion is taken as equal to the fully-softened shear strength of the soil to cover the case where the clay adjacent to the pile is fully-wetted and, therefore, at its softest. For this condition a factor of safety, for shaft resistance, of 1 is permissable. However, if the clay is not wet a value of shaft adhesion of $(0.45 \times \overline{C}_u \div 2)$ may be used, where $\overline{C}_u$ is the average soil shear strength over the depth of the pile, and factor of safety is 2.

When calculating the shaft resistance, the designer must select a pile length appropriate to the conditions. In the case of piling in open clay sites away from the influence of tree roots, the top 1 m of pile shaft should be assumed to offer no resistance. When designing

piles for sites where the roots of trees are expected, or have been found in a site investigation, an additional length of pile should be assumed, to allow for shrinkage of clay away from the pile surface. This additional length will depend on the expected depth of the desiccation by roots.

When piles are used for a site where trees have been removed and swelling of the clay can be expected, the load in the piles will be reduced by the upward force of the swelling clay. This force may be enough to put part of the pile into tension, and reinforcement will be required. It is prudent to reinforce the pile over its full length.

In extreme cases, the swelling force on the pile and on ground beams may be sufficient to lift the pile. In this case, either a slip surface should be provided by sleeving the pile to reduce friction or the length of the pile increased to resist the force.

Pile design for swelling soils requires the attention of a qualified engineer.

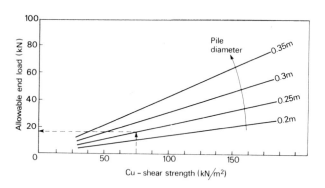

Fig 3 Pile end load

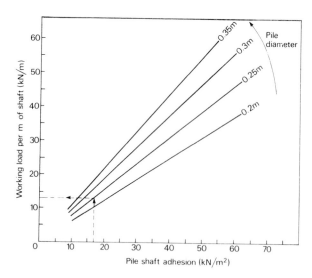

Fig 4 Pile shaft load

Design example

As a simple example of the use of the design aids presented in Figs 3 and 4, the following case is considered.

The maximum pile load for a particular scheme will be 67 kN. The undrained shear strength given in the site investigation report has an average value of 75 kN/m². The site investigation also revealed the presence of fine roots, from nearby trees, to a depth of 1.8 m.

Assuming a pile diameter of 0.25 m, Fig 3 shows the allowable end load as about 16.5 kN. In the absence of a value for the fully-softened shear strength and assuming that the piles will be concreted in dry weather immediately following boring, the value of shaft adhesion is calculated as $0.45 \times 75 \div 2 = 16.9$ kN/m².

From Fig 4, the shaft working load per m length of pile is found to be 13.5 kN/m. Therefore an effective pile lenght of $\frac{67 - 16.5}{13.5} = 3.74$m is required. To this must be added 1.8m to cater for the presnce of the roots, giving a final pile length of 5.54m.

Ground-beam design

Measurements carried out by BRE of the bending moments in beams supporting brickwork show that the magnitude and distribution of bending moments are influenced by the arching action of the brickwork itself. This 'composite action' between beams and brickwork allows beams to be designed for smaller than normal bending moments. This reduction in beam bending moment applies only to brick inner leaf construction and not to lightweight concrete block-work. Instead of adopting a moment of WL/12, based on a triangular distribution of brickwork load above the beam, reduced moments of WL/100, for walls with no openings or openings at mid-span, may be used. Lintels over door or window openings at mid-span act as struts and develop much of the composite action occuring in continuous brick wall cases. For walls with openings near beam supports a moment of WL/50 may be used. In these two cases W is the weight of the *rectangle* of brickwork above the beam. Assuming a worst beam loading of 50 kN/m, values of required beam depth and area of reinforcing steel, for various beam spans and widths, are given in Tables 1 and 2. The values in Table 1 have been calculated using a bending moment of $\frac{WL}{50}$, whilst for Table 2 a moment of $\frac{WL}{100}$ has been used. All steel specified is bottom steel.

Various limitations on stresses in reinforcing bars and on minimum beam depths are advised and these have been applied in Tables 1 and 2. Even with these limitations the depths of most of the beams could, on loading considerations alone, be much less (especially for the smaller spans) than the minimum practical depth of 200 mm recommended. (The beam designs therefore have an additional factor of safety built in since depths have been rounded up to a minimum of 200 mm).

In cases where foundations are designed to resist heave of the ground due to swelling, hogging may be introduced into beams, necessitating some top steel over the full span. In all other circumstances, the beams should experience only sagging in their middle halves. Top steel is, however, required immediately over pile heads and extending each side as far as quarter-span points, with appropriate shear reinforcements. If a door opening is situated at the end of a span, additional shear reinforcement is necessary.

The design method adopted in the tables assumes that the ground floor rests on the ground and is independent of the capping beams. If the floor is suspended, as is required in the case of swelling soil, consideration of the additional beam loadings will be required in the beam design.

Table 1 Beam design for moment = WL/50

Span (m)	Beam width (mm) 280		Beam width (mm) 330		Beam width (mm) 380	
	depth	steel	depth	steel	depth	steel
2	200	440	200	480	200	520
3	200	670	200	720	200	780
4	250	890	250	960	200	1035
5	300	1110	300	1200	250	1300
6	350	1330	300	1450	300	1550

(Each cell: Beam depth (mm) upper, Steel area (mm²) lower)

Table 2 Beam design for moment = WL/100

Span (m)	Beam width (mm) 280		Beam width (mm) 330		Beam width (mm) 380	
	depth	steel	depth	steel	depth	steel
2	200	310	200	340	200	360
3	200	470	200	510	200	550
4	200	630	200	680	200	730
5	250	790	200	850	200	920
6	250	940	250	1020	250	1100

Choosing a type of pile

This digest emphasises the need for a full investigation of ground conditions before deciding whether piles should be used or not, and stresses the importance of consulting a foundation engineer at an early stage. Types of piles and methods of installation are considered and a series of questions and answers is included, designed to lead to the correct choice of pile.

The approach to foundation design is substantially the same whether the structure is a small building or a large civil engineering construction. Discussions with a foundation engineer should take place as early as possible in the design stage so that the form of superstructure and foundation can be correctly chosen to suit each other. This requires adequate information about the ground conditions, expected loading and tolerable settlement of the structure, as well as the possible effects on adjoining property. Broadly speaking, different forms of piling have been devised to suit different ground conditions and the nature of the ground will largely determine the choice.

Unless the ground conditions are known accurately, it is impossible to reach a worth-while assessment of the situation. Information about the identities, strengths and compressibilities of all the strata likely to affect the foundations should therefore be obtained. Since the strata below the level of the pile points must carry the load, the site investigations should extend to a depth of at least one-and-a-half times the width of the structure below the anticipated pile point level. The presence of water-bearing sands or gravels should

be determined, especially if the water is moving or is under artesian pressure. The choice of the pile material will be influenced by the presence of chemically aggressive groundwater or soil which may cause deterioration of the pile material and, in harbour work, by the likelihood of attack by marine borers.

Types of piles

The sequence of strata determines how the piles will transmit load to the ground, whether by end-bearing or by 'skin friction'. With an end-bearing pile, the shaft usually goes through soft deposits and the base or point rests on bedrock or penetrates some distance into a stratum of dense sand or gravel so that the pile acts as a column (see Figs 1 and 2). A friction pile is embedded entirely in cohesive soil and obtains its support mainly by the adhesion or 'skin friction' of the soil on the surface of the shaft (Fig 3).

There is a further distinction between piles which are installed by forcing the soil to move out of the way,

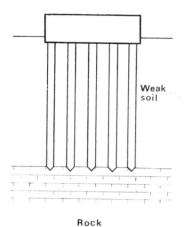

Weak soil

Rock

Fig 1

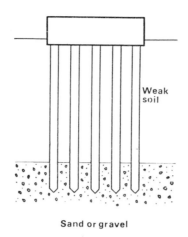

Weak soil

Sand or gravel

Fig 2

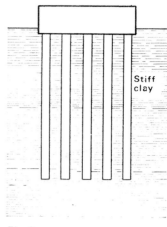

Stiff clay

Fig 3

such as happens when a stake is driven into the ground (these are known as 'displacement' piles) and those which cause no displacement because a hole is bored or excavated in the soil and the pile is formed by casting concrete in the hole (these may be termed 'non-displacement' or 'replacement' piles). **H**-section steel piles are usually thought of as 'small-displacement' piles.

Preformed solid piles of timber or reinforced concrete, and concrete or steel tubes or 'shells' with the lower end closed are clearly displacement piles. A displacement pile can also be formed by driving a steel tube with a detachable shoe or plug. As the tube is withdrawn, the shoe is left behind, while concrete poured into the tube runs out at the now open bottom to fill the void. The concrete is thus cast directly against the soil and is compressed or tamped in some way, depending on the particular proprietary system of piling. The hardened concrete forms the pile.

Replacement piles can be formed by driving an open tube, the bottom edge of which may be formed to a cutting edge, and extracting the soil core as the tube is sunk. When a suitable bearing stratum is reached, the tube is cleaned out and filled with concrete. A very common method of making a replacement pile is to form a borehole by auger or percussion methods, whichever is suitable, using temporary casing or lining tubes if needed to keep the hole open, and then to fill the borehole with concrete, withdrawing the casing tubes as the concrete is placed.

Preformed or cast-in-place piles may therefore be of either displacement or replacement type. Almost all cast-in-place displacement piles, precast reinforced concrete piles in modular lengths with special mechanical joints, bored piles and shell piles driven with the aid of a mandrel are installed by specialist piling contractors. However, it is the usual practice for a general civil engineering contractor to install preformed timber and steel **H** piles, some reinforced concrete piles preformed to the required lengths, and shell piles not requiring a mandrel.

Timber piles are usually made long enough to ensure that they will not need to be lengthened to accommodate normal ground variation or errors. Steel piles and tubes are easily shortened or lengthened and shell piles can be adjusted to length by the addition of further lengths of shell. Preformed reinforced concrete piles are now frequently built up from modular lengths supplied and driven by specialist contractors. The modular units are fitted with mechanical joints so that the piles can be lengthened during driving. The units are formed of high quality concrete under controlled conditions and transported to the site after they have cured. Like steel and concrete pile shells, the units are in convenient lengths and present no transport problems.

Cast-in-place piles of either displacement or replacement type are formed to the lengths required. Ready-mixed concrete is generally used for cast-in-place piles on urban sites.

Methods of installation

The traditional method of installing a pile is by means of a drop hammer, raised by a winch and allowed to fall on the pile head. Drop hammers are still in common use, together with compressed air, steam and diesel hammers. Loud noise and some vibration often accompany hammer-driven piling operations, but driving under carefully controlled conditions does not necessarily give rise to harmful vibrations, and noise can be reduced if the pile is driven by an internal drop hammer.

When the soil conditions are suitable, piles and casing tubes can be driven by vibration. The vibrator-driver brings the pile into vibration in the direction of its longitudinal axis. This breaks down the resistance of the soil, permitting the pile to sink under the combined weight of the driver and the pile. The chief source of noise in vibration driving is from the motors.

Boreholes up to 600 mm in diameter can be sunk using percussion tools on tripod rigs with compressed air or diesel winch motors. If the pile is short and of small diameter, a tractor-mounted auger might be used, but for bored piles over 600 mm in diameter, large truck- or crane-mounted augers or excavating rigs, using percussion tools and grabs within heavy casing tubes, would be used. The boring operation itself is relatively quiet but there will be noise from the motors. Piles used for underpinning may be installed by progressively adding short lengths to a pile, which is jacked into place. Small tripod rigs, needing no more than 2.5 m headroom, can form bored piles for underpinning.

Large piling rigs impose heavy loads on the soil, and the temporary work needed to get the rig to its worksite over weak ground can be a major item. If a large rig is needed for only a few piles the on-costs per pile may be unacceptably high.

Influence of the ground

The choice of piles for buildings and bridges can usually be made by satisfying the following questions:

1 Is the soil sensitive to an important degree?

Many alluvial soils of recent origin are sensitive, i.e. they are reduced in strength when remoulded. Highly sensitive soils need careful handling, and if piling must be used both the foundation engineer and the contractor should be guided by local experience.

2 Can heaving of the ground be tolerated?

When displacement piles are driven, the soil in the vicinity is displaced and heaving may occur. Generally this does not matter on an open site, except that redriving each pile after adjacent piles have been driven will be advisable if the piles are end-bearing. Heaving caused by displacement piles may result in damage to adjacent existing structures and the associated lateral thrust may cause bursting if displacement piles are driven within a cofferdam. In such cases, replacement piles or 'small-displacement' piles are required.

3 Does the soil contain boulders or beds which would impede piling operations?

With ground of this sort, it is best to look again at the design to see if piling can be avoided. If piling is still considered to be the best solution, then only trial will show if the boulders can be pushed aside by driven preformed piles or shell piles. If beds of resistant material must be penetrated, this may be done either by preboring or by 'spudding', which is the process of breaking through the obstruction by dropping or driving a strong steel probe, the pile then being inserted in the resulting hole and driven on. Boulders or resistant beds can be tackled by percussion tools and grabs working inside a tube which, if left in place, would follow normal caisson methods of foundation construction. If the tube is withdrawn as concrete is placed, the resulting foundation would be regarded as a pile.

4 Can the noise and vibration of hammer driving be tolerated?

If the answer is 'no', then clearly some form of pile not requiring driving must be used. The choice of an alternative will be limited to some form of bored or excavated pile.

5 If the pile is to be end-bearing, will the base or point be in water-bearing granular soil?

When a replacement pile, such as a bored pile or a tube from which the soil core is removed, is sunk to water-bearing sand or gravel, it is very difficult to prevent the ground around the base becoming loosened by inflow of water into the borehole. A preformed driven pile would be the better choice if it satisfies other requirements.

6 How strong is the soil through which the pile shaft will pass?

Clearly, in the case of a cast-in-place displacement or replacement pile, in which the concrete is cast directly against the soil, the soil itself has to be strong enough to support the column of wet concrete until it sets. Ground which is so weak or loose that a casing is required to prevent inflow of soil into a borehole needs special care to avoid the formation of 'waists' or gaps in the piles when the casing is withdrawn. Normally the use of a sufficient head of concrete of adequate workability, combined with continuous checks of the concrete level during extraction of the casing, is sufficient to ensure sound workmanship. In particularly adverse conditions, as, for example, where there is a strong groundwater flow, the use of a permanent casing may be advisable. A preformed pile can be used, either a displacement pile (r.c., closed tube, or shell pile) or a replacement pile, such as a permanent tube, open at the bottom and driven with simultaneous extraction of the soil core.

If the soil is strong enough, cast-in-place displacement or replacement piles are possible, depending on the decisions on the previous questions.

If the soil is a firm clay, a borehole may be formed without casing and the base enlarged, if required, by undercutting without the need of roof support.

7 Is the soil chemically aggressive?

The material of which the pile is constructed must be chosen with regard to durability in its given situation, and if either the groundwater or the soil is likely to attack pile materials this must be considered. The need for a particular material may determine the choice of the pile type; for example, where very highest quality concrete must be used, this demands a factory-made precast unit. The advice of chemists should be sought, but in the long run practical experience of similar conditions forms the best guide.

Economic considerations

When comparing the cost of piling with another form of foundation, the overall cost of the structure should be considered.

Where two or more types of pile would serve equally well, then invitations to tender should be spread among competing specialist piling systems and the fullest possible information about the site (its location and the details of the site investigation) and the settlement and loading demands of the structure should be given.

Meeting structural requirements

The ability of a pile to carry load and the amount it settles under load are functions of the ground and the shape and method of construction of the pile. For an end-bearing pile, the cross-sectional area at the point or base is important. For a friction pile, the area of shaft surface and the adhesion or 'skin friction' of the soil on the surface determine the load carried. Various specialist piling systems make provision for increasing the base area, for compressing cast-in-place concrete against the soil, for corrugating the shaft surface and so on, with the intention of improving the bearing capacity of the pile. Loading tests are usually necessary to check the claims made for any proprietary system.

The type of structure may have an overriding influence on the choice of pile type. Where part of the length of the pile will be left standing above the ground, as in harbour or bridge work, or where the pile has to be placed through water, a preformed pile is needed and the choice between a displacement or a small-displacement pile (in this case probably an open-ended tube or box pile) often depends on the problems of installation. Bracing is not easily fixed to reinforced concrete piles, but can be bolted or welded to steel piles.

The ease with which the head of the pile can be bonded into a pile-cap varies with the type of pile. Precast reinforced concrete and prestressed piles have to be stripped down to expose bars for bonding. On the other hand, cast-in-place concrete piles and shell piles filled with concrete are formed to the correct elevation and bond-bars inserted. Steel **H**-section piles may need shear connectors to transfer the load to the pile.

Further reading

BRE Digests

63 Soils and foundations: 1
64 Soils and foundations: 2
67 Soils and foundations: 3
240 Low-rise buildings on shrinkable clay soils: 1
241 Low-rise buildings on shrinkable clay soils: 2
242 Low-rise buildings on shrinkable clay soils: 3

British Standards Institution

BS 5930: 1981   Site investigations
CP 2004: 1972   Foundations

Damp-proofing solid floors

This digest discusses briefly site drainage and the principles of damp-proofing solid floors. Tables show the effects of ground moisture on floor finishes and the protection afforded by various damp-proof membranes.

Principles of damp-proofing

Oversite concrete and floor screeds do not keep back all ground moisture. This rises towards the surface, where it either evaporates or accumulates under a less pervious material.

The tolerance of some common floor finishes to moisture is classified in Groups **A**–**D** (*see* Table 1), which range from finishes which combine the functions of flooring and damp-proofing to those for which reliable protection against damp is always needed.

For the intermediate groups, in particular Group **C**, some judgement must be exercised in deciding whether or not to provide a membrane. Similarly, a choice must be made between hot-applied and cold-applied membranes for use under the more moisture-sensitive floorings. Consideration of the following factors will help to assess the degree of risk.

Figs. 1-3. Some typical effects of rising dampness and adhesion failure.

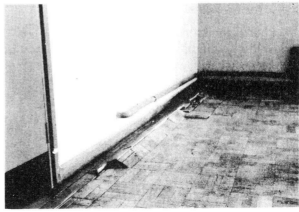

Table 1 Effects of rising moisture on floor finishes

Group	Material	Properties
A Finish and damp-proof membrane combined	Pitch mastic flooring Mastic asphalt flooring	Resist rising damp without dimensional or material failure
B Finishes that can be used without extra protection against damp	Concrete Terrazzo Clay tiles	Transmit rising damp without dimensional, material or adhesion failure
	Cement/rubber latex Cement/bitumen Composition blocks (laid in cement mortar)	Transmit rising damp slowly without dimensional or material failure and usually without adhesion failure
	Wood blocks (dipped and laid in hot pitch or bitumen)	Transmit rising damp slowly without material failure and usually without dimensional or adhesion failure. Only in exceptional conditions of site dampness is there risk of dimensional instability
C Finishes that are not necessarily trouble-free but are often laid without protection against damp	Thermoplastic flooring tiles PVC (vinyl) asbestos tiles Acrylic resin emulsion/cement Epoxy resin flooring	Under severe conditions dimensional and adhesion failure may occur. Thermoplastic flooring tiles may be attacked by dissolved salts
D Reliable protection against damp needed	Magnesium oxychloride	Softens and disintegrates in wet conditions
	PVA emulsion/cement	Dimensionally sensitive to moisture; softens in wet conditions
	Polyester resin flooring Polyurethane resin flooring Rubber Flexible PVC flooring Linoleum Cork carpet Cork tile	Lose adhesion and may expand under damp conditions
	Textile flooring	Dimensional and material failure, and usually adhesion failure occur in moist conditions
	Wood block laid in cold adhesives Wood strip and board flooring Chipboard	Acutely sensitive to moisture with dimensional or material failure

Wetness of site

This is influenced by the nature of the soil, the presence or absence of hardcore beneath the site concrete, and the slope of the ground. On some sloping sites, foundations can interfere with natural drainage, with consequent build-up of water pressure on the underside of the floor. In these cases, a ditch dug along the upper sides of the building, draining to a lower level, will help. The ditch may be filled, if it has a land drain in the bottom, with coarse material up to top-soil level.

Solid floors should not be subjected to water pressure unless specifically designed to withstand it; the problem then becomes one of tanking, and reference should be made to British Standard Code of Practice CP 102.

Temperature to be maintained in the building

The effect of a temperature gradient is to concentrate moisture in the cooler part and to lower the moisture content of the warmer part. Thus, if the floor surface is colder than the ground below it, moisture will tend to rise and collect near the surface;

protection against dampness is then advisable. In a permanently heated building, the risk is less, though with floor warming, a sandwich damp-proof membrane is necessary whatever the finish.

Sea-salt contamination of concrete aggregate and fill

Sea salt has two undesirable effects: it tends to keep the floor damp and it reacts with lime from the cement, liberating caustic alkali, which can contribute to an attack on floorings and their adhesives. Where sea salt is present, a damp-proof membrane is necessary.

Position of membrane

Surface membranes permit floor laying to follow completion (including cooling or hardening) of the membrane with no delay for drying time. They do not interfere with the bond between screed and base concrete; a screed can, therefore, be laid monolithically to a thickness of only 12–25 mm, or in separate construction to a minimum thickness of 40 mm (*see* Digest 104). The thicker surface membranes may also serve as a levelling compound on a well-finished concrete slab without screed or on a slightly irregular screed. Surface membranes are, however, susceptible to damage by subsequent trades; with mastic asphalt or pitchmastic membranes there is a risk of indentation under heavy loads. They should therefore be laid only just in advance of the floor finish.

If sulphates are present in hardcore under the floor or in the ground water, a surface membrane will give no protection against sulphate attack of the base concrete or screed and the risk of sulpho-aluminate expansion will be high.

Sandwich membranes located between concrete base and screed should be protected against damage by subsequent trades by laying the screed as soon as possible after completion. Hot-applied membranes can be covered by a screed as soon as they have cooled; cold-applied solutions or emulsions are likely to require several days to apply and

harden. The membrane effectively eliminates any bond between screed and base; a screed laid on a sandwich membrane should therefore be at least 50 mm thick.

Any of the sheet materials recommended for use as sandwich membranes can be used below the site concrete but the base on which they are to be laid must be structurally sound, to avoid fracture of the membrane, and the surface should be sufficiently smooth to avoid puncturing the membrane. A blinding layer of weak concrete or sand, on a consolidated bed of hardcore, provides a suitable base. A membrane in this position protects the site concrete and screed against attack by any sulphates present in hardcore or ground water and permits bonding of screed to concrete base. It has, however, the disadvantage that both the concrete base and screed must be allowed time to dry before a moisture-sensitive finish can be laid.

Table 2   Materials for membranes

Material	Standard or grade	Comment
Hot-applied Mastic asphalt	BS 1410: Mastic asphalt for flooring (natural rock asphalt aggregate) BS 1076: Mastic asphalt for flooring (limestone aggregate) BS 1451: Coloured mastic asphalt for flooring (limestone aggregate)	May be used as a floor finish (*see* BS CP 204); if used as an underlay to a floor finish, the thickness should be not less than 12 mm. A compressible underlay is not recommended but glass-fibre may be used. All are suitable for surface membranes.
	BS 1097 (limestone aggregate) BS 1418 (natural rock asphalt aggregate)	When loaded, can withstand hydrostatic pressure; suitable only for sandwich membranes.
Pitch mastic	BS 1450: Black pitch mastic flooring BS 3672: Coloured pitch mastic flooring	Normally used as a floor finish but may form a surface membrane to protect other finishes. Its indentation characteristics make it less suitable than mastic asphalt.
Pitch	BS 1310: Coal tar pitches for building purposes (Grade R & B 40)	Should be laid on a primed surface to give an average thickness of 3 mm (3 kg/m^2); suitable only for sandwich membranes.
Bitumen	Should have a softening point of 50–55°C; this corresponds to a penetration number of 40–50 at 25°C	
Cold-applied Bitumen solutions, coal tar pitch/rubber emulsion, or bitumen/rubber emulsion	Not defined by any BS Specification or Code	BS CP 102 recommends 0·6 mm minimum thickness but this is for broad guidance only. The solids content will usually have been adjusted to give adequate coverage by two or three coats; the material should not be thinned by dilution or spread in thinner coats than recommended by the manufacturer. Suitable only for sandwich membranes.
Pitch/epoxy resin		Although applied in thin layers, the material is strong enough and its adhesion to concrete is usually sufficient to make it a satisfactory base for a variety of floor finishes. It cannot tolerate any cracking in the surface to which it is applied. Generally used as a surface membrane.
Sheet material Polythene film	0·12 mm thick (500 gauge)	Suitable for sandwich membranes. Joints must be properly sealed; the welting method normally used appears satisfactory. Where there is risk of damage by subsequent screed-laying operations, material about twice as thick (1000 gauge) may be used with confidence.
Composite	Polythene and bitumen, self-adhesive; thickness is in excess of 1·5 mm	Adhesion simplifies joint treatment and reduces risk of tearing.
Bitumen sheet	Bitumen sheet to BS 743	Suitable for sandwich membranes. Joints must be properly sealed.

Properties required of damp-proof layers

A damp-proof membrane must be impervious to *liquid* water; it must also have at least as high a resistance to the passage of water *vapour* as the flooring it is designed to protect.

Hot-applied membranes are considered to have the higher vapour resistance. Cold membranes of adequate thickness also have a high vapour resistance, but in practice they may have thin spots.

An integral waterproofer incorporated in the concrete or screed is not a satisfactory alternative to a damp-proof layer.

Suitable damp-proofing materials are listed in Table 2. Site experience shows that not all are equally effective but if the materials are laid to the recommended minimum thicknesses, dampness troubles are more likely to arise from poor workmanship and bad detailing than from any deficiencies in the membrane materials. If flooring laid over a membrane shows early trouble, the cause is unlikely to be a defective membrane; the latter will usually require several months to show in the form of a flooring failure.

Drying

A long delay before laying the finish is unavoidable for all sandwich membranes, because the screed has to be left to dry out. Even under favourable conditions this may take as long as one month per 25 mm thickness. Thus, a 50 mm thick screed would take at least two months to dry. Where a membrane is introduced below the site concrete, a 150 mm thick slab and screed would take at least six months to dry sufficiently for a moisture-sensitive finish to be laid. A device for testing the dryness of a screed is described in Digest 18.

Continuity

All damp-proof layers must be continuous with the damp-proof courses in adjoining walls and with damp-proof membranes in adjacent floors. Where necessary, a vertical damp-proof course must be provided to link membranes at different levels, as shown in Fig 4.

A floor that is finished in part with material that needs no protection against ground moisture and elsewhere with material that does require protection, must be provided with continuous damp-proofing of the whole area, or each area of moisture-sensitive flooring must be protected by tanking—*see* Fig 5.

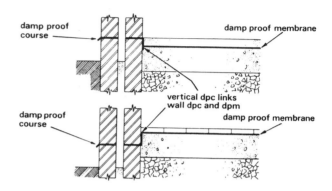

Fig 4

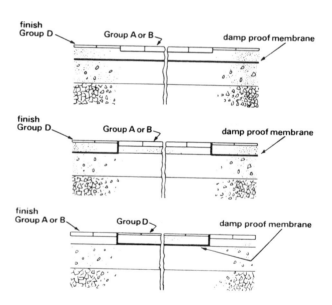

Fig 5

Heat losses through ground floors

Digest 108 explained the basis of calculating standard U-values and dealt in some detail with wall and roof constructions. For ground floors, either solid or suspended, it is not possible to calculate U-values from first principles but the value of a basic construction can be adjusted according to the nature of the floor finish and any insulation.

Solid ground floors

A solid floor, laid in contact with the ground, with or without a bed of hardcore, is exposed to the air on only one face. The heat flow from inside the building to the outside air is indicated by the flow lines in Fig 1. The greater the distance it has to travel the less is the quantity of heat lost. A U-value for a solid ground floor must, therefore, take account of the size and edge conditions of the slab.

The results of an examination of this problem, published over twenty years ago,[1] still form the basis of the conventional method of dealing with heat loss calculations through ground floors as set out in the CIBS 'Guide'.[2] Table 1 shows the basic U-values for a range of sizes and shapes of solid floor in contact with the ground; the values given are applicable to dense concrete floors, with or without a bed of hardcore. Because the thermal conductivities of ground and slab are similar, the values may be used for slabs of any thickness. They will not be affected by a hard dense floor finish such as granolithic concrete, terrazzo, clay tiling etc or by a thin finish of little insulation value such as thermoplastic tiles.

In applying these values, the full temperature difference between inside and outside should be used. During the early life of a building, heat flows into the ground to raise it to its final equilibrium temperature; because of the high thermal capacity of the ground, this may take 6–12 months, with an increased demand on the heating during the early period. Steady-state conditions are applicable only to a narrow band round the edge of the floor slab but, nevertheless, the convention is adopted of basing heat loss calculations on a U-value for the whole floor and this will not lead to great error after the ground has been warmed to its equilibrium temperature.

The effect of moisture content on the thermal conductivity of masonry materials is discussed in Digest 108,[3] which describes the standard assumptions to be made for moisture contents of walls in protected and exposed situations. No such assumptions are required for solid ground floors.

Table 1 U-values for solid floors in contact with the earth

Dimensions of floor	U-values			
	Four exposed edges		Two exposed edges at right-angles	
metres	W/m² °C		W/m² °C	
Very long × 30	0·16*	6·25	0·09	11·11
× 15	0·28*	3·57	0·16	6·25
× 7·5	0·48*	2·08	0·28	3·57
150 × 60	0·11	9·09	0·06	16·67
× 30	0·18	5·55	0·10	10·0
60 × 60	0·15	6·66	0·08	12·5
× 30	0·21	4·76	0·12	8·33
× 15	0·32	3·12	0·18	5·55
30 × 30	0·26	3·84	0·15	6·66
× 15	0·36	2·77	0·21	4·76
× 7·5	0·55	1·82	0·32	3·12
15 × 15	0·45	2·22	0·26	3·84
× 7·5	0·62	1·61	0·36	2·77
7·5 × 7·5	0·76	1·32	0·45	2·22
3 × 3	1·47	0·68	1·07	0·93

* Applies also to any floor of this breadth and losing heat from two parallel edges (breadth then being the distance between the exposed edges)

Figures in italics are reciprocals of the U-values ie the air-to-air resistance

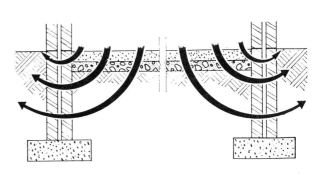

Fig 1 Heat flow through ground slab

Insulation of a solid ground floor

If a floor finish or screed affording some useful degree of thermal insulation is to be used, the U-value of the floor can be calculated accurately enough for most design purposes by taking the reciprocal of the basic U-value, ie the total air-to-air resistance (shown in italics in Table 1), adding the resistance of the additional material and then calculating the reciprocal of the combined resistances to obtain the U-value of the floor.

Assuming, for example, that a concrete floor size 15 m × 7·5 m exposed on all four edges is to be covered with 20 mm softwood flooring:

From Table 1, the basic U-value is 0·62 W/m² °C and its total resistance, the reciprocal, is 1·61

From Table 5, the thermal resistivity of softwood is 7·7 m °C/W; the thermal resistance of 20 mm

material is therefore $\dfrac{7 \cdot 7 \times 20}{1000}$ =0·15

total air-to-air resistance of insulated slab =1·76

U-value =1/1·76 =0·57

The effect of an overall layer of insulation (Fig 2) can be calculated in the same manner, by adding the thermal resistance of the insulation to that of the basic floor. The efficiency of the insulation is not, however, constant over the whole area of the floor because the greatest loss through an uninsulated floor is from the edges and the cost of overall insulation is seldom justifiable. An alternative that will give nearly as good results is to treat only the edges

Table 2   Corrections to Table 1 for edge-insulated floors

Dimensions of floor	Percentage reduction in U for 25 mm min edge insulation extending to a depth of:		
metres	0·25 m	0·5 m	1·0 m
Very long × 30	3	7	11
× 15	3	8	13
× 7·5	4	9	15
60 × 60	4	11	17
30 × 30	4	12	18
15 × 15	5	12	20
7·5 × 7·5	6	15	25
3 × 3	10	20	35

of the slab. This can be done in various ways (Fig 3). A vertical layer of insulating material (a) can be used; this should extend from finished floor level down to a depth of not less than 250 mm, but can with advantage be taken down to the top of a strip foundation. Alternatively (b) a horizontal strip about one metre wide can be laid in conjunction with a vertical strip through the full thickness of the floor around all exposed edges. Insulating material used in any of these positions should be of a type that is unaffected by moisture either in its performance or durability, or it should be protected from ground moisture. Data sheets which set out the properties of many insulating materials are included in 'Thermal insulation of buildings'.[4]

Corrections to Table 1 to allow for the effects of edge insulation as in Fig 3 (a) are given in Table 2. The detail shown in Fig 3 (b) will have a performance at least as good as with the same amount of insulation used as in 3 (a).

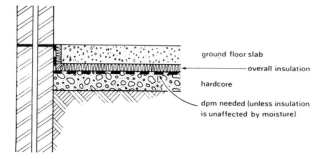

Fig 2 Overall floor insulation

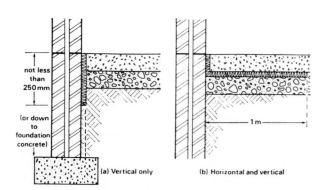

Fig 3 Edge insulation

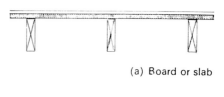

(a) Board or slab

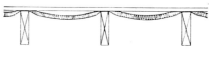

(b) Blanket, quilt or foil

Fig 4 Insulation above joists

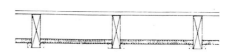

Fig 5 Insulation between joists

Table 3 Suspended floors directly above ground

Dimensions of floor	Basic thermal resistance (any floor structure) $R_{si}+R_a+R_e$	U-values: timber floors		
		Bare or with linoleum, plastics or rubber[1]	With carpet or cork[2]	With any surface finish and 25 mm quilt[3] (as Fig 4b)
metres	$m^2{}^\circ C/W$	$W/m^2{}^\circ C$	$W/m^2{}^\circ C$	$W/m^2{}^\circ C$
Very long × 30	5·35	0·18	0·18	0·16
× 15	2·82	0·33	0·33	0·26
× 7·5	1·67	0·53	0·52	0·37
150 × 60	7·13	0·14	0·14	0·12
× 30	4·58	0·21	0·21	0·18
60 × 60	5·90	0·16	0·16	0·14
× 30	4·02	0·24	0·23	0·20
× 15	2·54	0·37	0·36	0·28
30 × 30	3·42	0·28	0·27	0·22
× 15	2·34	0·39	0·38	0·30
× 7·5	1·55	0·57	0·55	0·39
15 × 15	2·03	0·45	0·44	0·33
× 7·5	1·44	0·61	0·59	0·40
7·5 × 7·5	1·27	0·68	0·65	0·43
3 × 3	0·75	1·05	0·99	0·56

(1) assuming $R_s = 0.20$
(2) assuming $R_s = 0.26$
(3) assuming $R_s = 0.86$

Suspended ground floors

A suspended ground floor above an enclosed airspace is exposed to air on both sides but the air temperature below the floor is higher than the outside air temperature because the ventilation rate of the underfloor air space is very low. The U-values are therefore lower than was assumed in the past, when the underfloor temperature was taken as the temperature of the outside air.

Table 3 gives the basic thermal resistances of suspended ground floors excluding the resistance of the structure, which must be added in order to calculate the U-values. The figures in column 2 are the sums of the inside surface (ie the floor surface) resistance R_{si}, the resistance of an airspace R_a ventilated by 2000 mm² gaps per linear metre of boundary and the resistance of the earth R_e. To these basic resistances must be added the resistance of the proposed floor structure together with any added insulation R_s. The reciprocal of the sum of these resistances is the U-value.

The results of this calculation for timber floors, either bare or covered with a thin finish of low thermal resistance (R_s assumed to be 0·20), are given in column 3. U-values obtained with a covering of higher thermal resistance (R_s assumed to be 0·26) are given in column 4. U-values obtained with any surface finish and 25 mm quilt, as shown in Fig 4b (R_s assumed to be 0·86), are given in column 5.

Insulation Additional insulation of a suspended wooden ground floor is commonly provided either in the form of a continuous layer of semi-rigid or flexible material laid over the joists (Fig 4) or semi-rigid material between the joists (Fig 5). With concrete or hollow pot floors it will usually be more convenient to place the insulation above the structural floor.

The thermal resistance of boards or slabs laid over joists (Fig 4a) and of airspaces, or of overall insulation above the structural floor must be added to the basic resistance (column 2 of Table 3) and the resistance of the floor structure to calculate the U-value. Standard thermal resistances for airspaces between the various layers of the construction are given in Table 4. Blankets and quilts laid over the joists will be effective only over their uncompressed area between the joists; foils are effective only where they operate in conjunction with an airspace—again, therefore, only between the joists. This is unimportant, however, because the resistance of the joists compensates for the absence of insulation.

Table 4 Standard thermal resistance of unventilated airspaces

Type of airspace		Thermal resistance* $m^2{}^\circ C/W$
Thickness	Surface emissivity	
5 mm	High	0·10
	Low	0·18
25 mm or more	High	0·22
	Low	1·06
High emissivity planes and corrugated sheets in contact		0·11
Low emissivity multiple foil insulation with airspace on one side		1·76

* Including internal boundary surface

Vapour barriers The introduction of an insulating layer on the underside of the floor raises questions as to the incidence of condensation on the colder faces of the construction and, consequently, of the need for a vapour barrier. A vapour barrier could set up a dangerous situation in a wood floor in the event of the space within the floor collecting water either by spillage or by leakage from plumbing or heating installations. The water could not then escape by draining or evaporating to the airspace below the floor and evaporation through the flooring would be so slow that dangerous conditions conducive to fungal attack could persist for a long period. The designer usually has no control over future treatment of the floor, particularly as to the nature of any finish that may be laid later. An impervious or nearly impervious finish such as pvc, rubber or linoleum sheeting would give good protection against spillage but in the event of leakage within the thickness of the floor it would further aggravate the situation. The safest course is not to provide a vapour barrier to a floor that is constructed of or incorporates wood.

References

1 Journal IHVE Vol 19 (Nov 1951) pp 351–372

2 CIBS Guide Section A3, 1980. The Chartered Institution of Building Services, 222 Balham High Road, London SW12 9BS

3 BRS Digest 108: Standard U-values

4 Thermal insulation of buildings; C C Handiside, D J Melluish: HMSO London 1971

Table 5 Thermal properties of some materials

Material	Density kg/m^3	Conductivity (k) $W/m°C$	Resistivity (1/k) $m°C/W$
Asbestos insulating board	750	0·12	8·3
Carpet		0·055	18·2
—wool felt underlay	160	0·045	22·2
—cellular rubber underlay	400	0·10	10·0
Concrete	2400	1·83	0·55
Cork flooring	540	0·085	11·8
Eelgrass blanket	80–215	0·039–0·049	25·6–20·4
Fibre insulating board	260	0·050	20·0
Glasswool quilt	25	0·04	25·0
Linoleum to BS 810	1150	0·22	4·6
Mineral wool —felted	50	0·039	25·6
	80	0·038	26·3
—semi-rigid felted mat	130	0·036	27·8
—loose, felted slab or mat	180	0·042	23·8
Plastics, cellular —phenolic foam board	30	0·038	26·3
	50	0·036	27·8
—polystyrene, expanded	15	0·037	27·0
	25	0·034	29·4
—polyurethane foam (aged)	30	0·026	38·5
PVC flooring / Rubber flooring		0·40	2·5
Straw slab, compressed	350	0·11	9·1
Wood —hardwood		0·15	6·7
—plywood		0·14	7·1
—softwood		0·13	7·7
Wood chipboard	800	0·15	6·7
Woodwool slab	500	0·085	11·8
	600	0·093	10·8

For a more comprehensive list, see CIBS 'Guide' [2]

Increasing the fire resistance of existing timber floors

This digest explains how the fire resistance of existing floors can be increased to periods of up to one hour. It discusses the addition of protection to the underside of the ceiling, over the floor boarding and between the joists, and the problems of improving fire resistance when the joists are to be exposed to view from below. Floors which are improved as described should generally give a satisfactory standard of fire performance but the precise improvement depends on the details of construction and the condition of the existing floor. The final decision as to suitability must rest with the building or fire authority.

Because this digest can give guidance only of a general nature, few jobs will fall precisely into the simple examples that are given (joist sizes and spacing may differ for example) and expert advice will have to be sought. In most cases, therefore, it can merely alert the reader to the problems that may be met.

The principal revisions in this new edition are to Tables 1 and 2 and are the result of further work carried out by the Fire Research Station and changes in the characteristics of premixed lightweight plasters.

Where there is an alteration, extension or material change of use of a building, regulations may require the period of fire resistance of existing timber floors to be increased. As with other structural elements, the fire resistance of a floor depends upon it satisfying criteria for specified periods. They are:

stability: the resistance to collapse or excessive deflection under load

integrity: the resistance to the formation of cracks or gaps which could lead to fire spread

insulation: the ability to restrict excessive transmission of heat.

Normally the floor should satisfy all criteria for the full period, but Building Regulations also prescribe a 'modified half-hour' floor for small houses which must satisfy the stability criterion for thirty minutes and the integrity and insulation criteria for fifteen minutes.

The method of test for floors is exposure of the underside to fire and therefore the fire resistance of timber floor constructions depends primarily on the protection given by the ceiling; once a ceiling has been penetrated the joists and underside of the floor boarding become exposed to fire. Although the fire resistance of an element of construction applies to the complete assembly, the stability of any individual member supporting a fire-resisting membrane must be considered. Plain-edged floor boarding or tongued and grooved boarding with significant shrinkage contribute little and the period of fire resistance of the floor is effectively the collapse time of the ceiling membrane. Tongued and grooved boarding with closed joists or added surfacing can contribute additional time to integrity and insulation.

The addition of a hardboard or plywood surface enables a plain-edged boarded floor (or sub-standard tongued and grooved floor) to be considered as a good-fitting tongued and grooved floor construction for the purposes of its maximum contribution to integrity and insulation. Although existing lath and plaster ceilings may possibly contribute as much as twenty minutes or so to the fire resistance of a timber floor, this will depend on the condition and key. Greater thicknesses of plaster will not necessarily provide additional protection and because of the added weight may well fail earlier than thinner plaster. It is possible for floors with timber boarded ceilings below to achieve even a full half-hour fire resistance period but this depends on board thickness, tongue size and joint profile, and on the joist size and span. In all constructions the fixing of component parts is critical to the behaviour of the floor when exposed to fire.

It is possible to increase the fire resistance of suitable existing timber floors by certain types of suspended ceiling systems but care is necessary to ensure that the assembly of any proprietary system is strictly in accordance with an appropriate tested specification together with any recommended modifications. In this respect, most fire-protecting suspended ceiling systems have been tested to assess the protection they can give to steel beams under fire resistance test conditions and where assessment of the behaviour under timber floors is possible their contribution is much less because the timber is more vulnerable; added protection is therefore necessary. Test data under BS 476: Part 8 may be unsuitable for assessment purposes where the test was not carried out with furnace pressure conditions appropriate to the integrity criterion.

Methods

Protection added to the underside of the existing ceiling Table 1 shows the additional protection required for some typical existing ceiling constructions to upgrade the fire resistance to either a half-hour or one hour. Although added layers can increase the performance of a floor, available fixing methods may not be able to carry the extra weight.

Protection applied from above Table 2 gives constructions which can be used if protection must be added from above, for example where an ornate ceiling is to be retained or where access cannot be gained to the storey below. Methods involve either filling between the joists after lifting the floor boards or applying an additional floor finish above the existing boarding, or both. In both the methods of joist infill described, it is essential that the protective material is in intimate contact with the joists to protect them from burning for as long as possible and that the existing ceiling is in a sound condition. It is also important that the added protection is independently fixed and supported, and therefore will not fall when the existing ceiling collapses.

Protection leaving joists exposed below To leave the joists exposed, the recommended protections involve either adding to the flooring above or placing protection between the joists to form an interrupted ceiling, or both.

Joists must be of a size which will enable them to retain structural stability even after some charring of the timber has occurred. Table 3 shows the amount of charring which may occur with different timbers under the heating conditions of the BS 476: Part 8 test and from this the reduction in section size can be calculated. For assessing stability, normal practice applies except that the stresses should not exceed 2.25 times the permissible long-term dry stresses given in CP 112: Part 2 when the minimum initial breadth of the section is 70 mm or greater, or twice the permissible long-term dry stresses when this dimension is less than 70 mm; deflection should not exceed 1/30th of the span. When

Table 1 Additional ceiling protection
(a) Floors with good-fitting, 21 mm tongued and grooved boarding

Required period of fire resistance	Existing ceiling construction	Protection fixed below existing ceiling
half-hour	13 mm fibre insulating board with 5 mm gypsum plaster finish	9.5 mm plaster board
		6 mm asbestos insulating board
one hour	Timber lath and 16 mm plaster	9.5 mm plasterboard with 13 mm lightweight aggregate gypsum plaster finish
		13 mm lightweight aggregate gypsum plaster (metal lathing grade) on metal lath
	9.5 mm plasterboard with skim coat	9.5 mm plasterboard with 13 mm lightweight aggregate gypsum plaster finish
		13 mm lightweight aggregate gypsum plaster (metal lathing grade) on metal lath
		2 layers of 9 mm asbestos insulating board laid to break joint
	12.7 mm plasterboard with skim coat	9.5 mm plasterboard with 13 mm lightweight aggregate gypsum plaster finish
		13 mm lightweight aggregate gypsum plaster (metal lathing grade) on metal lath
		12 mm asbestos insulating board

(b) Floors with plain-edged boarding or badly-fitting tongued and grooved boarding

Required period of fire resistance	Existing ceiling construction	Protection fixed below existing ceiling
half-hour	Timber lath and 16 mm plaster	12.7 mm plasterboard
		6 mm asbestos insulating board
one-hour	Timber lath and 16 mm plaster	13 mm lightweight aggregate gypsum plaster (metal lathing grade) on metal lath
		12 mm asbestos insulating board
	9.5 mm plasterboard with skim coat	9.5 mm plasterboard with 15 mm lightweight aggregate gypsum plaster finish
		12.7 mm plasterboard with 13 mm lightweight aggregate gypsum plaster finish
	12.7 mm plasterboard with skim coat	9.5 mm plasterboard with 15 mm lightweight aggregate gypsum plaster finish
		12.7 mm plasterboard with 13 mm lightweight aggregate gypsum plaster finish
		13 mm lightweight aggregate gypsum plaster (metal lathing grade) on metal lath

Table 1 is applicable only when the floor construction conforms to the dimensions shown in Fig 1
In the case of plaster finishes to lath, the dimensions given are those from the face of the lath.

there is insufficient sacrificial timber to maintain structural stability for the full period of fire resistance, the amount of joist permitted to remain exposed can be reduced by adjusting the position of the ceiling protection relative to the depth of the joists. It is permissible to build up joists to provide sacrificial timber; if this is done, at least ten minutes extra allowance for charring should be provided and the screw fixings should be countersunk at least 6 mm with the holes made good. Table 4 provides information about flooring and protection between joists which will provide either a modified half-hour or a full half-hour floor.

Fixing

Adequate fixing of the additional protection is of paramount importance. When fixing below an existing ceiling, nails or screws must penetrate new work and be driven into the joists to a depth which will ensure that the ceiling remains in place during the intended period of protection. Nailing must be carefully done to minimise damage to the existing ceiling but it must be accepted that some damage will be done, especially to old lath and plaster ceilings. Thus the new work, including fixings, will be supporting some of the weight of the existing ceiling. With lath and plaster ceilings, where the added protection is to incorporate boarding, it is recommended that chicken wire is securely fixed under the existing ceiling by nailing to the joists and the ceiling battened out to receive the new boarded protec-

tion. This ensures that should the existing plaster become detached, its weight is not transferred to the added protection. The battens also overcome the problem of an existing uneven plaster surface and will permit the use of conventional fixing techniques. The lengths of nails and screws should be determined according to the method of protection selected. Nails for plasterboard should be galvanised and be of the correct specification where boards are to be plastered. Table 5 gives recommended fixings for plasterboard and asbestos insulating board. The table assumes that the plasterboard is fixed directly to the joists; in practice, therefore, an allowance may have to be made for the thickness of the existing ceiling which in some cases may make this method impracticable. Metal lathing should be fixed at 100 mm centres with galvanised clout headed nails and should be spaced away from the background by some suitable means to give a 6 mm gap. Alternatively, an appropriate proprietary brand should be used.

All new plaster requires a proper key, either plasterboard (or similar) or metal lathing. The use of bonding agents is not recommended in connection with ceilings contributing to the fire resistance of a floor. Although the minimum width of joists (for example) are given, the recommended 'trade' practice should apply in respect of minimal backing, edge clearance of nails, etc.

Table 2 Protection applied from above

Required period of fire resistance	Existing construction		Examples of additional protection: see key below
	Floor boarding	Ceiling	
half-hour	None (eg existing roof space)	9.5 mm plasterboard with skim coat	1
	plain edged	16 mm plaster on wood lath	2
One-hour	21 mm good-fitting tongued and grooved	16 mm plaster on wood lath	3
	plain edged	16 mm plaster on wood lath	2 and 3
	plain edged	9.5 mm plasterboard	2 and 3

Additional protection

1 Not less than 25 mm of mineral fibre insulating material (formed from crushed rock or blast furnace slag) laid between the joists, supported by wire netting placed immediately over the ceiling: the netting to be well turned up and stapled to the joists sides. New floor boarding to be 21 mm good-fitting tongued and grooved

2 Not less than 4.8 mm medium or high density hardboard, or plywood of similar thickness, nailed at not more than 150 mm centres on the line of joists to the existing floor to break joint; joints to coincide with the line of the joists

3 25 mm lightweight aggregate gypsum plaster (metal lathing grade) trowelled between joists in conjunction with expanded metal lathing or chicken wire well turned up and fixed to the joist sides. To prevent staining the existing ceiling, polythene sheet can be placed before the plaster infill.

Note: In methods 1 and 3 the nails or staples should penetrate into the joist sides to a minimum depth of 20 mm

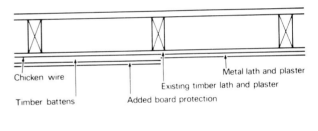

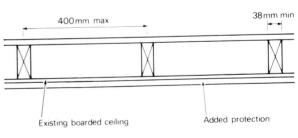

Fig 1 Protection added to underside of existing ceiling

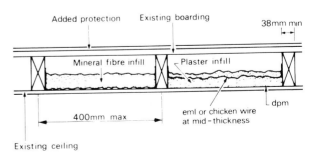

Fig 2 Protection applied from above

Table 3   Charring rates of timber*

Timber	Depth of charring in:	
	30 mins	60 mins
All structural species listed in Table 1 of CP 112: Part 2: 1971, except those listed below.	20 mm	40 mm
Western red cedar	25 mm	50 mm
Oak, utile, keruing (gurjun), teak, greenheart, jarrah	15 mm	30 mm

*From BS 5268: Pt 4: Section 4.1

Provided no dimension is less than 25 mm, a timber joist will char at a steady rate on all faces; the rates in Table 3 apply to each face exposed to fire. Allowance should also be made for increased depth of charring at arrises; this approximates to a radius equal to the calculated depth of charring. However, for periods of 30 minutes or less where the least dimension of residual section is not less than 50 mm, rounding is insignificant and may be disregarded.

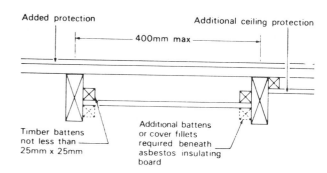

Fig 3   Exposed joists

Table 4   Protection leaving joists exposed to view from below

Required period of fire resistance	Construction to provide fire resistance	
	Protection between joists	floor boarding, etc
half-hour modified	9.5 mm plasterboard or 9 mm asbestos insulating board board	21 mm good-fitting t and g boarding
		19 mm wood chipboard or plywood with tongued joints
	12.7 mm plasterboard or 9 mm asbestos insulating board	16 mm good-fitting t and g boarding
half-hour	12.7 mm plasterboard or 9 mm asbestos insulating board	21 mm good-fitting t and g boarding
		19 mm wood chipboard or plywood with tongued joints
	12.7 mm plasterboard with 5 mm gypsum plaster skim coat	15 mm good-fitting t and g boarding
	12.7 mm plasterboard or 9mm asbestos insulating board	Plain-edged boarding with 4.8 mm medium or high density hardboard, or plywood of similar thickness nailed at not more than 150 mm centres on the line of joists to the existing floor to break joint; joints to coincide with the line of the joists.

See Fig 3 for details of joist spacing and battens

Table 5   Recommended fixing for plasterboard with no allowance for existing ceiling

Thickness of plasterboard	Nail length	Spacing
9.5 mm	30 mm	150 mm centres
12.7 mm	40 mm	150 mm centres

For asbestos insulating board, screws should be at centres not exceeding 300 mm and should penetrate the joists by 40 mm.

Asbestos Some of the constructions recommended involve the use of asbestos insulating boards; the Health and Safety Executive issue advice about safety when working with this material. Where the use of one of the new generation of asbestos-free boards is being considered, advice regarding its suitability should be sought from the manufacturer.

Design of timber floors to prevent decay

Most species of timber, especially softwoods, are liable under certain conditions to attack by the 'dry rot' fungus, *Merulius lacrymans,* which feeds on the timber, destroying it in the process. In persistently wet conditions, wood may be attacked by the 'cellar fungus', *Coniophora cerebella*; the effect is often called 'wet rot'.

An outbreak of dry rot can spread quickly, cause serious damage, and prove troublesome and costly to eradicate; prevention, therefore, is all-important. There are two possible courses—use timber that is naturally resistant to dry rot (eg Western red cedar, Californian redwood or yellow cedar) or take precautions in design and construction with less resistant species. To be immune from attack, the moisture content of the timber must be kept below 20 per cent (based on its oven-dry weight). Accordingly, the timber must be nearly in this condition at the time of fixing and everything possible must be done to keep the moisture content below 20 per cent thereafter. For the most part, this can be achieved by careful attention to the principles of good building construction—full provision against the entry of rain and ground moisture, thorough drying of the structure on completion, and efficient heating and ventilation to minimise condensation. Nevertheless, in the more inaccessible parts of a building—under floors, behind skirting and panelling, etc.—unsuspected damp conditions may persist unless precautions are taken.

Selection and storage of timber

Only sound, well-seasoned timber should be used; any that shows signs of incipient decay should be rejected. If possible, the conditions under which it has been stored should be ascertained and nothing allowed on the site which comes from a yard in which careless stacking or unclean conditions are tolerated.

Care taken in storage at the timber yard will be largely wasted unless it is matched by similar care on site. If the timber cannot be stored inside a building, it should be stacked on bearers so as to avoid contact with the ground. Dry, well-seasoned timber should be closely stacked, to minimise absorption of atmospheric moisture, and wholly covered with tarpaulins or polythene sheeting around and under the stack as well as over it.

If the timber is moist when it reaches the site, it should be open-piled so that air can circulate round each piece to promote further drying; the stacks should have top cover but the sides should be left open so as not to hinder air flow through the stack. If the stacks are within a building, windows should be left open.

Timber that has been treated with water–borne preservatives will not have been re-dried in a kiln unless this was specially ordered; normally, therefore, it will need to be open-piled and air-dried.

The moisture content of floor joists and battens should not exceed 22 per cent at the time of fixing; under normal drying conditions it will then quickly fall to 20 per cent and lower.

To prevent undue drying shrinkage, floor boarding and blocks, at the time of laying, should have a moisture content not more than about 2 per cent higher than they are expected to attain in use in a dried-out building; this final value is about 14 per cent where heating is intermittent, or 12 per cent where heating is continuous; softwood boarding may be fixed at a moisture content of up to 18 per cent if some gapping of the joints is acceptable.

Types of floor
Unventilated ground floors

Wood block floors. Wood blocks laid in hot-applied bitumen or pitch adhesive require no additional protection against rising moisture; the adhesive, in which the blocks are dipped, should form a continuous layer and keep them out of contact with the concrete. Cold bitumen emulsions, however, cannot be relied on to give adequate protection, and blocks laid with this type of adhesive should be protected by a sandwich type damp-proof membrane (*see* Digest 54) or by an underlay of mastic asphalt, using an adhesive which is compatible with the asphalt.

Board or strip flooring. Board and strip flooring may be nailed to battens fixed to the concrete sub-floor by one of the methods illustrated in Fig 1. Protection by an impervious membrane is essential for these floors.

A surface membrane will protect the floor against rising ground moisture and also against the effects of residual construction moisture in the screed, but it will be pierced by the legs of the flooring clips or by the flooring nails. A sandwich membrane need not be pierced but sufficient time must be allowed for the concrete above the damp-proof layer to dry before the boards are fixed. The time necessary for this will depend on the density and thickness of the concrete and on the drying conditions, but since in the absence of heating facilities it may be a very long period, the sandwich method is perhaps less useful in practice. Failure to dry out the floor screed thoroughly may lead to decay in these floors and the risk will be greatly increased if impervious floor coverings, such as rubber, linoleum, plastics, etc., are laid prematurely.

The damp-proof membrane should make a watertight joint with the damp-proof course in the walls, etc., the membrane being extended vertically if necessary. Materials suitable for use as damp-proof membranes are listed in Digest 54.

All battens should be impregnated with preservative. Brush application of a preservative to the underside of the boarding is also recommended; for this purpose it will normally be advisable to avoid creosote or any preservative which might creep or bleed through and disfigure the exposed surface of the flooring.

Tongued and grooved boarding should be used, so that water used for washing down, or spilled accidentally, will not readily pass through the joints. If any water reaches the underside of the boarding,

it will be slow to evaporate and dangerous conditions may persist for a considerable time.

Ventilated ground floors

Ground floors of boarding on joists have a relatively large air space beneath them. To minimise the evaporation of water into this space, the sub-floor should be covered with a bed of good-quality dense concrete or a hot applied damp-resisting coating (solum) to BS 2832; the latter should be laid on a well-compacted base of hardcore, blinded with ashes to form a level surface free from fissures. The surface of the concrete bed or solum should not be lower than the level of the surrounding ground, or alternatively, the site should be drained so that inundation of the area cannot occur. The air space should be thoroughly ventilated and, if this is efficient, no preservative treatment of the timber is necessary.

For efficient cross-ventilation, there should be a clear depth of 150 mm between the underside of the floor joists and the site covering and sufficient air-bricks to provide at least 3000 mm² *open area* per metre run of external wall. The airbricks should be placed as high as possible on opposite walls and sleeper walls should be built honeycombed. Care should be taken to avoid unventilated air pockets such as may occur near a bay window; ducts should be formed under hearths and under solid floors wherever these might interrupt cross-ventilation.

Airbricks should not be built in to the north walls of buildings which are situated in a frost hollow, particularly if the underbuilding or crawl-space is a deep one; otherwise, there is a risk that in some weather conditions condensation may occur on the underside of the floor near the airbricks. The risk will be greatest below rooms that are unheated or intermittently heated, such as bedrooms. On sloping sites where a deep underbuilding cannot easily be avoided, the need for a second damp-proof course near ground level should be considered. If a terrace around the building is cut into the hillside, it may be desirable to bring the level of the concrete bed or solum at least up to that of the terrace, for in these circumstances drainage of the terrace may not always be able to cope with the volume of rain-water run-off from the hillside. The concrete bed or solum should be stepped so as to coincide approximately with the finished level of the surrounding ground.

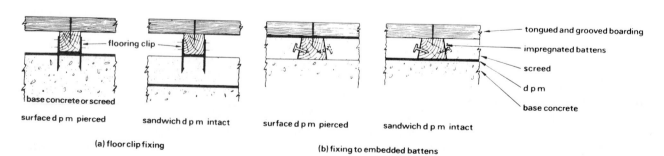

Fig 1 Board and batten fixing

Tongued and grooved boarding should be used because, if under-floor ventilation is as efficient as it should be, objectionable draughts would pass through the open joints of plain-edged boarding.

The thermal insulation of floors of this type can be improved by providing a layer of insulating material below the boarding. In a properly constructed and ventilated floor, this should not increase the risk of dry rot.

A damp-proof course should be provided in all sleeper walls and other supports that are in contact with the ground. The ends of joists should be cut back clear of the external walls (*see* Fig 2).

Upper floors

Dry rot in upper floors is rare because they are not exposed to moisture rising from the ground and the air above and below them is usually dry. No special precautions are required except that timbers built into walls that might become damp should be treated with preservative.

Board and batten floors (Fig 1) might be used on upper floors of *in situ* reinforced concrete, hollow beam or similar construction, but the damp-proof membrane would normally be omitted. However, structural floors of these types, possibly with the addition of a concrete screed, may contain a considerable quantity of residual construction water, and if a lightweight concrete is used the drying-out time will be substantially prolonged. Flooring should not be laid until drying-out is well advanced. Brush application of a preservative would then give temporary protection to the battens until drying-out is complete; the treatment could usefully be extended to the underside of the floorboards. Pressure impregnation, although not essential, would not only give protection during drying-out but would also continue to protect the battens from damage by accidental spillage, etc.

Wood block and parquet flooring laid on concrete, hollow tile or similar structural upper floors do not require special protection against fungal attack, but the concrete and screeds should be dry before the flooring is laid.

Floor coverings

Impervious floor coverings such as linoleum, rubber and plastics can safely be laid over floors that have been properly constructed in accordance with the foregoing recommendations, provided that residual construction moisture is not trapped below them. There may be some risk, however, in covering old timber floors, even when these have behaved satisfactorily for many years; the timber may have been kept at a safe moisture content mainly by evaporation from the upper surface, in which case the laying of an impervious covering might allow the moisture content to rise above the danger limit. Laying such coverings on a new boarded floor above a screed or slab which has not properly dried out could have a similar effect.

Skirtings

The absence of any protection on the back surface of a skirting and early painting of the exposed surface have the effect of raising the moisture content in skirting boards fitted to newly plastered walls that have not dried out. The risk of fungal attack is greatest when the wall is plastered right down to the floor and when skirtings are fixed above solid floors that are still wet.

All timber to be fixed in contact with new walls should, therefore, be given two brush-applied coats of preservative on the contact face. Impregnation would give still better protection; the use of preservatives that are soluble in water or certain organic solvents would allow for the normal painting of exposed surfaces.

Preservative treatment

Even with sound design and construction, it is necessary in some situations to treat the timber with a preservative. The effectiveness of this in eliminating or reducing the risk of attack will depend upon the thoroughness of the treatment. Any such treatment should be regarded as providing an extra margin of safety, the small cost of which, in comparison with the high cost and inconvenience entailed by fungal attack, is worth while in any situation where dampness, however slight, can occur. The treatment is further justified by the protection it affords against insect attack.

Timber to be treated with preservative should be clean and dry. The preservative may be applied either by brushing or by impregnation. Where permanent dampness cannot be avoided, timber

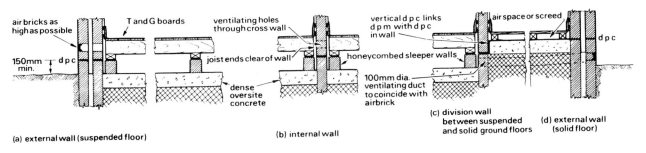

air bricks as high as possible

T and G boards

ventilating holes through cross wall

vertical d p c links d p m with d p c in wall

air space or screed

150mm min.

d p c

joist ends clear of wall

dense oversite concrete

honeycombed sleeper walls

100mm dia. ventilating duct to coincide with airbrick

d p c

(a) external wall (suspended floor)

(b) internal wall

(c) division wall between suspended and solid ground floors

(d) external wall (solid floor)

Fig 2 Ventilated ground floors

should be impregnated. The maximum protection will be obtained if the timber is impregnated after all cutting and boring has been done; if this is not possible, preservative should be brushed liberally on to any cut surface.

Brush application gives less protection and should be used only where dampness is likely to be slight and temporary, as, for example, in those parts of a new building that can be expected to dry out fairly quickly.

Some care is needed in choosing the preservative to be used. In some situations the persistent smell of creosote and other preservatives of the tar oil type may be objectionable; also they tend to creep into and stain adjacent materials such as plaster. Alternatives are available in the organic solvent and water-borne types of preservative; see references below.

Method of determining the dryness of the sub-floor

A simple form of instrument measures the relative humidity of a pocket of air in equilibrium with the sub-floor (Fig 3). It consists of a paper hygrometer in a vapour-tight mounting housed in a well insulated box. Provision is made for sealing the edges of the instrument against the surface to be tested—Plasticine is a convenient material for this purpose—and for reading the hygrometer scale whilst the instrument is in position on the floor.

The instrument should be sealed firmly to the floor surface for not less than four hours to allow the entrapped air to reach moisture equilibrium with the concrete base before a reading is taken. A longer period is preferable and can sometimes be obtained conveniently by placing the instrument in position overnight and taking the reading in the morning. If readings are to be taken at several points with only one instrument available, subsequent positions may be covered by impervious mats (bitumen felt, polythene sheeting, etc.) about one metre square, laid down when the instrument is placed in its first position, to speed up the later readings.

When the hygrometer readings fall to 75–80 per cent, the sub-floor can be assumed to be sufficiently dry for flooring to be laid.

The use, instead of a hygrometer, of anhydrous copper sulphate (which turns blue in the presence of moisture) or of anhydrous calcium chloride (which liquefies), is not recommended.

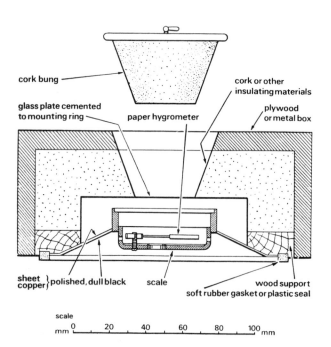

cork bung

glass plate cemented to mounting ring

paper hygrometer

cork or other insulating materials

plywood or metal box

sheet copper } polished, dull black

scale

wood support
soft rubber gasket or plastic seal

scale
mm 0   20   40   60   80   100 mm

Fig 3 Apparatus for measuring dampness

Further reading

Decay in buildings—recognition, prevention and cure Tech Note 44: 1969 Princes Risborough Laboratory (free on application to Distribution Unit, BRE)

Decay of timber and its prevention K St G Cartwright and W P K Findlay; HMSO (London) 1976. £4.50

BS 144 : 1973 *Coal tar creosote for the preservation of timber*

BS 913 : 1973 *Wood preservation by means of pressure creosoting*

BS 1282 : 1975 *Guide to the choice, use and application of wood preservatives*

BS 3051 : 1972 *Coal tar creosotes for wood preservation (other than creosotes to BS 144)*

BS 3452 : 1962 *Copper/chrome water-borne wood preservatives and their application*

BS 3453 : 1962 *Fluoride/arsenate/chromate/dinitrophenol water-borne wood preservatives and their application*

BS 4072 : 1966 *Wood preservation by means of water-borne copper/chrome/arsenic compositions*

BS 5268 : Part 5 : 1977 *Preservative treatments for constructional timber*

BS CP 102 : 1973 *Protection of buildings against water from the ground*

Sound insulation of party floors

In a Building Research Establishment survey of dwellings built during the 1970s, 44 per cent of the floors tested failed to achieve the performance standard given in the Building Regulations for insulation against airborne sounds and 63 per cent failed to achieve the standard for insulation against impact sounds.

To help select suitable party floor constructions, this digest gives data on the performance of common types and shows examples of features which can affect performance.

Requirements of Building Regulations

The Building Regulations for England and Wales (1976) and the Building Standards (Scotland) Regulations 1981 incorporate mandatory requirements to limit sound transmission between dwellings. Both Regulations contain two provisions under which constructions are deemed-to-satisfy these requirements. One stipulates the use of one of the construction types specifically described in the Regulations, and the other is in the form of performance standards. To comply with the performance standards in England and Wales it is necessary to supply evidence from tests which demonstrates that the average performance of at least four examples of a construction similar to that proposed satisfied the performance standards. In Scotland, the actual construction is required to meet the performance standards.

Comparison with performance standards

Floors are required to provide insulation against airborne sounds, such as conversation, and impact sounds, such as footsteps. To compare the performance of a particular design with the performance standards the insulation against both types of noise of four or more examples must be determined at each of the sixteen 1/3 octave bands in the frequency range 100 Hz to 3150 Hz.

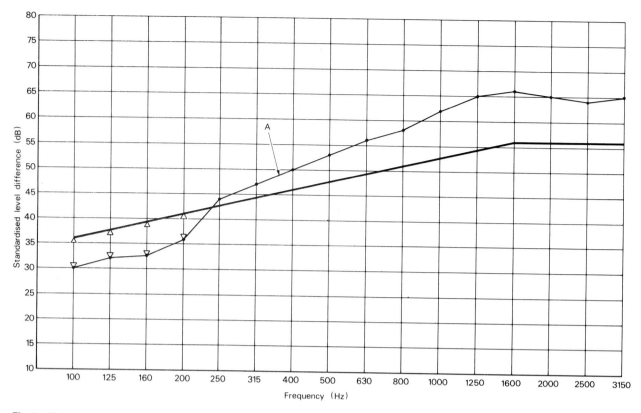

Fig 1 Airborne sound insulation
In the example shown the AAD is: 6 + 5 + 6 + 5 = 22dB

Fig 2 Impact sound transmission
In the example shown the AAD is 11 + 10 + 10 + 7 + 5 = 43dB

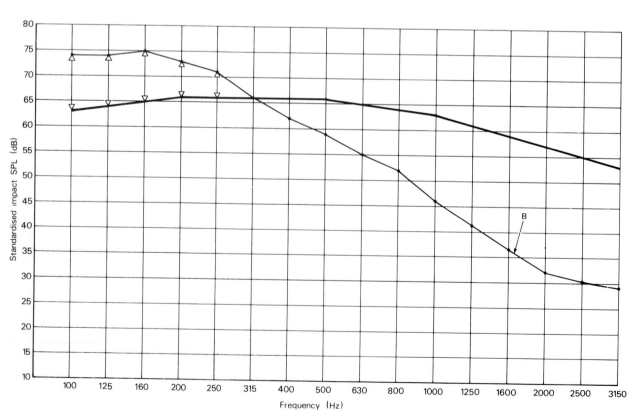

The method of comparison is shown graphically in Figs 1 and 2. In Fig 1 the thick line represents the reference curve for airborne sound insulation of party floors. To quantify the performance of a particular floor design, the average of the measured values (represented by line A) at each frequency is subtracted from the corresponding reference value, and the positive results are summed. The sum is called the Aggregate Adverse Deviation (AAD); it must not exceed 23 dB to satisfy the performance standard given in the Regulations.

In Fig 2 the thick line represents the reference curve for impact sound transmission of party floors. To quantify the performance, the reference value is subtracted from the average of the corresponding measured values, line B, at each frequency and the positive results are summed. Again, this sum is called the AAD and it must not exceed 23 dB.

Design considerations

Generally speaking, floors can be designed to provide insulation against airborne sounds in one of two ways. The first is by having a high surface mass (ie mass per square metre expressed in kg/m^2). The second is to use a floating floor in which the walking surface 'floats' on a resilient layer supported by the structural base. The insulation required against impact sounds can be provided either by laying a soft covering on the walking surface or by using a floating floor. The function of a soft covering is self evident but the requirements and function of a resilient layer are more complex.

Resilient layer The resilient layer should prevent vibrations induced in the walking surface travelling into the structural base and the walls. To do this it must be continuous across the base (ie not bridged by rubble or service pipes etc) and also turned up round the edges between the walking surface and the walls. The resilient layer behaves as a spring and its stiffness must be chosen with regard to the mass of the walking surface to ensure that it acts as a vibration isolator for frequencies above 100 Hz. Fibre resilient layers (ie glass fibre or mineral wool) are usually sold by density rather than stiffness so the correct density must be specified. Acoustically, the thicker the resilient layer the better the isolation at low frequencies; however, if the layer is too thick the floor may feel soft and be liable to cracking.

For a normal floating concrete screed a fibre resilient layer should have an uncompressed thickness of 13 mm to 25 mm and a density of at least 36 kg/m^3. Pre-compressed expanded polystyrene is also suitable provided the correct grade is used.

Recommendations for resilient layers in timber floating floors are given in *Floor constructions* under type (f).

For practical reasons it is generally better to build a separate floating floor for each room rather than to attempt to float partition walls.

Flanking transmission Floors often fail to achieve their potential insulation because of flanking transmission down the walls. Generally, sound can travel vertically between flats by paths involving the party floor, partition or party walls, and the inner leaf of the external wall. Heavy concrete floors provide some restraint to the walls which support them, or are tightly bonded to them, and this reduces flanking transmission along the walls. This is why the Building Regulations require that concrete floors extend to the outer face of the inner leaf of any adjoining external wall and are tied or bonded to every adjoining separating or internal loadbearing wall. The reduction in flanking transmission is often sufficient to make restrictions on the mass of the flanking walls unnecessary. However, to improve thermal insulation, it is becoming increasingly common to build large windowless areas of wall at the gable end. Limited evidence suggests that, in some cases, flanking transmission has been significant and so the use of blocks in the inner leaf having a surface mass of at least 120 kg/m^2 is recommended in this situation.

There is insufficient evidence to show whether dry-lined flanking walls perform differently from plastered ones.

Lightweight timber floors do not restrain the flank walls and so they can only be effective with heavy supporting walls or lightweight plasterboard on timber frame types which do not radiate sound efficiently.

Floor constructions

The following information is based mainly on data collected during a BRE survey of physical sound insulation performance. The conditions for inclusion in the survey and the detailed results have been published in BRE current papers listed under *Further reading*. The survey was carried out unselectively and floors were tested as built; they did not necessarily comply with manufacturers' recommendations on workmanship and detailing etc.

The floors encountered during the survey have been grouped into the following categories:

(a) Heavy solid concrete with soft covering.
(b) Floating concrete screed on a solid concrete base.
(c) Floating concrete screed on hollow concrete beam or beam and hollow block base.
(d) Timber raft floating on a solid concrete base.
(e) Timber raft floating on a hollow concrete beam or beam and hollow block base.
(f) Lightweight timber raft and platform floors.
(g) Pugged timber joist floating floor.

A summary of performance of four main types of floor ((b), (c), (d) and (f)) is given in Table 1; more detailed information follows.

Table 1 Sound insulation performance of four main types of floor

Floor type	Airborne AAD	Impact AAD
	Average dB	Risk of exceeding 23dB expressed as a percentage
Timber raft floating on solid concrete base (d)	12	8	23
Screed floating on solid concrete base at least 125 mm thick (b)	11	14	34
Timber joist raft and platform (f)	22	45	80
Screed floating on hollow beam or beam and block base (c)	27	59	68

(a) Heavy solid concrete with soft covering

Too few examples of this form of construction have been found in the BRE survey to allow statistical analysis. However, the evidence available supports the surface mass requirement of not less than 365 kg/m^2 given in the Building Regulations. A thick, soft floor covering must be used to provide insulation against impact noises.

(b) Floating concrete screed on a solid concrete base

The basic design is shown in Fig 3. Most types tested were cast in-situ but a few used floor-sized panels. For both types, the solid structural base was generally at least 125 mm thick; this corresponds to a surface mass of at least 300 kg/m^2. For both types the average insulation against airborne sounds was about 11 dB AAD with 5 per cent exceeding 31 dB AAD. Floors with bases thinner than 125 mm are likely to perform less well. The performance against impact sounds is more difficult to specify because it covers a very wide range, including examples with construction faults. A histogram of the results is shown in Fig 4; this shows that about 5 per cent had AADs exceeding 103 dB. The fact that over half the examples tested provide good insulation suggests that the basic design is satisfactory but that it is susceptible to lack of attention to detail.

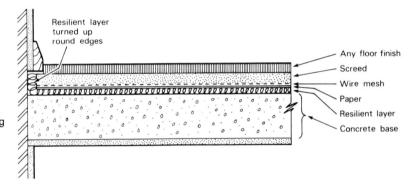

Fig 3 Schematic of concrete screed floating on concrete base

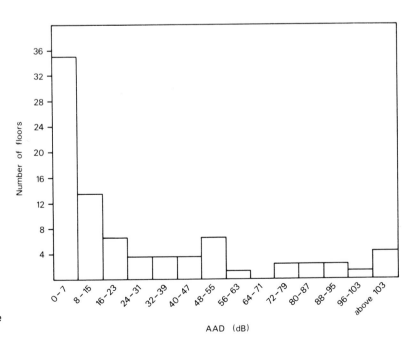

Fig 4 Distribution of impact AAD values for floating concrete floors with dense concrete base and fibre or polystyrene layer

(c) Floating concrete screed on a hollow concrete beam or beam and hollow block base

Hollow beam or beam and hollow block floors are usually designed to satisfy the Building Regulations minimum requirements by having a mass not less than 220 kg/m². The two versions provide a similar standard of performance which is lower than that of the heavier solid corcrete type. For insulation against airborne sounds the average AAD is about 27 dB AAD, with 5 per cent exceeding 57 dB AAD. The insulation against impact sounds is again difficult to specify because it covers a wide range and includes examples with construction faults. However, as only about 32 per cent of the sample had AADs not exceeding 23 dB it is likely that performance will be lower than for the heavier type (b).

(d) Timber raft floating on a solid concrete base

The basic design is shown in Fig 5. The insulation against airborne sounds was about the same as that of the version with a floating concrete screed. However, the insulation against impact sounds was less variable, with an average of 14 dB and with only 5 per cent worse than 35 dB. This design seems to be less susceptible to bridging and poor detailing than the floating concrete screed version and the space between the battens provides a convenient run for service pipes etc.

A resilient layer of glass fibre or mineral wool seems to give better performance than expanded polystyrene sheets or strips of resilient material only under the battens. Satisfactory results have been obtained from an expanded polystyrene layer with the floor surface laid directly on it without battens.

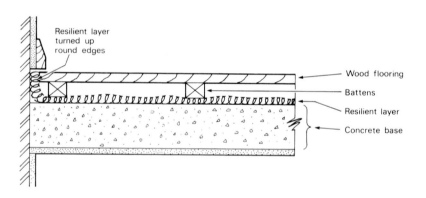

Fig 5 Schematic of timber raft floating on concrete base

(e) Timber raft floating on a hollow concrete beam or beam and hollow block base

There is insufficient evidence to indicate how this type performs but it is likely that the insulation against airborne sounds will be similar to the concrete screed version (c); for design, the remarks for type (d) apply.

(f) Lightweight timber raft and platform floors

Typical designs for these floors are shown in Figs 6 and 7. These designs are successful only when used with either heavy masonry flank walls (eg whole brick or equivalent party walls and half brick or equivalent inner leaves of external walls containing windows), or lightweight plasterboard on timber frame types, on all four sides.

The two types of floor provide a similar standard of performance. For insulation against airborne sounds, the average AAD was about 22 dB with 5 per cent worse than about 42 dB. The insulation against impact sounds was worse, the average AAD being about 46 dB with 5 per cent worse than 83 dB.

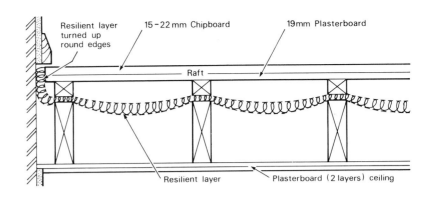

Fig 6 Schematic of raft floor adjoining heavy masonry wall

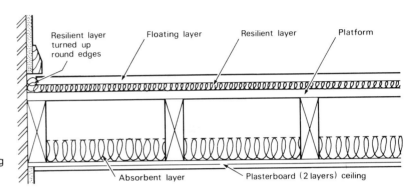

Fig 7 Schematic of platform floor adjoining heavy masonry wall

The following improvements might be made to the typical designs illustrated; the suggestions do not, however, guarantee compliance with the performance standard in the Building Regulations nor are they necessarily the only ones which can improve performance.

Raft types 18mm T & G chipboard on 19 mm plasterboard, laid on battens running parallel to the joists and supported on 25 mm thick mineral wool of about 140 kg/m^3 density; 100 mm of fibre absorbent (as used for insulation in roof spaces) laid between the joists on top of the plasterboard ceiling.

Platform types 18 mm T & G chipboard on 19 mm plasterboard floating on a 25 mm thick mineral wool layer of about 70 kg/m^3 density; this to be on a 12.5 mm plywood platform; 100 mm of fibre absorbent laid between the joists on top of the plasterboard ceiling.

For both types the ceiling can be 19mm + 12.5 mm plasterboard. The resilient layer must not be punctured by nails.

(g) Pugged timber joist floating floor

The basic design is shown in Fig 8. Too few examples have been found in the BRE survey to give information on performance. However, it must be stressed that this type of floor can be used only with flanking constructions which minimise sound transmission, such as those suggested for type (f).

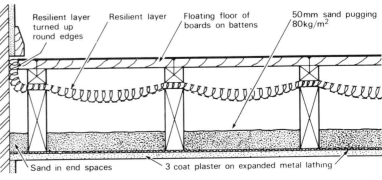

Fig 8 Schematic of pugged timber joist floating floor

Check list of factors affecting performance.

Ensure that the material used as a resilient layer is of a recommended grade and thickness.

Ensure that the structural base is level and smooth before laying the resilient layer.

Check that there are no gaps between the strips or slabs of resilient material that could allow the wet screed to contact the base.

If the resilient layer has a paper face this should be laid 'up' under a concrete screed but 'down' under a timber raft.

Remove all nails used temporarily in the installation of a floating timber floor and make sure that permanent nails do not bridge the resilient layer.

Turn up resilient layers round the edges to prevent the floating layer touching the walls.

Leave a narrow gap between the bottom of the skirting board and the floating layer.

In a concrete floating floor, the best place acoustically for service pipes etc is in the structural base or levelling screed. They must not bridge the resilient layer.

Wood-wool slabs used as permanent shuttering for cast in-situ floors have been found to reduce sound insulation.

Arrange for rooms of similar function to be vertically above each other where possible.

Further reading

BRE Digests

104   Floor screeds
143   Sound insulation: basic principles
187   Sound insulation of lightweight dwellings
252   Sound insulation of party walls

SEWELL, E C and ALPHEY, R. S. Field measurements of the sound insulation of floating party floors with a solid concrete structural base. BRE Current Paper 3/79

SEWELL, E C and ALPHEY, R S. Field measurements of the sound insulation of timber-joist party floors. BRE Current Paper 2/81

SEWELL, E C, ALPHEY, R S and SAVAGE, J E. Field measurements of the sound insulation of party floors with floating screeds and hollow precast concrete (or concrete and clay) structural base. BRE Current Paper 8/81

UTLEY, W A and CAPPELEN, P. The sound insulation of wood-joist floors in timber-frame constructions. BRE Current Paper 46/78

Floor screeds

Recent investigations of floor screed failures, some involving remedial work of tens of thousands of pounds, have demonstrated that published guidance on design, workmanship and supervision too often goes unheeded.

The principal sources of reference have been examined in detail so as to find and resolve any inconsistencies and, in consequence, this digest, first published in 1969 has been expanded to include some matters that were not dealt with, or were insufficiently emphasised, in the original edition. Some of the earlier recommendations have been slightly modified in detail to bring them into line with those made elsewhere, for example, in British Standard Code of Practice CP 204; the differences were, in most instances, the result of rounding up or down when converting imperial units to rational metric equivalents.

Rational design of a floor screed begins with consideration of the whole floor as an element—structural base, screed and finish together. If the floor has to incorporate a barrier against rising dampness —ground-water under a solid floor or condensation on the underside of a suspended floor—if it has to accommodate any special services or a floor-warming system, if it must meet a standard of thermal or sound insulation, the whole element must be designed with these requirements in mind. All too often a structural slab is designed, sometimes even laid, before such needs are considered, leaving them to be dealt with by means of various sandwich layers and screed.

It should be emphasised that a screed does not provide the final wearing surface of the floor.

The need for a screed

Smooth surface It is often possible to make the surface of an *in situ* concrete base smooth enough to suit the proposed floor finish, for example, by the use of a power float or power trowel. *In situ* bases and some that are of precast units may be designed so that an adequate surface can be produced simply by means of a levelling compound. In any other circumstances, a screed will usually be necessary.

Falls The most efficient and economical way to provide surface falls is to form them in the structural base. A screed laid on a level slab and finished to falls must not be thinner in any part than the appropriate minimum thickness recommended below; over most of its area it will, therefore, be wastefully thick, merely to provide falls.

Sandwich constructions Damp-proof membranes and insulating materials are often located between structural base and screed. If the screed is properly designed and laid, a satisfactory job results, but alternative design solutions should be examined before making a final selection. For example, in the range of floor constructions for sound insulation shown in Digest 103, the cost of a resilient layer, a floating screed and a 'hard' floor finish may be higher than that of a 'soft' floor finish on a solid base—and the risk of failure may be greater.

In general, the fewer the layers that comprise a floor, the less will be the risk of failure.

Thermal insulation A floor screed of lightweight concrete provides better insulation than dense concrete. But a comparison of efficiency and cost with other means of providing the same standard of insulation should form part of the process of selection, bearing in mind that under thin materials, for example, flexible pvc flooring, a dense topping to the screed might be needed.

Services The thickness of a floor screed can conveniently accommodate services—pipes and cables. In first cost, this may provide the cheapest solution, but should any fault develop in a pipe or cable, or if access is required for any other reason, the floor finish must be disturbed and the screed broken up with risk of damage to other services. Location of a fault is likely to prove difficult. Because screed thickness is reduced above an embedded pipe, cracking along this line is more likely no matter how generous is the thickness of the screed.

Underfloor warming—Heating cables or pipes are often embedded in a floor screed to provide a space-heating system. Some of the problems associated with heated screeds are discussed on page 5.

Dense concrete floor screeds

Bond and thickness The thickness of a dense concrete screed should be related to the state and nature of the base on which it is to be laid, ie its age when the screed is to be placed and the strength of the bond likely to be attained.

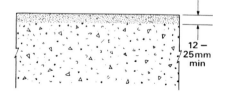

Monolithic—screed placed within three hours of base

Monolithic construction—When a screed is laid on an *in situ* concrete base before it has set (within three hours of placing), complete bonding is obtained. Maximum restraint is thus provided on the shrinkage of the screed and, because screed and base can shrink together, there is a reduction in the potential differential shrinkage between them. A thickness of only 10 mm is all that is necessary; layers thicker than 25 mm should be avoided if the effects of the shrinkage forces arising from the screed are to be restricted. Undoubtedly monolithic construction offers the best chance of eliminating problems of cracking and curling but the decision to lay the screed monolithically with the base must be made at the design stage so that the work may be planned to make this possible. The screed will, in effect, be laid in bays that coincide with those of the structural base and must be finished near the design level if thin floorings are to be used.

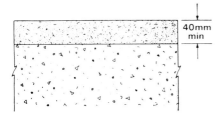

Separate—more than three hours' interval

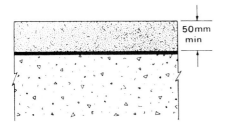

Unbonded—on damp-proof membrane

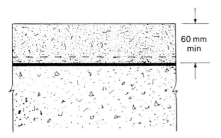

Unbonded and with heating cables

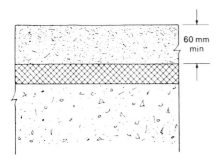

Floating—on compressible material

Separate construction—Once the base has set and hardened, monolithic construction can no longer be used. The strength of the bond between screed and base will then depend on the thoroughness with which the base has been prepared. For maximum bond, the base should be thoroughly hacked by mechanical means, cleaned and damped to reduce suction, then grouted immediately before the screed is placed. A bonding agent may be used as an alternative to grouting. Obviously the amount of preparation considered to be adequate will vary enormously, but assuming a good average standard has been achieved, a minimum thickness of 40 mm should suffice.

Unbonded construction—There are many bases with which it is impossible to achieve a bond, for example damp-proof membranes, concrete containing a water-repellent admixture and concrete that has been impregnated with oil and grease. Although bonding to a base of weak material, eg cellular concrete, is possible, the restraint imposed by such a base can only be slight. The screed should, in such circumstances, be designed and laid as if it were unbonded. Because there is no useful bond it is necessary to have a screed at least 50 mm thick, or, if it contains heating cables, at least 60 mm thick.

Floating—A screed laid on a compressible layer of sound-insulating material should be at least 60 mm thick, or, if it contains heating cables, at least 75 mm thick.

Division into bays To avoid random cracking and to reduce curling it used to be considered necessary to lay all dense screeds in bays.

It is, however, difficult to ensure that screeds laid in bays will not show slight curling or unevenness at the junctions of bays. These show as undulations when thin floorings are used, particularly in large areas and if their surfaces are highly polished. Undulations are difficult and expensive to eliminate but random cracks are generally considered to be easily repaired.

It is now recommended that screeds should be divided into bays only if they are to contain underfloor warming cables (*see* page 5) or are intended to receive an *in situ* floor finish. There should, however, be a joint in the screed corresponding to any joint in an *in situ* structural base but these do not necessarily have to coincide.

When a screed is to be laid in bays, these should not exceed 15 m²; the ratio between the lengths of the sides should be no greater than 1 : 1½. Long narrow bays should be avoided. Many specifications call for screeds to be laid in strips 3 m wide; it must be recognised that where this is done there is a risk of curling at the edges of adjacent strips.

Edges should be vertical and should abut at joints. Building paper, polythene sheeting, fibreboard, etc, placed in these joints are likely only to assist differential movement between bays and sometimes make trowelling more difficult; they should not be used. When the bays shrink, the gaps left between them will, although small, be sufficient to cater for most likely thermal movements.

Expansion joints Expansion joints are required only where similar joints are provided in the main structure and these are unlikely to be needed at intervals of less than 30 m.

Materials
Cement—Portland cement to BS 12 is commonly used and is satisfactory for most conditions.

Aggregates—Good grading helps to improve workability and permits low water/cement ratios. The most suitable aggregates are given in BS 882.

Mix design Mixes made with Portland cement will start to shrink soon after placing and will continue to do so for a long time. The effects of shrinkage can be minimised by good mix design, by restraint (ie bond strength), by limiting differences in shrinkage that can occur between layers of concrete of different mix proportions or states of dryness and by careful curing (*see* page 4).

Mix proportions should be specified by weight of the dry materials. For screeds up to 40 mm thick, cement and sand $1:3-4\frac{1}{2}$ (by weight) is suitable. The mixes less rich in cement are likely to have lower shrinkage. For thicker screeds fine concrete of $1:1\frac{1}{2}:3$ (cement: fine aggregate: coarse aggregate) using 10 mm maximum coarse aggregate is suitable.

Only sufficient water to produce a mix that permits thorough compaction with the means available should be used. A simple test is to squeeze a handful of the mix—it should ball together but it should not be possible to squeeze water out of it. A lower water content is possible in a mix to be compacted by machines than in one that is to be hand-compacted. Although the mix should be as dry as possible, failures have arisen because mixes have been too dry to permit adequate compaction. This usually results in a generally weak screed or at least a weak layer in contact with the base. The surface layer

of strong material is often no more than 5 mm thick and collapses under impact loads such as are applied by some types of office chair. Weak material in contact with the base leads to poor adhesion and also increases the differential shrinkage stresses that can be set up between the top and bottom of the screed. Shrinkage differences of this kind, coupled with poor adhesion, may cause curling at the corners and edges of the screed. Lower water/cement ratios can be achieved with workability aids but care should be exercised to minimise air entrainment.

Placing and finishing The screed mix should be placed as soon as the base is ready, both to ensure that good contact is made with any grout before it sets and to minimise the time during which damp-proof membranes, insulation materials, etc, are liable to be damaged.

For small thicknesses, compaction of the mix on to a rigid base is not difficult. To ensure thorough compaction of screeds more than 40 mm thick, these should be laid in two courses each at least 20 mm thick but with the first layer thicker than the second. The mix must be the same for both layers and the upper must be placed as soon as the lower has been compacted. Thorough compaction is more difficult on resilient bases, eg sound insulation quilts, and careful supervision is needed to ensure that this is achieved.

The finish required on the screed will depend on the type of flooring that is to be laid. Most commonly, the slightly open texture produced by a wood float or the closely knit smooth finish produced by a steel trowel will be required.

It is sometimes argued that a good steel-trowelled finish cannot be achieved on a fine concrete screed. Where there is likely to be difficulty, the fine concrete can be surfaced with a thin layer of a cement and sand mix. This layer should be about 5–10 mm thick and it should be placed before the fine concrete has set. Alternatively, the amount of sand in the mix can be increased to a small extent provided that the overall cement/aggregate ratio is unchanged, or a levelling compound may be used at a late stage in the work.

Curing For at least the first week after a screed has been laid it should be covered with waterproof sheeting to prevent drying as much as possible. During this period of curing, the screed gains strength and the onset of drying shrinkage is delayed; when drying is then allowed to start, the material is better able to resist the shrinkage stresses. Curing compounds should not be used as these will prevent adhesion of most flooring materials to the screed.

Drying The amount of water used in making a screed is necessarily greater than is required to hydrate the cement and there is surplus water to be removed before many floorings can be laid safely. Apart from the adverse effects of moisture on these floorings, the water in the screed will contain alkalies, derived from the cement, which can attack some flooring materials and adhesives. The only way to eliminate excess water in the screed is to allow it to evaporate. The slower the rate of drying the lower is the risk of cracking and curling. No particular drying period can be specified because this will depend on many factors, such as the quality and thickness of the screed and the heating and ventilation within the building. A rule-of-thumb method often quoted is that one month should be allowed for every 25 mm of screed thickness; this is useful for forward planning of building operations but no finish should be laid until the screed is shown by a reliable test to be sufficiently dry. Test methods are discussed in Digest 18 and BS CP 203.

The temptation to use hot-air blowers, underfloor heating, or other means of accelerating drying should be resisted at least for the first four weeks or so.

Protection Because a screed is not designed to function as a wearing surface, it must be protected against abrasion and impact until the flooring is laid. Alternatively, the chance of some damage must be accepted and allowance made for repairs. A balance should be achieved between the need to promote drying and the need to protect the surface where necessary by covering with plywood, hardboard, planks, etc.

Heated screeds

Careful attention should be paid to reducing drying shrinkage and minimising its effects, particularly by mix design, thorough compaction and curing. If monolithic laying can be organised, this will involve the least risk of failure, but if a separate construction is adopted, preparation of the base should be thorough (*see* page 3) so as to obtain the benefit of the maximum bond that can be achieved.

However, in many installations no bond is possible between screed and base. Although the thickness of a heated screed commonly lies within the range of 60–75 mm, which is regarded as adequate for a floating screed, the thermal gradient across the thickness of the screed increases the risk of curling. For this reason, the higher figure (75 mm) should be adopted for a floating screed that is also to be heated.

When an electrically heated screed is to be placed on thermal insulating material or on a damp-proof membrane, it is convenient first to place a bed of cement and sand about 10–15 mm thick, on which the heating cables can be placed without risk of contact between cables and insulation or membrane. This layer may form part of the total screed thickness; if, however, it sets and hardens before the screeding operation is continued, then the required minimum thickness (60 mm) of screed must be laid on it. The screed must be carefully and thoroughly packed around the cables. During screed-laying, the cables should be monitored so that faults can be rectified before the screed has set and hardened.

Heated screeds should be divided into bays not greater than 15 m². Where cables pass from one bay to the next. they should be looped and wrapped as the cable supplier recommends to avoid fracture by shrinkage of the screed; pipes may be either wrapped or coated with bitumen.

Floating screeds

The use of floating screeds to reduce the transmission of impact noise through upper floors is discussed in Digest 103. The screed should be not less than 60 mm thick, or if it incorporates heating elements, 75 mm thick. The screed material must be prevented from seeping through the sound-insulating layer or penetrating at the joints to form solid bridges between the screed and the base slab; a continuous layer of impervious material—polythene sheeting, building paper, etc—well lapped at all joints is effective for this purpose.

It is usual to provide 20–50 mm mesh wire-netting in the floating screed. This is normally laid directly on the impervious sheeting to protect the sheeting and the quilt from mechanical damage during screed laying.

Because the curling of separate bays in a floating screed can lead to difficulty with the floor finish, room-size panels are often adopted, but if these exceed 15 m² by a substantial amount it must be accepted that the risk of curling and cracking is increased.

It is suggested on page 4 that a thin layer of cement and sand can be used to bring a fine concrete screed to a smooth surface. If this is too rich in cement, or too thick, it could encourage a floating screed to curl.

Other screed materials

Synthetic anhydrite Synthetic anhydrite (anhydrous calcium sulphate) is a by-product of hydrofluoric acid manufacture and has different properties from natural anhydrite. It is used with specially graded aggregate—1:2½ by volume—to form screeds having the following characteristics:

(a) Almost all the water used is combined as water of crystallisation. The amount left to evaporate is thus very small and under normal drying conditions the laying of moisture-sensitive floorings can be considered from about ten days after placing the screed.

(b) The material loses strength when it becomes wet. It must therefore be laid only on bases that are dry and likely to remain so.

(c) Drying shrinkage is very low. Large areas can be laid without joints and with no risk of curling.

(d) Minor damage can be repaired quickly and easily.

(e) The material is not bonded to the base and so for level bases preparation is unnecessary.

(f) Drying out during the first two days must be avoided or there will be insufficient water to combine with the anhydrous calcium sulphate. Dustiness and failure to gain sufficient strength may result.

(g) The minimum thickness is 25 mm.

(h) Over compressible material, eg a glass silk quilt, in floating floor construction, the minimum thickness should be 40 mm.

(i) A screed that contains underfloor warming cables should be not less than 30 mm thick; a greater thickness will be needed to provide thermal storage capacity in an off-peak system.

Modified cement and sand   Because the basic characteristics of dense screeds impose limitations on design, there have been many attempts to increase the versatility of the screed by the use of admixtures. The best known of these have water-repellent properties (for example, metallic soaps) and are often assumed to provide adequate substitutes for damp-proof membranes. Not only is this assumption false but they introduce drying problems because the movement of water by capillary action is inhibited.

There are many proprietary screeds which are basically dense screeds modified by the inclusion of materials in emulsion form. Materials that have been used alone or in combination are bitumen, polyvinyl acetate, acrylic resins and some synthetic rubbers. The inclusion of these is aimed at improving adhesion to the base, thereby permitting thinner screeds to be laid. These emulsions tend also to improve the resistance to cracking, despite the fact that emulsion/cement/aggregate mixtures tend to have higher drying shrinkage than similar mixes containing water instead of emulsion. It is often claimed that these screeds dry out faster than unmodified ones. As they are usually thinner, less drying time may be required but no general guidance on this issue can be given.

Lightweight aggregate concrete   As a floor screed, its most important property is its low density which enables it to be used in the thickness required to provide falls or to accommodate services with only the minimum increase in the load imposed on the structural floor. Advantage can also be taken of its thermal properties. It is not suitable for use as an electrically heated screed. Lightweight aggregates and some of the properties of fully compacted concrete made with them are discussed in Digest 123. Screeds of no-fines lightweight aggregate concrete are not considered.

This type of screed should be not less than 40 mm thick. If the proposed floor finish is incapable of spreading point loads (for example, thermoplastic or pvc (vinyl) asbestos tiles, flexible pvc, rubber or linoleum), a topping of cement and sand at least 10 mm thick will be required. To reduce the risk of cracking and to minimise the effects of shrinkage, the topping should be no richer than 1 : 4 and it should be laid monolithically with the lightweight screed.

Generally

Surface texture The surface finish should be related to the kind of flooring that is to be laid on the screed. The slightly rough surface left by a screeding board drawn across screeding battens will be suitable for many floorings, for example, magnesium oxychloride. A wood float finish may be necessary for others, for example, wood block, but for most sheet and tile floorings the smooth dense surface produced by steel trowelling is necessary. The standard of the finish will depend ultimately on the skill of the operative.

Level Some useful information on tolerances in terms of what can reasonably be expected of the floor surface is given in BS CP 204. It is important to bear in mind that insistence on very close limits may result in higher costs. The limits for floor surfaces given in the code are generally applicable to screeds. Briefly, the permissible deviation from level depends on the area involved; for large open areas, a deviation of 10 mm can be tolerated. Localised deviations of 3 mm in any 3 m would normally be acceptable in a nominally flat floor.

Hollowness If the adhesion of a screed to its base is examined by tapping the surface with a rod or hammer, a hollow sound indicating poor adhesion might be detected in some areas, most commonly at the edges and corners of bays. Only if the hollow areas have actually lifted by a visible or measurable extent, so that there is a risk of fracture under superimposed loads, should the screed be considered unsatisfactory on this account.

Sheet and tile flooring made from thermoplastic binders

Sheet and tile floor finishes for non-industrial premises are nowadays frequently made from mixtures consisting essentially of fillers, pigments and thermoplastic binders. This Digest discusses materials other than linoleum and natural rubber together with some of the problems that have arisen in their use, and the sub-floor requirements. A section at the end describes the constitution of the various types of material, and their manufacture and availability, and will provide a background for an understanding of the problems discussed in the earlier sections.

The information given on the composition, manufacture and uses of flooring made from thermoplastic binders should be read in conjunction with the relevant British Standard Specifications and Codes of Practice. These are as follows:

BS 2592 : 1955   Thermoplastic flooring tiles
BS 3260 : 1969   PVC (vinyl) asbestos floor tiles
BS 3261 : 1960   Flexible PVC flooring
BS CP 203 : 1969   Sheet and tile flooring

In addition to the materials listed above, brief reference is made in this Digest to PVC floorings not covered by BS 3261, and to synthetic rubbers. The latter are introduced for the sake of completeness, though the Station's experience of their behaviour in practice is not yet sufficient to provide detailed information.

Sub-floors

All the types of flooring described will conform to the contours of the sub-floor which should, therefore, be even, smooth and rigid. Otherwise the appearance of the finished floor will be affected and any raised portions will show signs of wear more quickly than the rest of the floor. Any sub-floor can be levelled and smoothed, and suspended timber floors can be made more rigid by the use of suitable underlays. The choice of these depends on the situation in which they are to be used and detailed consideration of underlays such as mastic asphalt,

emulsion/cement mixtures, plywood and hardboard is given in BS CP 203 : 1969.

Whilst these sub-floor requirements are comparatively easily met, the most difficult problem associated with sub-floors is the exclusion of moisture. Dampness in sub-floors is the commonest cause of premature failure of floorings fixed with adhesives. The problem arises because the finishes, the adhesives and in some cases the sub-floor (e.g. magnesium oxychloride cement or timber) can be affected by moisture. The commonest sub-floor for any of the materials under discussion is, however, concrete used in the form of a screed (see Digest 104). It is with moisture in this screed that the following remarks are concerned.

Moisture in the screed can derive from water used to mix the screed or base concrete on which it is laid, and from water that can on wet sites rise through concrete in contact with the ground. In each case the water contains alkalis derived from the Portland cement, and can soften all adhesives normally used and give rise to considerable moisture expansion of some of the finishes. With thermoplastic and vinyl asbestos tiles, alkaline moisture produces a curious effect which will be discussed later.

Water rising from the ground or from the base concrete can be prevented from reaching the screed by taking the precautions discussed in Digest 54 and detailed in BS CP 102, Protection of buildings against water from the ground.

In making the cement/sand screed the amount of water used is always much greater than that required to hydrate the cement. Nearly all the excess water must be removed before the floor finish is laid, irrespective of whether the finish, e.g. thermoplastic and vinyl asbestos tiles, has good tolerance to moisture. The only way to eliminate excess water from the screed is to allow it to evaporate. No particular drying period can be specified because the time required will depend on many factors, such as the quality and thickness of the screed, and the heating and ventilation within the building. A rule-of-thumb method often quoted is that one month should be allowed for every inch of the screed thickness. This figure is useful for forward planning of building operations but no finish should be laid until the screed is shown to be sufficiently dry by a reliable moisture test. Various test methods have been devised and of these a method based on the use of a paper hygrometer fitted into an insulated box has been found by the Station to be both simple and reliable. Details of the apparatus and method of use are given in Digest 18 and BS CP 203 : 1969.

Tests that are of little value are those relying on the use of anhydrous calcium chloride, anhydrous copper sulphate or phenolphthalein. In the presence of moisture, calcium chloride becomes visibly damp and copper sulphate turns blue, but the amount of moisture necessary to produce these changes is so small that they can occur even when the screed is sufficiently dry to install the floor finishes. It is generally believed that drops of an alcoholic solution of phenolphthalein placed on concrete will always turn purple when the concrete is too wet to lay the finish. Unfortunately, the colour change can occur even when the concrete is sufficiently dry, and in certain circumstances it will even remain colourless on wet concrete.

The effect of alkaline moisture is the same for all flexible floorings. The edges of the sheet or tile lift and bubbles appear in the surface. Usually the adhesive remains firmly attached to the underside of the finish but leaves the concrete surface completely. Occasionally the adhesive is attacked so severely that it is converted to a brown or black liquid that oozes up between the joints.

Thermoplastic and vinyl asbestos tiles are much more resistant to alkaline moisture but sometimes the adhesive is attacked in the manner just described. Alkalis can, however, produce failure peculiar to these tiles. Water rising through the base concrete penetrates the joints and on evaporation deposits salts, mainly sodium carbonate, from the concrete on the edges of the tiles; the salts tend to creep inwards from the joints over the surface of the tiles, and when dry, characteristic white bands about 25mm wide are formed around the edges, which have been described as 'window framing'. This condition, though unsightly, is not necessarily harmful, and the salt deposits can be removed by careful cleaning. In severely damp conditions, however, thermoplastic tiles can absorb these salts, and the pressures set up within the tiles as the salts crystallise are sometimes sufficient to cause delamination and ultimately powdering of the edges of the tiles.

Uses

Thermoplastic tiles may be used in most non-industrial situations. The tiles are not resistant to grease and oil but are satisfactorily used in domestic kitchens.

Vinyl asbestos tiles tend to have better abrasion resistance than thermoplastic tiles. They have good grease and oil resistance and are more suitable for domestic kitchens or even industrial canteens : they are not, however, suitable for industrial kitchens.

Flexible PVC flooring is produced in such a wide variety of forms that a suitable type can be found for most non-industrial situations and in some instances for industrial situations also. Some are tough enough to withstand truck traffic but it is difficult to fix them so as to prevent the stretching and splitting this produces. In places where a jointless floor is desirable, such as in industrial chemical laboratories or hospitals, it is possible to make a continuous floor finish impervious to liquids by hot air welding of adjacent sheets. Sometimes sheets are butt jointed and welded ; in other cases a rod of material of similar composition to the sheets is welded into a gap left between the sheets or one formed by edge trimming.

A disadvantage of PVC flooring is that it is more easily damaged by cigarette burns than some other materials, but it is doubtful whether any floor finish should be expected to withstand abuse of this kind.

The characteristics of synthetic rubber flooring are much the same as those of natural rubber flooring but they have the advantage of higher resistance to solvents, grease and oils, and freedom from the surface crazing often associated with natural rubber flooring.

Adhesives

There are few difficulties associated with adhesives for flooring so long as it is realised that adhesives cannot act as damp-proof membranes. Even on a dry base there are some problems involved in laying flexible PVC flooring on adhesives. Tar from an adhesive can diffuse slowly through the thickness of the flooring to produce indelible brown stains on the surface. Adhesives containing tar are not therefore recommended.

Some adhesives cause flexible PVC flooring to shrink and produce unsightly gaps around the tiles. This shrinkage is quite different from that shown by dimensionally unstable material (BS 3261 : 1960 includes a test for this) and is produced by movement of plasticiser from the tile into the adhesive. The shrinkage is high (0·7 per cent has been observed) and because the plasticiser softens the adhesive there is a tendency for the tiles to move under traffic and for very wide gaps to appear.

The problem can be solved by using an adhesive that is resistant to plasticisers. Water emulsions of synthetic resins or synthetic rubbers form the basis of most suitable adhesives but the choice of adhesive must normally be left to the manufacturer of the flooring, since he is likely to use a range of plasticisers any of which might bleed into particular adhesives.

Maintenance

To retain the initial appearance of the floor finishes discussed in this Digest it is necessary to maintain them by polishing. The polishes available may be divided into two categories: (i) emulsions in water of resins, waxes or blends of these; and (ii) pastes or liquids in which wax is dissolved in white spirit, turpentine or other solvent. Emulsion polishes can be used on all the materials without risk of damaging the finish, but solvent-based polishes should never be used on thermoplastic tiles since the solvents soften the binders in these. Excessive use of polish should always be avoided, since it leads to slipperiness and high dirt retention. Worn or dirty coats of polish can be removed by washing with a solution of a neutral detergent and subsequently rinsing with clean water.

Two common kinds of markings which may present problems of flooring maintenance are those produced by black rubber in footwear, castor tyres and protective thimbles on the legs of metal furniture, and those produced on the floorings of motor showrooms by rubber tyres.

The scuff markings first referred to can be removed by rubbing with scouring powder and fine steel wool and, on materials other than thermoplastic tiles, by wiping with a cloth moistened with turpentine or white spirit. The markings in motor showrooms, however, are indelible as they are caused by interaction between the antioxidants in the rubber tyres and the floor finish. Here, prevention is the only real answer, although careful choice of pattern in the flooring can help to mask the effect. Mats, metal strips, or thin sheets of polyethylene are effective safeguards in preventing contact between tyres and floors.

Composition

Thermoplastic binders

These are termed thermoplastic because they soften when heated and harden again on cooling. At normal temperatures they are usually brittle unless blended with plasticisers. Large quantities of flooring employ the following binders:

Pitch and petroleum bitumen—dark brown to black substances obtained from the distillation of coal and petroleum respectively.

Gisonite—a dark brown naturally occurring asphaltic material.

Coumarone resins—pale yellow substances found in coal tar naphtha. Extensive processing, including polymerisation, is necessary before they can be used for flooring.

Vinyl resins—white resins synthesised from acetylene or ethylene. Important members of this group are polyvinyl chloride (PVC), copolymers of vinyl chloride and vinyl acetate containing up to 15 per cent of the acetate, and copolymers of vinyl chloride and vinylidene chloride.

Plasticisers

Plasticisers are usually oily liquids having high boiling points and low volatility. They are used to increase the pliability of the binder during the manufacturing process and to provide some measure of control over the flexibility of the finished product.

Fillers

These are used mainly to reduce material costs but they have subsidiary uses, e.g. carbon black may sometimes act as a reinforcing agent or even as a means of providing an electrically conducting material, and asbestos fibre helps to improve the handling properties of hot material during the manufacturing process. Most of the powdered fibres used are of mineral origin, e.g. calcium carbonate and china clay. Cellulosic fillers such as sawdust are seldom used since products containing them are more sensitive to moisture: further, they sometimes lead to high dirt retention by the finish.

Stabilisers

Stabilisers are used mainly to prevent degradation of some of the thermoplastic binders during manufacture, but they also protect the finished flooring subsequently when this is exposed to strong sunlight.

Manufacture and Availability

Thermoplastic flooring tiles

Thermoplastic tiles are made by heating and masticating binders, plasticisers, short-fibre asbestos, powdered mineral fillers and pigments. The resulting hot mass is passed between rollers, which combine heat and pressure, to produce a sheet of appropriate thickness from which the tiles are produced, usually by die-cutting. At ordinary temperatures the material is brittle so that it cannot be marketed in sheet form. The binders range from petroleum bitumen and pitch in the very dark coloured tiles through gilsonite to coumarone-indene and coumarone-styrene resins in the lightest colours. Many of these tiles are now produced with a small proportion of plasticised PVC; they are more flexible and more resistant to grease. The dark binders and their associated fillers and pigments are cheapest and this is reflected in the lower cost of the dark tiles. They are produced in a variety of plain colours and marbled patterns; other patterns, e.g. one simulating the grain and colour of timber, have been made.

PVC (vinyl) asbestos tiles

PVC (vinyl) asbestos tiles formed a natural development from thermoplastic tiles. They are manufactured in the same way with approximately the same ratio of binder to filler: the difference lies in the binder, which consists mainly of vinyl chloride polymer or of copolymers of vinyl chloride with vinyl acetate. The binder allows the production of tiles having clearer, brighter colours and greater flexibility than thermoplastic tiles, though the material is too inflexible to allow of its marketing in sheet form.

Flexible PVC flooring

Flexible PVC flooring is made in both sheet and tile form and in the same thicknesses as vinyl asbestos tiles. The binders used are polyvinyl chloride, copolymers of vinyl chloride or blends of these. It should be noted that although the binding medium may not be entirely polyvinyl chloride it is common practice to refer to the binders as PVC: to avoid confusion this description will be used here. Powdered minerals are the most commonly used fillers but some flooring contains a small proportion of asbestos fibre. The ratio of binder (plasticised resin) to filler can vary very widely; some materials contain as much as 85 per cent of binder, whereas others may contain only 25 per cent or even less. The prices of the finished products when compared on the basis of equivalent thicknesses give some indication of the proportion of binder, as this is the most expensive ingredient.

The most important processes in the manufacture of PVC flooring include the following:

(1) The binder and its compounding ingredients are heated and masticated to form a hot mass from which sheets are produced by calendering. Sheets up to 3 mm thick can be satisfactorily produced in this way, but it is often easier to manufacture thinner sheets which are then pressed together in layers or laminated with other materials such as bitumen-saturated paper felt, cellular rubber and cellular PVC. When similar sheets of thin material are laminated together it is often difficult and sometimes impossible to distinguish the finished product from one made to the full thickness in one operation. Frequently the backing has the same composition, apart from pigmentation, as the face, so as to allow trimmings or offcuts, which would otherwise be scrapped, to be re-used.

(2) A cold paste of the plasticised binder is spread on to a supporting layer such as needleloom felt or hessian. The paste is then heated and a tough film is formed when it gels. This process lends itself to the production of embossed patterns.

(3) Pelletised material is formed into blocks and these blocks are sliced into tiles. Particular patterns, e.g. simulated terrazzo, can be produced by this method.

Methods (1) and (2) are used for the production of PVC flooring having a jute hessian backing. Hessian may also be used to support material during production, in which case it is stripped from the product before it is distributed.

Synthetic rubbers

There is a small but increasing use for flooring of a group of materials generally referred to as synthetic rubbers. These materials resemble natural rubber flooring in appearance and can be produced on conventional rubber manufacturing equipment. Tiles may be cut from calendered sheet or produced individually in moulds to give the same wide range of thicknesses and sizes that are available for natural rubber flooring. The binders used include chlorosulphonated polyethylene, styrene-butadiene copolymers, and butyl and nitrile rubbers.

Clay tile flooring

This digest describes methods of laying clay floor tiles to avoid risk of failure by arching or ridging. Cement mortar bedding on a separating layer of sheet material gives satisfactory service. This method, and the newer ones of laying by the 'thick bed' (also sometimes referred to as 'dry bed' or 'semi-dry bed') technique or by using thinly-applied adhesive compounds, are described below. More detailed guidance can be found in BS CP 202: 1972, Tile flooring and slab flooring.

Classes of tile available

For general use

Two classes are available, floor tiles and quarry tiles the difference being as stated in BS 1286 : 1974 : 'floor tiles are manufactured to narrower limits than quarries and are made by the compaction of powder method, usually from refined and blended ceramic powders but some are made from neat clay powders ; quarries are made from stiff plastic clays by extrusion or other plastic process'. Both types are divided into two classes, as shown in the following table :

	Maximum water absorption (%)
Ceramic floor tiles	
fully vitrified	0.3
vitrified	4.0
Quarry tiles	
class 1	6.0
class 2	10.0

For special uses

Slip resistance. Improvement in slip resistance can be obtained with ribbed or studded surfaces, particled surfaces (shot-faced or pin-head finish) or with non-slip aggregates incorporated in the wearing surface. 'Slip-resistant' tiles are more difficult to keep clean. In some areas, industrial kitchens, for example, there is always the possibility of greasy films being formed on the surface, and unless extra care is taken to eliminate these films, the benefit of the special surfaces will probably be nullified.

Chemical resistance. Clay tiles in general have good resistance to chemical attack but for use in severe conditions tiles should meet the requirements of BS 3679 : 1963.

Frost resistance. Most floors will not be subjected to frost attack in normal service but if this is likely, e g if used externally, the frost resistance of the tiles should be verified by reference to the manufacturer. There is no standard method of test.

Bases for tiling

Rigidity

The base on which the tiling is to be laid must be rigid and stable, e g concrete slabs, precast concrete or hollow clay units ; most wood joist-and-board floors are not suitable.

Falls

Any falls required in the finished floor should be formed other than in the bedding of the tiles although the thick semi-dry method of bedding offers some opportunity to form slight falls in the thickness of the bedding.

Smoothness

Thick semi-dry bedding can be applied directly to a good 'spade-finished' surface of concrete. The thickness of bed can accommodate some irregularity in the surface of the base. For other methods of laying, the base must have a smooth surface; a structural concrete slab can be finished to a satisfactory surface by mechanical means but it is more usual to apply a screed or levelling compound.

Methods of laying

Good laying techniques are designed to prevent bonding between the bedding and the base so that relative movement between them is not restrained.

Bedding on a separating layer (see Fig 4).

A separating layer of sheet material such as polythene or building paper is spread over the base—whether concrete slab or screed. Adjacent sheets should be lapped 100 mm to prevent any bond between bedding and base. The tiles are then laid on the sheet in as thin a bedding of cement and sand mortar as will produce a level floor. A thickness of 13 mm is common but a thinner bed, say 10 mm, may be possible on a smooth base. Where heavy traffic or sharp impacts are likely, the thickness of bedding may be increased to a maximum of 20 mm but its thickness should be less than that of the tiles. The only purpose of a separating layer is to avoid forming a bond between bedding and base. Tiles may therefore be bedded directly on to a damp-proof membrane or on to any surface treated so as to eliminate bonding, e g surfaces coated with curing compounds. An exception is mastic asphalt, where a separating layer lapped 50 mm is required wherever cement/ sand bedding layers are used.

'Thick bed' method

No special preparation of the base is required but it may be necessary to dampen the surface to reduce suction. A semi-dry mix of cement and sand not richer than 1 : 4 should be packed on to the base to a thickness which should not be less than 20 mm but may be as thick as 75 mm; a thickness of 40 mm produces good results. The area of bedding placed in one operation should allow grouting and tiling to be completed whilst the bedding is still plastic. The surface of the compacted bedding should be spread with a 1 : 1 cement and sand slurry about 3 mm thick. The floor tiles are normally laid dry and are tapped into the slurry. A separating layer is not required with this method.

'Thin bed' (adhesive) fixing

Proprietary cement-based and other types of adhesive are available. They should conform to the requirements of Appendix B of Part I of BS CP 212. They should be used according to the instructions of the manufacturer, at a thickness not exceeding

Fig 1   Arching of floor tiles

Fig 2   Ridging of floor tiles

5 mm. Adhesives bond the tiling to the base but the bedding material is sufficiently resilient to tolerate some slight movement between tiling and base without ill effect.

Arching of tiles

The above methods of laying avoid risk of failure of floor tiling by arching or ridging (see Figs 1 and 2). A feature of this type of failure is the way in which the tiles separate cleanly from the bedding; there should be no risk of confusion, therefore, with failures caused by sulphate attack on the concrete base, where the whole floor may bulge upwards (see Digest 75).

Shrinkage of the screed

A newly laid screed shrinks during drying, the tiles do not; indeed some tiles may undergo a small but non-reversible expansion early in their life. If the tiles are firmly bonded by their bedding to the screed surface, considerable stresses can be set up which in the most severe cases are eventually relieved by areas or rows of tiles lifting. In typical instances, failure would occur during the first year after laying. Thin tiles rise more readily than thick ones.

Thermal movements

Failures similar in appearance can be caused by thermal movement in conditions that exclude screed drying shrinkage as a cause of failure, that is in new tiling laid on an old concrete base, or in tiling which has behaved satisfactorily for many years. It may occur after a prolonged cold spell because concrete contracts two or three times as much as clay tiles and a sufficiently low temperature may produce sufficient stress in the tiling to cause lifting. Drying shrinkage and differential thermal movement often act together in causing failure; the stresses set up by one may be insufficient to produce lifting until augmented by the stresses of the other.

Expansion of tiles

In common with most ceramic materials clay tiles may expand slightly due to gradual uptake of moisture, although with highly vitreous low porosity tiles the expansion is insignificant. The mechanism of expansion is not fully understood but it probably involves both physical adsorption of water vapour and chemical hydration. Expansion is most rapid in the first few days after manufacture but can continue at a reduced rate for many years. Long-term expansion is the most likely cause of failure of tiled flooring when this occurs after some years of satisfactory service (see Fig 3).

Special requirements for bedding

Bitumen bedding

If the base is to be subjected to high temperatures, e g around boilers and heating installations, bituminous bedding is recommended. This should consist of 1 part of aqueous bitumen emulsion and $2\frac{1}{2}$ parts of soft dry sand by volume, The bedding should be laid only on a dry surface, primed by brushing a coating of bitumen emulsion over it. The minimum of water should be added to the composition to improve the workability of the mix.

Fig 3   Failure caused by long-term expansion of tiling

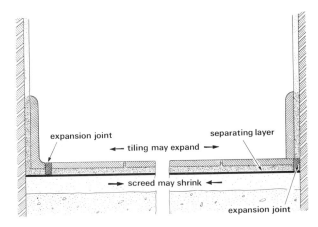

Fig 4   Use of expansion joints (left) between tiling and skirting and (right) between tiling and wall

Corrosion-resistant bedding

Where there is risk of chemical attack, special corrosion-resistant jointing compounds should be used and in the severest cases the compound should be used for bedding as well as jointing. More detailed recommendations are given in Digest 120. It should be borne in mind that chemical attack can derive from seemingly harmless liquids such as milk and fruit juices.

Expansion joints

Expansion joints with suitable compressible material should be provided around the perimeter of every clay tiled floor and at abutments against piers, machine bases, etc. They may be formed either between tiling and coved skirtings, or against walls, where they are lapped and concealed by a skirting (see Fig 4). If the area of flooring requires it, additional expansion joints should be provided at intervals of about 4.5 m across both the length and width of the floor.

Heated floor

Clay tiling is suitable for use on floors that incorporate a heating system. If the bedding is to be other than cement and sand, its suitability for use on a warmed floor should be verified with the manufacturers. The thermal resistance of the tiles is not significantly different from that of concrete but the heating engineer should be informed of the proposed thickness of tiles and bedding. The provision of expansion joints as outlined in the preceding paragraph is important.

Fire performance of walls and linings

The rate of growth of a fire in a building is partly determined by the nature and disposition of the contents of the fire compartment and partly by the design of the building and the materials from which it is constructed. This digest discusses the role of room linings and wall construction in the growth and spread of fire. An important factor which influences the spread of fire within a compartment is the burning characteristics of the materials exposed and this aspect is considered in detail. Of other factors, the thermal properties of the ceiling and walls are discussed briefly but the degree of ventilation has not been considered. Lateral spread of fire from a compartment is prevented by ensuring that the walls or partitions enclosing it have fire resistance and the requirements for this are considered in the latter part of this digest. Fuller details on fire stopping can be found in Digests 214 and 215.

Fig 1

Room linings

Internal linings form large areas of continuous surface which may be heated by the burning contents of a compartment. When hot, these linings will transmit heat principally by radiation to materials not yet involved in the fire, and should the linings burn, the flames will heat uninvolved materials. The contribution to fire growth from combustible linings is particularly important if heat evolves at an early stage in the fire during which that released by the burning contents has not yet reached a significant level. Some indications of the fire hazard of combustible lining materials are given by the ease of ignition, rate of spread of flames over the surface under fire conditions and the rate at which the material will contribute heat to a fire. The results obtained in standard tests are heavily dependent on the exposure conditions and many other factors and cannot be interpreted as describing fundamental properties of the materials.

In the UK the standard methods of test are BS 476: Part 4 which determines whether building materials are non-combustible within the definition given in the Standard; BS 476: Part 7 which tests the rate of spread of flame over the surface of a material and BS 476: Part 6 which measures the rate of heat release under given fire conditions. The ignitability test of BS 476: Part 5 has slight relevance as it indicates the risk of ignition from a small flame similar to a match.

Although non-combustible materials do not contribute directly to fire growth and spread, their thermal insulation properties and heat capacity can affect the development of a fire. Thus, materials with good thermal insulation allow a more rapid rise in temperature in the fire compartment which, in turn, may lead to the earlier ignition of other combustible materials present. Conversely, walls, floors or ceilings of high heat capacity soak up heat from the fire and tend to slow its rate of growth. Experience with real fires and results of experimental work on traditional linings in model rooms, combined with a knowledge of the test ratings obtained by many types of materials, enables the surface spread of flame test and the fire propagation test to be used within Building Regulations as a basis for controlling wall and ceiling linings in different situations. However, a complete indication of all the hazards associated with a lining under fire conditions, including its use in conjunction with other materials or in new forms of construction, cannot always be predicted from the results of the standard tests and may need to be assessed by analysis of the total system. When considering a lining system for test the sample must include any layer which, because of its thermal or combustible properties, is likely to affect the overall fire performance. Even when a non-combustible substrate is specified, its thermal properties can significantly affect the performance of a combustible finish and the test result is directly applicable only to systems based on a substrate of similar thermal properties. If this substrate is thin, then the asbestos insulating board or substitute which is used to back all specimens subjected for test may also affect the fire performance and should be considered to represent a typical non-combustible insulating base. Similarly, where the product under test consists exclusively of a thin or quickly destructible material, the insulating board which is used in the tests as a backing may also affect the fire performance. A warning is given in published results of surface spread of flame and fire propagation tests[1][2][3][4] where it is considered that the material backing a listed product may affect the result. Advice should be sought, therefore, before attempting to apply the test data to systems incorporating other substrates.

No information on the effects of ageing or overpainting is provided by tests on new samples, nor can the performance of a multiple system be predicted from tests on individual components.

Building Regulations prescribe minimum acceptable test ratings for room linings in different occupancies and situations. The general requirement is for Class 1 under BS 476: Part 7 but this is relaxed in carefully defined situations, eg ceilings in domestic buildings, to allow a limited use of Class 3 surfaces. Where the highest degree of protection is required, eg in circulation spaces which often constitute escape routes, Building Regulations introduce a Class 0 rating. By definition, this refers to materials which are non-combustible throughout or which achieve a Class 1 rating for surface spread of flame and also have fire propagation indices * $I \leqslant 12$ and $i_1 \leqslant 6$ obtained in BS 476: Part 6. Regulations also specify the circumstances under which thermoplastic materials are acceptable in Class 0 situations. Materials which do not reach the required test performances, or are unclassifiable because they fall away from the test sample holder before the test duration has elapsed, are sometimes permitted but limitations are imposed on the maximum areas acceptable and the spacing between those areas.

For the purposes of the regulation dealing with the 'restriction of spread of flame over surfaces of walls and ceilings', the surface of any glazing is controlled but door frames, window frames, fitted furniture, architraves, skirtings etc are not.

Untreated timber and its derivitives can generally achieve a Class 3 rating; however, the use of flame-retardant treatments will enable these materials to achieve Class 1 and Class 0 but they cannot make combustible materials non-combustible nor do they usually reduce significantly the rate of charring away of timber in a fire. The types of treatment involve either surface application or impregnation and their action varies; for example, the treatment may provide an impervious barrier over the surface of the

*Fire propagation index $I = i_1 + i_2 + i_3$, where sub index i_1 is derived from the first three minutes of test. A high initial index (i_1) indicates an initially rapid ignition and heat release.

material or when heated it may cause a reaction which inhibits combustion or insulates the surface of the material. Advice on such treatments forms the subject of FPA and TRADA publications[5][6] which also consider practical aspects such as the type of surface to be treated, over-painting, weathering and smoke emission. The mechanical resistance and durability of surface treatments should always be questioned, many being degraded by regular wetting, eg by rain or condensation.

The choice of lining material will frequently involve consideration of layered or laminated systems. It is therefore important that the methods of fixing or bonding used on site will not permit premature delamination in the event of fire, resulting possibly in a markedly different response by an otherwise 'satisfactory' finish or veneer. One of the problems associated with delamination is the exposure of the combustible substrates to the fire sooner than designed for. The problem of early delamination is exemplified by the behaviour of thick paint films. Where finishes of similar paint base are allowed to accumulate on a surface the overall heat output may not, after ageing, vary significantly from that of the original three-coat system because the overall combustible content is low. Where the base varies, eg where an emulsion coat is applied to an existing gloss finish and is subsequently over-painted by gloss, delamination of the film may occur at the interface. Ignition of subsequent layers can result in fragments of flaming film falling during the early stages of a fire.

Certain plastics materials, because of their softening characteristics, cannot be assessed in the tests for fire performance of building materials. Thermoplastic materials soften and melt in a fire. Those which do so before they ignite do not contribute significantly to fire spread if they fall away from the flames, although falling hot material may be a hazard to people beneath. Materials which ignite and burn while falling may result in rapid fire spread. The performance depends on the type of plastics material, thickness of sheets and the way they are held in position. The Building Regulations, therefore, stipulate the use of certain quality control tests for burning characteristics specified in BS 2782: 1970. Whilst these are not designed to assess fire hazard they provide a measure of flammability of the constituent material and, coupled where necessary with restrictions on fixing methods, permissible area, separation etc, provide a method of control.

Fire resistance

The fire resistance* of a wall (or partition) is determined by subjecting one side of a 2.5 × 2.5 m (mini-

*Defined in BS 4422: Part 2 as 'the ability of an element of building construction to satisfy for a stated period of time some or all of the criteria specified in BS 476: Part 8, namely resistance to collapse, resistance to flame penetration and resistance to excessive temperature rise on the unexposed face.

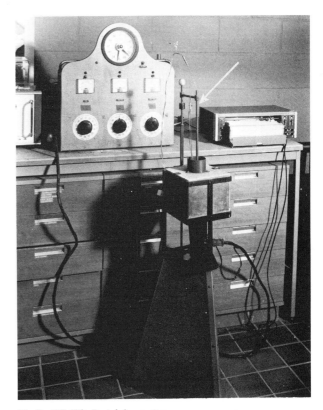

Fig 2 BS 476: Part 4 Apparatus
The specimen, 40 × 40 × 50mm is suspended from the insertion rod (arrowed) in a cylindrical furnace heated to 750°C, and is exposed for 20 minutes.

Fig 3 BS 476: Part 6 apparatus
The specimen, 228 × 228 × 50mm maximum, is placed in the recess (arrowed) and bolted against the face of the furnace. The temperature in the furnace flue during the test period of 20 minutes is compared with that obtained using a standard asbestos board specimen.

Fig 4 BS 476: Part 7 apparatus

The specimen, 900 × 230 × 50mm max is located in the holder (arrowed) and is exposed to heat from a 900mm square radiant panel. The extent of flame spread after 1½ minutes and after 10 minutes is used to classify products as shown in Fig 5.

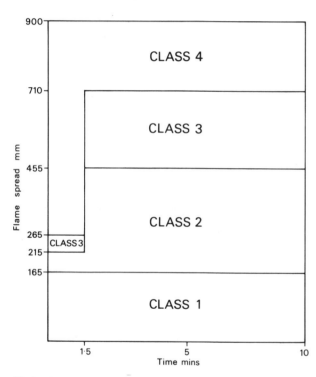

Fig 5 An indication of classification limits for large-scale spread of flame test (based on Fig 2 of BS 476: Part 7)

mum) specimen to a furnace which is controlled to follow a time/temperature curve in which the temperature, measured by thermocouples at specified locations, rises by 821°C after 30 minutes and 1133°C after four hours (Fig 6). The performance of the specimen is expressed as the time in minutes for which the appropriate criteria of stability, integrity and insulation are satisfied. Although the stability criterion is applied to both loadbearing and non-loadbearing constructions the interpretation is not the same for each case.

Failure is deemed to have occurred in the case of,

Stability: when collapse takes place;

Integrity: when cracks or other openings develop through which flame or hot gases can pass which can cause flaming of a cotton wool pad. Where the level of radiation is such that the cotton wool test cannot be used, failure shall be deemed to have occurred if a crack or fissure exists or develops exceeding 6 mm × 150 mm;

Insulation: when the mean temperature of the unexposed surface of the specimen increases by more than 140°C above the initial temperature, or by more than 180°C at any point.

Depending upon its situation and function within a building, a wall may be expected to fulfil different requirements in the event of fire. Most fire resisting walls used to separate buildings, enclose compartments and contain fire will be required to provide a barrier to the passage of fire from one side or the other and must therefore be able to satisfy each of the three criteria from either side for a prescribed period. Other situations arise where fire resistance is not required from both sides and where the construction may have to satisfy the criteria to different extents. Examples of different wall situations/requirements are given in Table 1.

External walls

The nearness of a building to its boundary determines the probability of its being a danger to other buildings on adjoining sites if it is 'on fire' or of its being at risk itself from a neighbouring building involved in fire. External walls may have windows and other areas in them which provide no barrier to fire; they may have combustible material fixed externally as a cladding and this is more easily ignited by radiation from a neighbouring fire; or they may in some areas fail to provide adequate or any resistance to the passage of fire. All such areas are designated 'unprotected' for Building Regulations (England and Wales) purposes; the Building Standards (Scotland) Regulations use the term 'opening' to describe similar areas.

The Building Regulations require different performances from external walls depending upon distance from boundary. In walls which are not located on or near the boundary, Regulations control the extent of permitted limits of unprotected areas or openings.

Where regulations permit external walls to have fire resistance only from the inside, stability and integrity are required to be satisfied for the full period; but insulation is required for only 15 minutes (see Table 1). This means that satisfactory designs will be different from other types of wall required to maintain insulation for the full period.

In a single-storey portal framed building, the designer may wish to leave the rafters unprotected; where the portal frame is built into or supports an external wall, the siting of the building in relation to the boundary has to be taken into consideration. If these walls are so sited that under the Building Regulations the whole elevation cannot be 'unprotected' it must be ensured that any collapse of the 'rafters' will not also result in premature collapse of the external wall. Advice on this aspect is contained in Appendix 1 to DOE Circular 91/73[7].

Loadbearing walls

Occasionally, a loadbearing wall is so positioned that it forms part of the structural frame of a building but does not perform a separating function; in this event the construction would be judged only by the criterion of stability. Such a wall, while it may have to withstand the effects of fire from both sides at once, is difficult to test in the existing designs of furnace which can apply heat to only one side. Most constructions which are satisfactory when tested from each side separately are not adequate when heated from both sides at the same time.

Glazed screens

Because of the transmission of radiant heat through ordinary wired glass, constructions incorporating such glazing cannot satisfy the heat insulation requirement for more than a few minutes although they are able to achieve results in terms of stability and integrity. The function and location of a screen will dictate whether it may be fully glazed, incorporate glazing to a limited extent, be glazed above a

minimum height or not at all, eg if there is a risk to people escaping past the screen or if ignition can occur of combustible materials stacked in close proximity on the side remote from the fire.

However, where walls or screens incorporate a new glazing system which has been shown by test to achieve full insulation, the above limitations do not apply.

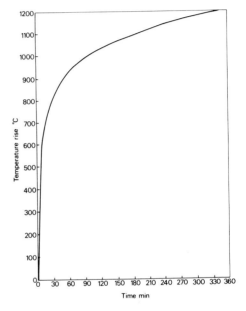

Fig 6 Standard time-temperature curve BS 476: Part 8: 1972

Table 1 Provisions as to method of test and minimum period of fire resistance (Based on Table 1 to Regulation E1 of the Building Regulations 1976)

Part of building	Method of test	Minimum period as to—BS 476: Part 8: 1972 (or Part 1: 1953)		
		Stability	Integrity	Insulation
External wall situated 1 m or more from relevant boundary (excluding any part of such a wall which is described in item 2 of the table to the regulations).	exposure of inside of wall to test by fire	*	*	15 min
External wall situated less than 1 m from any point on relevant boundary	exposure of each side of structure separately to test by fire	*	*	*
Separating wall				
Compartment wall				
Wall situated between a 'small' garage and a house to which it is attached or of which it forms part	exposure of garage side of wall to test by fire	*	*	*

(* denotes period of fire resistance specified by the regulations)

Framed walls

The contribution to integrity and insulation of the linings on each side of a symmetrical framed wall construction attacked by fire from one side cannot be assumed to be identical. Once the exposed lining is penetrated, the unexposed side will be attacked on its inside face and will generally fail in a shorter time. Thus a framed wall, each lining of which could in theory satisfy the integrity and insulation criteria for 20 minutes (if exposed to fire from either side), would achieve an overall performance of less than 40 minutes for the complete wall. The lining first exposed to the fire will alone contribute to the stability of the frame.

Possible points of weakness in such walls are joints and junctions, the method and type of fixings, charring of combustible framework and expansion of steel studs. Suitable forms of linings can be constructed from combustible as well as non-combustible materials.

Examples of load bearing framed constructions are given in a BRE Report[8].

Combustible material penetrating fire resisting construction

Timber joists and purlins built solidly into masonry separating and compartment walls should not normally render ineffective the resistance of such walls to the effects of spread of fire where there is no significant gap between the timber member and masonry. The charring rates of timber exposed to the standard heating conditions of BS 476: Part 8 are such that a one-hour fire resisting wall is unlikely to be of so small a thickness that it will fail prematurely through 'passage of flame' along the timber member.

The charring rates given in BS 5268: Part 4, Section 4.1 vary with species—see Table 2.

However, floors should be so designed that the pulling out or displacement of the joists will not cause the premature failure of the wall, a situation of particular relevance where the floor does not have to achieve the same period of fire resistance as the wall.

Table 2   Charring rates of timber

Timber	Depth of charring in:	
	30 mins	60 mins
All structural species listed in Table 1 of CP 112: Part 2: 1971, except those listed below.	20 mm	40 mm
Western red cedar	25 mm	50 mm
Oak, utile, keruing (gurjun), teak, greenheart, Jarrah	15 mm	30 mm

Junctions between walls and other elements of construction

Allowance must also be made for possible interaction, under fire conditions, at the junction between a wall and the underside of a structural floor, and a wall and the perimeter of a fire protecting suspended ceiling, so as to minimise the possibility of disruption of components by distortion and consequent fire spread (Fig 9).

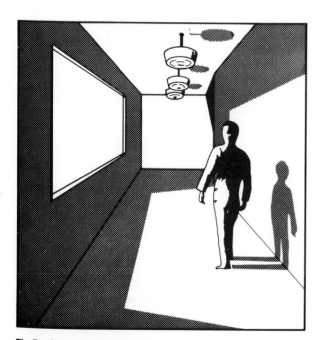

Fig 7   Glazed screen on escape route. People in the corridor can be exposed to radiated heat

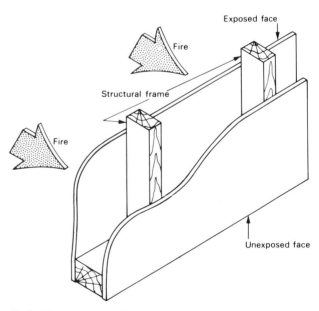

Fig 8   Fire resistance of framed walls

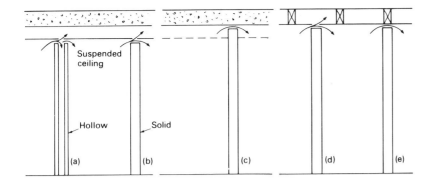

Fig 9 Possible routes (arrowed) for fire spread at the head of partitions ((c) and (e) are preferable) indicating the need to consider fire stopping

References

1 Results of surface spread of flame tests on building products; RW Fisher and Barbara FW Rogowski; BRE Report; HMSO London, 1976.

2 Results of fire propagation tests on building products; RW Fisher and Barbara FW Rogowski; BRE Report; HMSO London, 1976.

3 Fire test results on building products; surface spread of flame; RW Fisher; Fire Protection Association, London, 1978.

4 Fire tests on building products; fire propagation; RW Fisher; Fire Protection Association, London, 1980.

5 Fire retardant treatments for wood and its derivatives; Fire Prevention Design Guide 13; Fire and the Architect; Fire Protection Association, London, 1978.

6 Flame retardant treatments for timber. TRADA Wood Information, Timber Research and Development Association, March 1980.

7 Public Health Act 1961: Building Regulations; Notes for guidance on the relaxations or dispensations of Part E requirements; Department of the Environment Circular 91/73; HMSO, London, 1973.

8 Guidelines for the construction of fire-resisting structural elements. REH Read, FC Adams and GME Cooke. BRE Report, HMSO, London 1980.

British Standards

BS 476:   Fire tests on building materials and structures

        Part 4: Non-combustibility test for materials
        Part 5: Method of test for ignitability
        Part 6: Fire propagation test for materials
        Part 7: Surface spread of flame tests for materials
        Part 8: Test methods and criteria for the fire resistance of elements of building construction

BS 2782:   Methods of testing plastics

BS 4422:   Glossary of terms associated with fire

BS 5268:   Code of Practice for the structural use of timber
        Part 4: Fire resistance of timber structures
        Section 4.1: Method of calculating fire resistance of timber members (1978)

DD64   Guidelines for the development and presentation of fire tests and for their use in hazard assessment.

Other BRE Digests

208 Increasing the fire resistance of existing timber floors
214 Cavity barriers and fire stops: Part 1
215 Cavity barriers and fire stops: Part 2
220 Timber fire doors
225 Fire terminology
233 Fire hazard from insulating materials

Sound insulation of party walls

In a survey of dwellings built during the 1970s, BRE found that over 50 per cent of the party walls failed to achieve the performance standard given in the Building Regulations. To aid selection of a suitable party wall construction, this digest outlines the requirements of the Regulations, and provides information on the performance of some of the more common party wall constructions; it indicates the risk of a wall failing to achieve three levels of performance, the highest of which is the minimum performance requirement of the Building Regulations. The digest draws conclusions about the performance of different constructions and gives examples of features which can adversely affect performance. Whilst specialist knowledge is required to design buildings with very high sound insulation, application of the information given in this digest should contribute to a reduction in the risk of dwellings being built with inadequate performance.

Requirements of Building Regulations

The Building Regulations for England and Wales (1976) and The Building Standards (Scotland) (consolidation) Regulations 1971 incorporate mandatory requirements to limit sound transmission between dwellings. Both Regulations contain two provisions under which constructions are deemed-to-satisfy these requirements. One stipulates the use of one of the construction types specifically described in the Regulations and the other is in the form of a performance standard. To comply with the performance standard in England and Wales it is necessary to supply evidence from tests which demonstrates that the average performance of at least four examples of a construction similar to that proposed satisfies the performance standard. In Scotland, the actual construction is required to meet the performance standard.

Comparison with the performance standard

To assess the performance of a particular design the insulation of four or more examples must be determined at each of the sixteen 1/3 octave bands in the frequency range 100Hz to 3150Hz. An example is shown graphically in Fig 1, in which A represents the reference for party walls between houses and flats in England and Wales. To quantify the performance, the average of the measured values at each frequency is subtracted from the corresponding reference value and the positive results are summed. The sum is called the *Aggregate Adverse Deviation* (AAD) and it must not exceed 23dB to satisfy the performance standard given in the Regulations. The situation is similar in Scotland except that A applies only to walls between houses and B (also shown in Fig 1) must be used to assess walls between flats.

Interpretation of AAD ratings

A recent social survey has provided data which illustrates probable subjective responses to different levels of sound insulation. For example, with party walls complying with the Regulations, about two-and-a-half times as many occupants rated their insulation as very good or good as rated it poor or very poor. At around 48 dB AAD the numbers giving these ratings were approximately equal and at 80 dB AAD about two and a half times as many occupants rated their insulation as poor or very poor as rated it good or very good. The estimated risk of failure to reach these three performance levels for various types of party wall construction is given in Table 1.

Field performance of common constructions

Table 1 is based on data collected in the course of a BRE survey of physical sound insulation performance between dwellings built since 1970. The conditions for inclusion in the survey and the detailed results have been published in the BRE Current Papers listed under *Further reading*. The survey was carried out non-selectively and the dwellings included were tested as built; they did not necessarily comply with manufacturers recommendations with regard to workmanship and detailing etc.

The first four columns in the Table provide brief descriptions of each of 19 common constructions according to the following definitions:

Solid wall: A single leaf of dense concrete at least 170 mm thick, or of brick or blockwork at least 200 mm thick, or of no-fines concrete at least 225 mm thick. (All thicknesses exclude surface finish).

Cavity wall: Two leaves of brick or blockwork, each typically 100 mm thick, separated by a cavity and coupled by butterfly wall ties.

Dry-lined: Walls lined on both sides with a single layer of plasterboard, usually 9.5 mm thick, attached by dabs or battens.

Plastered: Walls plastered on both sides. No distinction is made between lightweight and traditional materials.

Concrete, autoclaved aerated: Walls built from autoclaved aerated concrete blockwork and having a surface mass below 250 kg/m^2.

Concrete, dense blockwork: Walls having a surface mass exceeding 415 kg/m^2.

Concrete dense: Solid walls built from large concrete panels or concrete poured in situ. Some examples had a plaster finish and some were fair-faced. The surface mass normally exceeds 415 kg/m^2.

Concrete, lightweight aggregate blockwork: This is a general term referring to blockwork containing various types of aggregate, including pulverised fuel ash, chemically stabilised graded wood particles and furnace clinker. The surface mass of walls built from such blocks, when plastered, normally exceeds 250 kg/m^2.

Concrete, no-fines: Solid walls plastered or rendered on both sides. The surface mass normally exceeds 415 kg/m^2.

Plasterboard on timber frame walls: Walls comprising two separate stud frames each supporting one leaf of the wall, each leaf being in the form of a laminate of plasterboard (or plasterboard and plywood) at least 32 mm thick, with the separation between the inner faces of the two leaves exceeding 200 mm and containing one or two sound-absorbing quilts over the whole area.

Table 1 Sound insulation performance of different constructions

Material	Type	Finish	Solid or cavity (cavity width mm)	Average AAD	Risk of failure to achieve stated AAD value (Risk expressed as a percentage)		
					23 dB AAD	48 dB AAD	80 dB AAD
Brickwork		DL	38 and wider	44	79	44	8.5
		DL	S	32	67	23	1.1
		P*	50 and wider	29	62	17	0.5
		P*	S	20	43	4.8	less than 0.1
Concrete: autoclaved aerated	Blockwork	DL	S	99	greater than 99	greater than 99	89
		P	50-70	67	92	72	35
		P	75 and wider	44	80	44	7.3
		P	S	49	82	49	14
Concrete: dense	Blockwork	DL	50 and wider	42	86	37	1.5
		P*	50 and wider	5	less than 0.1	less than 0.1	less than 0.1
		P*	S	13	14	less than 0.1	less than 0.1
Concrete: dense	Cast in situ or precast panels	F/P	S	7	1.4	less than 0.1	less than 0.1
Concrete: Lightweight aggregate	Blockwork	DL	50 and wider	42	77	41	7.2
		DL	S	44	83	43	5.2
		P	50-70	40	75	37	5.6
		P	75 and wider	41	81	37	3.1
		P	S	30	64	17	0.4
Concrete: no-fines	Cast in situ	P	S	13	25	0.8	less than 0.1
Plasterboard	Timber frame	—	200 and wider	6	less than 0.1	less than 0.1	less than 0.1

DL = dry lined
P = plastered
F/P = fair faced or plastered

* Samples restricted to party walls associated with external flanking walls which met, or were close to, deemed to satisfy requirements.

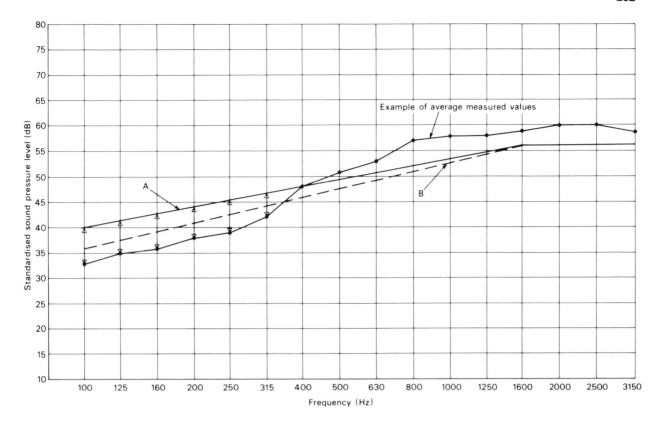

Fig 1 Example of calculaton of AAD
In the example shown the AAD related to Curve A is: 7 + 6 + 7 + 6 + 6 + 5 = 37 dB

The average AAD found for each type of construction is shown in Table 1. It is clear that the performance of a particular type of construction cannot be specified adequately by a single AAD value; this is because of the wide range of performance found for most types of construction. With present experience, variability must be regarded as an inherent feature of sound insulation performance. Some factors which may help to prevent bad performance are discussed later, but in general the causes of variability are not fully understood. Therefore, when assessing the suitability of a possible type of construction, it is prudent to consider the risk of failing to achieve various levels of performance. For example, only for six of the types listed in Table 1 is the risk of failure to achieve 23 dB AAD less than 50 per cent. For these same six types the risk of failure to achieve 48 dB AAD and 80 dB AAD are less than 5 and 0.1 per cent respectively.

The table has been prepared from data on individual walls, not groups of four. The values shown in the last three columns are best estimates, based on the means and standard deviations of the samples measured in the survey. Because of statistical uncertainties in the estimated values, small differences have little practical significance.

The table highlights the following points:

With masonry walls, mass is the main factor determining performance.

Lightweight constructions comprising two leaves of plasterboard on studwork (described in Digest 187) can provide a high standard of insulation. From the survey evidence, this construction seems to be reliable.

Solid and cavity versions of the same type of masonry wall usually provide fairly similar performance. Consequently there is little advantage for sound insulation in using cavity construction for masonry walls.

Plastered walls usually provide better performance than their dry-lined counter-parts. The difference depends on the wall type and is small for cavity lightweight aggregate blockwork walls but large for cavity dense blockwork walls. The dry-lined walls in the sample generally were not rendered. It is not known if rendering before dry-lining affects performance.

Factors affecting performance

The tabulated results are for typical constructions with no evidence of major faults. Even designs which normally provide adequate insulation may give poor results if such faults are present and so particular attention should be paid to the following details to avoid the more common faults:

Direct air paths through or round a party wall, even in the roof space, should be kept to a minimum by use of joist hangers where necessary and by careful sealing around any unavoidable penetrations of the wall. To reduce the risk of penetration, flush mounting fittings should not be attached back-to-back on the party walls, but separated by at least 200 mm. It is essential to make a wall airtight; even gaps having a total area of only 100 mm^2 in a 10 m^2 wall (0.001 per cent) may be sufficient to seriously limit performance, particularly at high frequencies.

Ceilings in upper-floor rooms should be of plasterboard or other airtight material of similar mass. Several examples of poor insulation have been found between bedrooms with lightweight ceilings.

It is advisable to continue the party wall construction, unmodified, right through the roof space. With cavity walls it is particularly important not to close the cavity with blocks supported on both leaves to form a base for a single leaf extension in the roof space.

A masonry party wall should be bonded to the inner or only leaf of the external masonry wall and not merely butt jointed.

Resilient thermal insulating materials (such as expanded polystyrene) which are attached to the flanking walls then plastered over may reduce the sound insulation. An adverse effect has also been found from wood-wool slabs used as permanent shuttering for concrete.

Minimum connections should be used between the leaves of cavity party walls consistent with structural stability. If, for structural reasons, butterfly wire ties cannot be used, it is better to use a solid wall of the required mass.

Air bricks and windows in adjacent dwellings should be separated by at least the minimum distance (690 mm) specified in the Building Regulations to minimise transmission via air paths outside the building or along the wall cavity.

The mass of a brick wall is significantly higher if the bricks are laid 'frog up' and filled with mortar instead of 'frog down' and hence the sound insulation performance will be improved.

Room Layout

Generally, designs which minimise common wall area are beneficial for sound insulation. For example, a wall will provide better sound insulation where it separates two rectangular rooms by forming one of the shorter dimensions rather than one of the longer dimensions. Similarly, stepped or staggered layouts between dwellings tend to improve performance. This applies mainly to airborne sounds, such as conversation or music. However, occupants are often disturbed by 'structure borne' sounds such as plumbing noises, kitchen activities, footsteps on stairs and banging doors. It is generally preferable to arrange for rooms of similar function to be juxtaposed at the party wall and to be vertically in line in blocks of flats.

Further reading

BRE Digests

143 Sound insulation: basic principles

187 Sound insulation of lightweight dwellings

BRE Current Papers

SEWELL, E C, and SCHOLES, W E. Sound insulation performance between dwellings built in the early 1970s. CP 20/78.

SEWELL, E C, and ALPHEY, R S. Field measurements of the sound insulation of party walls in timber-framed dwellings. CP 39/77.

SEWELL, E C, and ALPHEY, R S. Field measurements of the sound insulation of heavy solid concrete party walls. CP 43/77.

SEWELL, E C, and ALPHEY, R S. Field measurements of the sound insulation of plastered solid brick walls. CP 37/78.

SEWELL, E C, ALPHEY, R S, SAVAGE, J E, and FLYNN, S J. Field measurements of the sound insulation of plastered cavity masonry walls. CP 4/80.

SEWELL, E C, ALPHEY, R S, SAVAGE, J E, and FLYNN, S J. Field measurements of the sound insulation of plastered solid blockwork walls. CP 5/80.

SEWELL, E C, ALPHEY, R S, SAVAGE, J E, and FLYNN S J. Field measurements of the sound insulation of dry-lined masonry party walls. CP 6/80.

Rising damp in walls: diagnosis and treatment

This digest considers the causes of dampness in walls and offers a positive method for diagnosis of rising damp. It suggests possible remedial measures which can be taken to avoid rising damp such as providing a complete moisture barrier by insertion of a physical damp-proof course or the non-traditional method of chemical injection. The repair of areas of plastering damaged by damp is also included. This digest replaces Digest 27 which is now withdrawn.

Masonry walls which stand in water or in saturated soil and which contain no physical barrier to the upward flow of moisture, often have rising damp at heights in excess of 1 m. This height depends on several factors, such as the pore structure of the wall, the degree of saturation of the soil, the rate of evaporation from the wall surfaces and the presence of salts in the wall. Bricks and mortars have a complex pore structure in which the diameter of the pores varies widely, as does the pore size distribution in each component. This has an important effect on the height to which the damp will extend because, within limits, the smaller the pores the greater the vertical rise of moisture. Old walls may contain pores as small as 0.001 mm diameter, which can theoretically support a column of water far higher than 1 m.

For water to rise in a wall, a supply must be available at the base. If the ground surrounding the wall is saturated, this condition is achieved but if the ground is not saturated the soil will exert a suction that will oppose the upward capillary pull on the water in the wall. This suction is approximately equivalent to the negative pressure exerted by a column of water extending from the base of the wall to the water table. If the water table falls the height of the moisture in the wall will drop to a new level provided there is sufficient time for equilibrium to become established. Each period of heavy rain on the base of the wall will produce a temporary condition of saturation and the water level in the wall will begin to rise again. The level to which is rises depends on the amount of evaporation of water from a wet wall and on the resistance to the flow of moisture up the wall. If this resistance is high, as in a material with many fine pores, the effect of evaporation is most marked but if the wall material has many coarse pores, the height of dampness will be only slightly affected by normal rates of evaporation. Increasing the heat input to the structure will increase the rate of evaporation from the wall surfaces. The overall effect is to increase the rate of flow

of water up the wall but because of the resistance to flow this is likely to be accompanied by a reduction in the height to which the moisture extends. In addition, evaporation will occur from deeper in the pores of the plaster so that the rising damp seems to disappear. In summer, hot weather will increase the evaporation rate and lower the water table so the effect on rising damp can be even more striking.

Water drawn from the soil usually contains a low concentration of soluble salts and the rising water will also generally dissolve salts from the bricks or the mortar. These salts tend to increase the surface tension of the water which increases the upward pull but this will be partially offset by the increase in density of the solution and the consequent increased downward pull of gravity. When evaporation occurs the salt solution becomes more concentrated at the surface and finally the salts will crystallise out. This tends to block the pores, reducing evaporation and hence raises the level of dampness. These salts may also be hygroscopic and will absorb moisture from the air above some critical value of relative humidity so that the surface appears wet during wet weather although this dampness seems to disappear when the air becomes drier again.

All this suggests that under real, dynamic conditions rising damp in a wall is often in a rather sensitive equilibrium which may be considerably disturbed by changes in the heating of the building and in the level of the water table. The presence of hygroscopic salts tends to obscure any drying associated with such changes by keeping the wall more moist than it would otherwise be. If such salts are removed from the surface by removing the old plaster, and the heating system is improved, it is likely that the apparent dramatic improvement in the appearance of the wall surface will give the impression that the rising damp has been cured. It is against this background that the correct diagnosis of rising damp becomes important.

Diagnosis

Because of high remedial costs, it is essential that the diagnosis is as positive as possible to distinguish between rising damp and other sources of dampness. The presence of damp that has existed for some time is indicated by clearly visible signs such as damp patches on walls, peeling and blistering wall decorations, patches of efflorescence and possible rotting and splitting woodwork due to wet or dry rot. There is usually a damp and musty smell due to mould growth. Many of these visible signs may be absent if the dampness problem has recently developed or is caused by an intermittent and occasional source of damp such as rain penetration or condensation. The presence of rising damp is often indicated by a horizontal tide mark at a height of 1 m or so along a wall (Fig 1). However, the visible signs do not necessarily indicate the cause of the problem as there are a number of possible causes other than rising damp. They include:

(a) rain penetration through defects in construction or materials or leaking gutters or downpipes;

(b) water from defective plumbing systems and drains;

(c) condensation;

(d) contamination of surfaces by hygroscopic salts;

(e) water used in construction.

Penetrating damp from some external source is likely to create isolated patches of dampness that increase in size after periods of heavy rain and tend to disappear in long dry spells of weather. The patches may be near or well away from floor level on external walls. Where there is dampness, a close inspection should be carried out to ensure that water is not penetrating from such external sources. Time must be allowed after any remedial measures for the damp structure to dry (6 to 12 months) before seeking other causes of dampness.

Condensation may occur from the way in which a building is used or because of the design of the structure

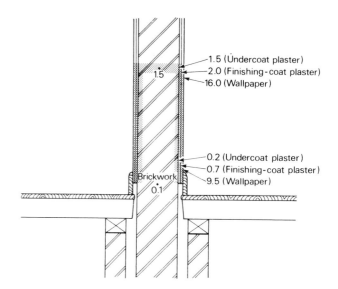

Fig 2 Concentration of salts in a party wall in which rising damp has persisted for 80 years. Figures show percentage, by weight, of chloride plus nitrate. The shaded area is heavily contaminated.

itself. Poor ventilation, low temperatures and the heavy use of such devices as paraffin heaters for local heating can raise the moisture content of the air to the point where the moisture condenses out on to any available cold surface. Serious condensation gives rise to large amounts of moisture running down non-absorbent surfaces such as single-glazed windows. On absorbent wall surfaces the condensation results in large damp areas which can support mould growth.

Moisture will move through a structure towards the surfaces where evaporation is taking place. The moisture will carry with it soluble salts either introduced with the moisture or already present in the structure. Salts will therefore concentrate on wall surfaces, regardless of the source of moisture that carries them there, and cause efflorescence. Old plasters tend to become contaminated with salts but this does not necessarily mean that rising damp is the cause. These salts might be hygroscopic and in absorbing moisture from the air, produce a damp wall surface. If non-hygroscopic, the salts will be unsightly and damage decoration but will not cause damp patches. The presence of hygroscopic salts does not necessarily indicate rising damp as the cause. However, rising damp usually concentrates hygroscopic salts on wall surfaces; these salts are mainly carried up from the foundations and surrounding soil (Fig 2).

Large amounts of moisture will be introduced into a newly built structure or into an existing dwelling subject to new extension work. This is an inevitable consequence of the building process which presents no long-term problems provided there is adequate ventilation and heating to allow the structure to dry.

Fig 1 Rising damp

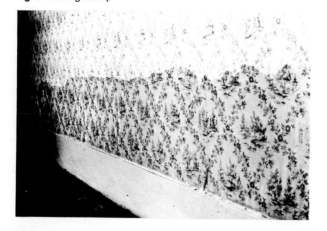

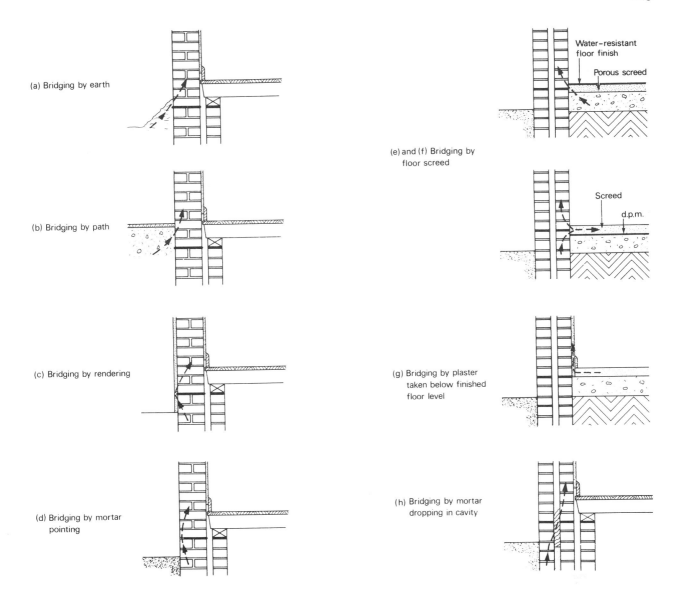

(a) Bridging by earth

(b) Bridging by path

(c) Bridging by rendering

(d) Bridging by mortar pointing

(e) and (f) Bridging by floor screed

Water-resistant floor finish

Porous screed

Screed

d.p.m.

(g) Bridging by plaster taken below finished floor level

(h) Bridging by mortar dropping in cavity

Fig 3 Bridging of damp-proof course.

Rising damp must, by definition, create moisture and a moisture gradient in the height and thickness of a structure, not merely surface moisture. The existence of such a gradient should be demonstrated before deciding whether or not a damp-proof course is really necessary. In many situations where rising damp occurs, it is often due to the bridging of an existing damp-proof course rather than the absence of one (Fig 3). Measurements of surface moisture are in themselves no indication that a genuine rising damp problem exists. The electrical meters commonly used by surveyors are responsive to both the amount of moisture present and to the salt concentration and are incapable of distinguishing between the two. Such meters quite commonly give high readings on the walls of old properties where some accumulation of salts inevitably occurs on internal surfaces. This does not mean, however, that the property necessarily has a dampness problem; high readings can be obtained from a wall where the concentration of salts is high, even if the wall is virtually dry. Nevertheless, as preliminary surveying instruments, these meters have a valuable role to play and will identify areas where further investigation is necessary.

To obtain more conclusive proof of the presence of rising damp the most satisfactory approach currently available is to obtain samples of the bricks, blocks or mortar at some depth in the wall. From these samples an accurate measurement of the moisture content of the wall can be obtained, together with an indication of the influence of any hygroscopic salts that may be present. The sampling technique, which is described in the Appendix, creates a limited amount of dust and slight damage to decorations. A wrong diagnosis could, however, lead to considerable unnecessary expenditure.

Interpretation of results

It is unusual for walls with moisture contents less than 5 per cent at their base to be severely affected by rising damp, though hygroscopicity caused by salts which may have migrated over many years can cause damage to the plaster and decorations.

Comparing the hygroscopic moisture content (HMC) with the moisture content as found (MC) gives an indication of which factor is controlling the dampness at any position. An HMC higher than the MC indicates that the dampness is due to moisture from the air rather than from the ground or some other source. An MC higher than the HMC indicates that water is coming from some source other than the air, such as rising damp or rain penetration.

If samples are taken at a sufficient number of heights the results can be plotted as shown in Figure 4 which illustrates two typical cases of rising damp where the moisture content is more than 5 per cent at the base of the wall and decreases with height.

Figure 4 (a) illustrates a situation where the moisture content in the lower part of the wall is dominated by rising damp above which there is a region in which the moisture content is controlled by the hygroscopicity of the wall. Figure 4 (b) illustrates a situation where the conditions at the base are similar to 4 (a) but where the upper region of the wall is gaining water from other sources, eg driving rain; the moisture content of the upper portion is above that due to any hygroscopic salts present and no significant moisture gradient exists.

It is not possible to list all the various moisture gradient profiles that can be obtained in this way but several important points need to be emphasised as a guide to interpretation.

Experience has shown that some building materials possess an HMC of up to 5 per cent even without the introduction of salts from external sources. Although only a rough indicator, the 5 per cent threshold does represent a reasonable general guide to whether or not some kind of remedial treatment is needed. This emphasises the importance of the difference between the HMC and MC measured on samples.

If only rising damp is present, there should be a definite moisture gradient from the base of a wall tapering off to a point where the HMC becomes equal to the MC. Other sources of moisture to a wall (eg rain penetration) will alter this gradient so that a precise diagnosis of rising damp cannot be made. It is important therefore to remedy other causes and allow time for remedial measures to take effect.

Rising damp is a seasonal effect, increasing in winter with rising water tables and falling in summer. This seasonal effect must be taken into account in any diagnosis since the problem could disappear in the summer months and return in the winter.

Fig 4 Results from typical cases.

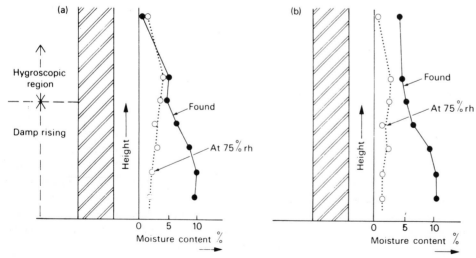

Treatment

Where rising damp has been diagnosed, treatment will involve either curing the source of the problem or masking its effects. Curing the problem at source is normally preferable and as a first step a building should be closely inspected to ensure that an existing damp-proof course is not being bridged. Earth piled against external walls should be removed and external render and internal plaster cut back to just above the dpc line. Improving the land drainage at the base of the wall may also help to cure the problem. In old houses with suspended wooden floors, the dpc usually runs in the mortar course at the top or bottom of the ventilation grills set in the external walls. The grills should be cleared of any obstruction since the presence of adequate sub-floor ventilation is most important. Suspended wooden floors should be checked for possible wet or dry rot. They may need extensive preservative treatment and the cutting out of any decayed timber. In many situations, the original dpc will be completely effective; a fact often overlooked when treatment is being considered.

The methods for installing a new dpc are described generally as 'traditional' (the insertion of a physical damp-proof course) or 'non-traditional'. It is strongly recommended that non-traditional methods should be considered only if they have been awarded an Agrement Certificate. The only one currently to satisfy this requirement is chemical injection. This is the only method which the Building Research Establishment considers suitable where insertion of a physical dpc is not possible. Physical dpc's can only be placed in brickwork or coursed stonework; random flint walls or rubble infilled walls are not suitable. Unusually thick walls can rarely be treated and it can be dangerous to attempt installations of this type for structural reasons if the walls have settlement cracks. Chemical injection systems can be used in most types of structure although flint walls and rubble infilled walls can be very difficult to treat successfully.

Where treatment of the source is virtually impossible, the alternative is simply to mask the effects of damp by using some kind of wall lining technique, such as plasterboard on battens or a proprietary system. This approach has the fundamental disadvantage that such remedies will cut down the evaporation rate from a wall and cause the dampness to rise further. Rising damp results from a dynamic equilibrium between the rate at which water is fed to the structure via the soil and the rate at which it evaporates away via air flow across the surfaces. Increasing the height and intensity of the dampness could pose serious longer-term dangers to wooden components such as window frames.

Physical damp-proof course

The only certain way in all circumstances of introducing an effective dpc into a wall is to insert a new physical membrane. Techniques for doing so have improved over recent years and the cutting of an old lime/sand mortar bed joint through the entire thickness of a 225 mm (9 inch) solid wall should, in most cases, present no problems.

A tungsten-carbide tipped chainsaw is usually used and the cut made in short lengths of about 1 m at a time. The membrane is loaded with mortar and inserted and temporary wedges used in the remaining gap to prevent settlement. Eventually the cut is back-filled with more mortar. In the standard solid 225 mm brick wall, the entire thickness of the wall can be cut from one side but, of course, great care has to be taken that all water and gas pipes and electrical wiring are moved out of the way. A new dpc, regardless of type, should if possible be inserted below the level of an existing suspended wooden floor and as close as possible to the top screed of an existing solid floor. Conditions vary enormously in this respect and usually some compromise is necessary in the siting of a new damp-proof course. Any gap between horizontal dpc and solid floor membrane should be closed if necessary with a tanking type of treatment.

The advantages of the physical techniques are that the membrane can be extended internally to form a vertical dpc between any solid floors and the horizontal course, and the membrane (usually flexible black polythene) is resistant to all acids and alkalis normally encountered in building materials. The disadvantages are cost, time taken and the disturbance created.

Chemical injection systems

These involve the use of silicone or aluminium stearate water repellents, either injected at high pressure or transfused into the wall under gravity or at low pressure. The high pressure systems are used most often with solvest-based silicones and aluminium stearates, whilst the transfusion methods are of necessity limited to the appliction of water-based silicones basically in the form of the water-soluble sodium methyl siliconate. The water-repellents are pore liners rather than pore blockers and hence allow the passage of some water vapour whilst preventing the rise of liquid moisture. The repellents are not intended to provide a damp-proof barrier against a substantial positive pressure of water and should not be used in basement areas subject to high water tables and penetrating damp. Another limitation is that the repellents in common use for damp-proofing work are not durable in the long term in highly alkaline conditions and their use is not recommended in newer buildings containing relatively fresh cement mortars. Available evidence suggests that high alkalinity is not a problem in older buildings with well weathered lime/sand mortar joints, unless perhaps the walls are exceptionally thick. Once injected, various curing and solvent evaporation processes occur resulting in polymerisation reactions and the weak bonding of the cured repellents to the material substrate. This bonding serves to keep the injected and cured material in place in the presence of active rising damp.

The efficiency of chemical injection systems depends on the efficiency of the fluid penetration of a damp structure. The repellents are injected or transfused into closely spaced holes in brick or mortar courses along the dpc line and treatment must be carried out at different depths in anything other than a single leaf wall to ensure penetration through the entire thickness of the structure. The transfusion methods carried out at low pressures with aqueous repellents should, in principle, penetrate more effectively than the high pressure systems since they depend almost entirely on diffusion processes which are the only physical processes that can eventually give complete penetration. The disadvantages are that diffusion processes are extremely slow and the danger arises that the slow curing aqueous repellent can be carried away in the presence of very active rising damp before an effective dpc is formed. In practice it is unlikely that an injection treatment will create a completely impervious barrier in a truly damp wall. The success of these systems in treating a case of genuine rising damp lies in reducing the moisture flow up the wall to such an extent that the dampness problem in practical terms disappears.

The treatment of rising damp by various chemical injection systems is perhaps best summed up by the general statement that all injection techniques are likely to be less effective in non-uniform materials and where moisture contents are quite high at the injection level. Fortunately, in practice, the latter condition is rare: evidence suggests that most cases of genuine rising damp involve low enough moisture levels for an injection technique to have a significant effect. As rising damp is a seasonal effect, injections are best carried out in late summer when water tables are at their lowest and the walls are relatively dry.

Replastering

Where a dampness problem exists, it usually leads to damaged internal plaster-work and a subsequent need for some replastering as part of remedial treatment. The main requirement of any new plastering is that it should act as a barrier to residual salts and moisture in a wall. Ideally it should have as high a vapour permeability as possible to help the evaporation of residual moisture and should be weaker than the background to which it is applied. Ordinary gypsum-based undercoats are not effective moisture barriers and should not be used. The rich cement-based undercoats usually applied by installers are effective moisture barriers in their own right. However, their vapour permeability is low and their strength very high. Some recent tests on a typical 1:3 cement/sand undercoat finished with Class C Gypsum plaster have shown the finished surface to remain completely dry with an evaporative air flow across it even with water under a positive pressure behind the system. Although a washed and well-graded sand was used no waterproofing additives or workability aids were incorporated. Results of this sort demonstrate the possibilities of a basic cement/sand system as a moisture barrier although the disadvantage of high strength and low vapour permeability remain. High strength may preclude their use direct on very weak backgrounds where lathing is needed to provide a base for the plaster.

Further reading

Installation of Chemical Damp Proof Courses, British Chemical Dampcourse Association Code of Practice, 1978.

BRE Digests

18 Design of timber floors to prevent decay
54 Damp-proofing solid floors
77 Damp-proof courses
89 Sulphate attack on brickwork
110 Condensation
125 Colourless treatments for masonry
163 Drying out buildings
198 Painting walls - Part 2: Failures and remedies

The Agrement Board PO Box 195, Bucknalls Lane, Garston, Watford, Herts.

APPENDIX

The sampling method

The basis is to drill samples from the wall and measure both their water content and hygroscopicity. Walls may contain considerable quantities of hygroscopic salts. Therefore, hygroscopicity should be measured to see whether the wall could have absorbed from the atmosphere the quantity of water found in the samples.

Location for test sampling

A damp location away from sources such as drains, dripping gutters or earth piled against walls should be chosen for examination. An internal wall is ideal if this appears to have rising damp. On external walls it is preferable to sample from the inside, though with a plastered wall this will usually require removal of small areas of plaster so that the mortar joints can be identified.

Collection of sample

A low-speed drill with a masonry bit of about 9 mm diameter is used. If the wall has mortar joints samples of the mortar should be taken, since in most cases the mortar will be wetter than the bricks. The outer 10 mm or so should be rejected, the sample being taken from 10 mm to about 80 mm depth. In brickwork, samples should be taken every two or three courses up to a level beyond the point where rising damp is suspected; it is usually worth taking at least one sample well above this height. The sample should be collected either in a small stoppered bottle for subsequent weighing or, if measuring moisture immediately in a carbide meter, in the scale pan provided. When using a carbide meter, part of the sample should be put aside for the hygroscopicity determination. The height of the drilled holes above ground level and position in the building should be measured and recorded. Tests have shown that the heat produced by drilling does not cause sufficient evaporation to affect significantly the accuracy if the drill bit is sharp and the material is not so hard as to make drilling difficult.

Measurement of moisture content and hygroscopicity of sample

The moisture content can be established either by a direct weighing and drying method or by a carbide meter. Tests have shown that a carbide meter gives an accurate measure of the water in a sample. The main advantage of the longer weighing method over a carbide meter is that is requires a smaller quantity (say one gram), whereas the minimum for the carbide meter is three grams. With the latter it is also necessary to keep separate samples for hygroscopicity measurement.

For most situations it is suitable to measure hygroscopicity at 75 per cent relative humidity; for most walls the effective relative humidity is less than 75 per cent and it is easy to provide a relative humidity of 75 per cent by using a saturated solution of common salt ($Na\ Cl$). A closeable vessel is required in which the sample can be placed over, but not in contact with, the solution of salt. A dessicator or an enclosed space similar to that shown in Fig 5 is suitable.

Procedure using a balance

1. Collect the samples in stoppered bottles.
2. Shake the bottle well before removing stopper. Then spread about 2 grams of the sample from the bottle on to a previously weighed Petri dish or watch glass of about 40 mm diameter (weight W_o) and weigh immediately (weight W_w).
3. Place immediately in enclosure at 75 per cent relative humidity. Leave for a time: overnight should be sufficient if the layer is only 1 to 2 mm deep.
4. Reweigh (W_{75}).
5. Place in an oven at about 100°C for about an hour. Remove and allow to cool. Reweigh soon after cooling (weight W_d).

6. Calculate the following:

Hygroscopic moisture content at 75 per cent RH (HMC) =

$$100\ \frac{W_{75} - W_d}{W_{75} - W_o}\ \%\ \text{wet wt}$$

Moisture content of sample when found (MC) =

$$100\ \frac{W_w - W_d}{W_w - W_o}\ \%\ \text{wet wt}$$

This procedure cuts down weighing to a minimum, but if the moisture content is required more quickly, part of the sample may be left in the bottle or put out on an additional dish and the moisture content of that found by weighing and oven drying.

Procedure using a carbide meter

When only a carbide meter is used (with a minimum quantity M), the procedure is as follows:

1. Collect at least 2M of sample.
2. Shake bottle and weigh out a quantity M.
3. Measure moisture content of M in the carbide meter. (This moisture measurement may have been carried out on site).
4. Place the remainder in a Petri dish and leave in the 75 per cent enclosure for sufficient time to achieve equilibrium: about 2 days.
5. Weigh out a quantity M from the Petri dish and test in the carbide meter.

Equipment required

Electric drill with low speed for drilling masonry.

Masonry bits of 9 mm diameter.

Weighing bottles with well-sealed stoppers. (Identify by numbering with a scribe or felt marker).

Dish or chute to collect the powder sample.

A closeable vessel in which samples can be placed over, but not in contact with, a solution of salt (Fig 5).

Either

Laboratory balance accurate to ± 1 mg. (Alternatively, weighing facilities may be available locally at a school or technical college.)

Oven able to be controlled to about 100°C. (A lower temperature just prolongs the drying whereas temperatures of much more than 100°C may affect the sample chemically.)

Or

Carbide meter. In practice it may be an advantage to use both oven drying and the carbide method.

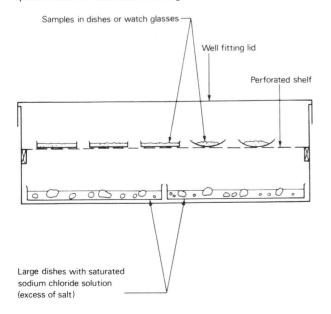

Samples in dishes or watch glasses

Well fitting lid

Perforated shelf

Large dishes with saturated sodium chloride solution (excess of salt)

Fig 5 Enclosure with 75 per cent relative humidity.

Cavity insulation

The thermal insulation of a masonry cavity wall can be greatly improved at modest cost by the introduction of insulating materials into the cavity. This can reduce the heating costs of a dwelling by up to 25 per cent (although in some cases the benefits will be taken, at least in part, in improved comfort) and if the cost of the insulation is considered in terms of an investment, it will often give a good return. In new constructions, the lower heating demand can allow economies in the cost of the heating installation. As well as a cut in heat loss, the inner face of the inner leaf will be warmer than if no insulation were present and there will be a consequent reduction in the risk of condensation.

But against these advantages must be weighed an increased risk of rain penetration through the wall in some conditions of exposure. This digest discusses this form of insulation and is based on several years experience of its use and on simulated rain penetration tests.

A continuous wall cavity, with properly designed and installed damp-proof courses and cavity trays, offers very good protection against penetration of rain. In driving rain conditions, water may not only be absorbed by the brick though capillary action; it can also leak through the outer leaf of facing brickwork and run down the cavity. The actual extent of the penetration of the outer leaf depends on its absorption capacity, on the quality of the jointing, and on the severity and duration of the driving rain. In a clear cavity, with correctly installed wall ties and detailing, the water flows freely and harmlessly down the inner face of the outer leaf to the base of the cavity unless deflected outwards through the leaf, for example by intervening cavity trays. Often walls are not perfectly constructed and rain penetration occurs even in unfilled cavities, caused, for example, by debris within the cavity or ties sloping downwards from the outer leaf. However, when cavity fill is introduced, the free flow of the water may be impeded and it is more likely to find any faults at cavity trays, vertical damp-proof courses or wall ties. Water may also cross to the inner leaf through gaps, fissures or voids in the fill. The extent and severity of this is discussed later.

The introduction of thermal insulation around electric cables carries a risk of the cables overheating, depending on the type of insulation and the loads on the cables. The insulation contractor should ascertain whether the space to be filled contains any cable runs and should advise whether the cables should be replaced by ones with larger conductor sizes.

Building Regulations

In new buildings

A number of Building Regulations relating to weather resistance of walls are applicable to new buildings and, in certain forms of construction, Regulations relating to fire may also impose limitations on the methods of cavity insulation.

In existing buildings

For the filling of cavities in most types of existing buildings in England and Wales, there is a 'Type Relaxation Direction' which, subject to certain conditions, directs that the Regulations relating to bridging cavities are dispensed with. Work covered by an Agrément or British Standards Certification scheme (the BS scheme applies at present only to urea formaldehyde foam) will satisfy most of the criteria. These schemes require operatives to undergo approved training. Where the Type Relaxation applies, the local authority requires notification at least seven days before the date of installation; where it does not apply (eg flats, maisonettes, buildings over three storeys or with unconventional walling) a longer application procedure is involved. The installer will usually deal with the application on behalf of the building owner.

The filling of cavities in existing buildings is not restricted by regulations in Scotland.

Insulating materials and installation

Materials fall into two types; those inserted during the construction of a wall in the form of slabs or boards, and those inserted into a completed wall by blowing or injection. These are in the form of loose fibres, beads, granules or foam.

New Walls

When cavity insulation is considered during design, the number of methods available is greater than for existing buildings because insulation can be introduced during construction. Furthermore, it can be ensured that detailing and materials are compatible with the insulation material having regard to the exposure of the building. If installation is to be delayed until after the walls are completed, the material can be injected into the cavity through the inner leaf; making good then forms part of the plastering work (it is usual in existing buildings to inject only through the outer leaf).

All types of cavity insulation inhibit ventilation of the cavity and the drying of masonry materials may, therefore, be slowed down. Normal practice of decorating with a permeable water-based emulsion should be followed as this will allow drying to continue. The application of an impermeable covering should be delayed until the inner leaf has dried sufficiently; this will usually be one full heating season.

Glass and rock fibre slabs

Although the slabs themselves are very effective barriers to water, the joints between them may be vulnerable if the slabs are not installed with care. Wide gaps between adjacent slabs must be avoided and any mortar droppings prevented or removed: good site supervision is therefore important. Often the inner leaf is built up first to a height of at least one slab, the slabs placed against this, and the outer leaf then built. With this order of construction, mortar can be extruded from the outer leaf into the joints between the insulating slabs. Subsequently, in driving rain, these extrusions can divert water into the joints and hence lead to penetration across the cavity. A better practice is to build the outer leaf ahead of the inner leaf and carefully to clean off the cavity side so that a smooth surface is presented to the exterior side of the fill.

Expanded polystyrene board

Insulating boards, usually 25 mm thick, are fixed to the inner leaf, leaving a clear cavity between the outer leaf and the boards; special fixings are available for the purpose. Again, good site supervision is important to make sure that the boards are restrained by the fixings against the inner leaf and do not lean across the cavity against the outer leaf. It is recommended that the cavities are designed to leave 50 mm clear with the boards in place, since it is difficult to keep a narrower space clear of mortar droppings. Agrément Certificates for this product specify different exposure restrictions, depending on the width of the remaining cavity. Whilst it gives a smaller increase in insulation than a method which fills the cavity, it is possible to use thicker board provided the cavity width is increased by an equivalent amount.

Completed walls

Urea-formaldehyde (UF) foam By far the most commonly used form of cavity fill in the UK, this accounts for well over half-a-million installations to date. The material is a low-density cellular plastics foam which is produced by foaming together in a 'gun' a mixture of a water-based resin solution, a hardener-surfactant solution, and compressed air. The foam, which has a consistency rather like shaving cream, is injected into the cavity where it subsequently hardens and dries. As it dries it will normally shrink and this will lead to fissuring. Occasionally the fissures are able to provide a bridge which will allow water to cross from the outer leaf to the inner leaf. When the foam is injected, and for some time after, it gives off fumes of formaldehyde gas. For a normal cavity wall of two leaves of masonry, plastered on the inner leaf, these fumes will rarely enter the house. However, there is a greater risk when the inner skin is vapour permeable (eg plasterboard or fair-faced brickwork), particularly if the outer skin is impermeable. Where the cavities to be filled are very wide (say 100 mm or more) the problem is more likely to occur; formaldehyde vapour can cause irritation to the eyes and nose but the extent of this effect depends on the sensitivity of the individual.

On the basis of the considerable amount of information and experience which has been accumulated for UF foam, two British Standards have been published which deal specifically with this fill. BS 5617 covers materials' standards for normal quality control of the foam and constituents. This allows a linear shrinkage of up to 10 per cent for samples taken on site. BS 5618 ia a Code of Practice for the technique of installation and gives rules for the climatic exposure conditions appropriate to this type of fill when used in masonry cavity walls.

Rock fibre Fibres coated with a water repellent are blown as tufts into the cavity where they form a water-repellent mat. Although the second most widely used fill in this country, the number of installations is much lower than for urea formaldehyde foam. Although the price of installation depends on location because of transport costs and other factors, the raw material cost is higher and so it will generally be more expensive than urea formaldehyde.

Polyurethane granules These are irregularly shaped granules usually between 5 mm and 20 mm across, made by chopping waste rigid polyurethane foam. At present the fill is most widely used in the north of England. Polyurethane is combustible and gives off toxic gases when burning. However, in conventional masonry/cavity/masonry walls, the material is normally sufficiently protected to prevent any hazard. The material should be kept away from hot surfaces such as flues built into or crossing the cavity.

Expanded polystyrene (eps) loose fills Expanded polystyrene beads are white spheres with a diameter between 2 mm and 7 mm. They are extremely free running and so very few filling holes are necessary. The wall is usually drilled high up, with additional holes under obstructions such as windows. The free running nature of this insulant can lead to an unnoticed escape of material where there are holes in the inner leaf, for example round joist ends or service pipes and ducts, so that particular attention must be paid to these points. Polystyrene granules are made by shredding waste eps bead board; they are about the same size as beads but since they are irregularly shaped they do not have the same properties and there is less risk of escape. Bonded eps beads are spherical beads which are thinly coated with adhesive as the fill enters the wall. The adhesive sets and so prevents subsequent escape.

Polystyrene is flammable, but as for polyurethane, this should not be a hazard in a conventional masonry-cavity/masonry wall. However, the fill should be kept away from hot flues. If expanded polystyrene comes into contact with pvc-coated electrical cable, plasticiser can migrate from the pvc leading to embrittlement of the cable insulation. Provided the cable is not disturbed, the electrical insulation will remain intact. Even so, the problem is best avoided by not using polystyrene in cavities where contact with such cables is likely to arise.

Glass fibre   This material was introduced recently as an alternative to rock fibre, and is installed by a similar method. However, it is less dense when installed and material costs are therefore lower. But the materials are not identical and they may behave differently. So far there are few installations from which its performance can be evaluated.

Polyurethane foamed in-situ   Two liquid components are mixed and injected into the cavity where they spontaneously foam and rise to fill the space; the foam adheres strongly to masonry and does not shrink. It has, therefore, been used to stabilise cavity walls where the wall ties have corroded but at the density required for this application the material cost is very high. A lower density foam has come into use recently specifically as a cavity insulant, but is at present the only material discussed in the digest not to have an Agrément Certificate.

Rain penetration - experience and simulated tests

Surveys on the extent and circumstances of rain penetration were carried out by the Agrément Board in 1970 and by BRE in 1973. Both surveys gave statistically meaningful results only for UF foam because of its predominant use over the other materials. Results were largely similar and showed that buildings with low exposure to driving rain had a low risk of rain penetration. The BRE survey of 30 000 UF-filled low-rise dwellings showed also that buildings filled some time after completion produced fewer reports of penetration (0.2 per cent) than those filled during or immediately after construction (3.3 per cent). The reasons for this significant difference are not altogether clear, but the ability of interior decorations to conceal dampness is one factor.

Simulated rain tests have been carried out by BRE on over 30 houses. In most cases the houses were tested before and after the installation of cavity insulation. Inspection of the empty cavities before filling showed a high number of faults such as sloping ties and debris but this was typical of other sites where cavities have been inspected. When tested, only in some cases did the faults cause water to cross the cavity; in a few of these significant dampness showed internally. The filled cavities however, showed a wide range of performance attributable to two principal factors: the brickwork of the outer leaf and the properties of the insulation. Where the outer leaf was of dense clay bricks, which are unable to absorb and retain water easily, leakage into the cavity (and in some cases across it) began soon after application of water to the outside surface of the wall. As the outer leaves of these walls allowed most of the applied water to leak into the cavity, the spraying presented a severe test to the cavity insulation and to any building fault within the cavity.

Blown-in rock fibre and polystyrene beads allowed least water penetration. In-situ polyurethane of intermediate density (about $30kg/m^3$) also showed good resistance and prevented water penetration at some wall ties which, before filling, had conducted water across the cavity. Very careful installation is required for this fill to achieve its full potential; material costs are high but cheaper, less dense polyurethane has proved less successful in tests.

Although attempts have been made in tests to simulate driving rain storms, using the results to predict performance in practice is complicated. One approach is to relate the performance of filled and unfilled walls and compare the risk of filling to the possibility of faults in unfilled cavities causing penetration. Tests indicate that the better materials may introduce faults equivalent to only small amounts of debris, whereas fissures in UF foam are usually equivalent to larger obstructions in an empty cavity. Whether such faults create problems depends on a number of factors but experience indicates that many poorly constructed cavity walls perform satisfactorily.

Clearly, one of the important factors governing the risk is exposure to driving rain. A widely used scheme in BS 5618, and in Agrément Certificates for some types of insulation, assesses the exposure of an individual building. It takes into account the local annual driving-rain index, the shelter provided by surrounding buildings and the local topography. The scheme sets lower limits of exposure for low-porosity stonework, concrete blocks and calcium silicate bricks than for clay brickwork, but tests and experience suggest that less absorbent clay bricks should be included with low porosity materials and therefore treated more cautiously.

Walls which are tile hung or clad, or have rendering in good condition, give adequate protection from driving rain.

Rain penetration - remedial measures

Rain penetration can usually be distinguished from other causes of dampness because it will follow spells of particularly heavy driving rain. Any remedial work must be based on sound diagnosis; it may be difficult to establish the part played by cavity insulation especially if there are building defects and if the insulation has been introduced before the structure has been tested by storms.

Remedial measures that have been used include insertion of more insulation materials, clearing obstructions from the cavity, and the use of colourless water repellents such as silicones. In rare cases it has been necessary to clad or render the wall, or to remove the material from the cavity.

Durability of material and walls

All the materials currently used for cavity insulation should be expected to last the lifetime of the building without significant deterioration; urea formaldehyde and polyurethane foams will do so if they are processed and installed correctly whilst granular materials are inherently durable.

Settlement of particle fills should be negligible since the vibrations to which buildings are normally subjected will not be sufficient to disturb the fill. Although blown fibre fills may appear from their nature to be susceptible to slump, observations of rock fibre have indicated that the fill still extends almost to the top of the cavity some years after installation.

With cavity insulation, the outer leaf will be colder than with an unfilled cavity. Also, the moisture content of the outer leaf can be expected to be somewhat higher, due to the lower temperature and, possibly, to restricted drying into the cavity. It has been suggested that this will increase the risk of frost damage to cavity-filled walls. Tests have shown that in cold weather the temperature of the external face is about 1°C below that of an unfilled wall and that the moisture content is indeed somewhat higher. Experience so far has shown that these differences are not a significant cause of frost damage, but where the materials in existing buildings already show signs of frost damage, or cracked rendering, which may permit higher than normal moisture contents in the outer leaf, insulation of the wall can be expected to increase the rate of deterioration.

If the external brickwork is painted, care should be taken to check the integrity of the paint film and to ensure a good standard of maintenance. Defects may allow water to penetrate into the brickwork and subsequent drying will be retarded by the paint on the one side and the fill on the other. Painting a filled wall should be carried out only when the wall has had ample time to dry.

References and further reading

The Agrément Board, PO Box 195, Bucknalls Lane, Garston, Watford, Herts.
British Standards Institution, Maylands Avenue, Hemel Hempstead, Herts.

BS 5617: 1978 - Urea formaldehyde foam for thermal insulation of cavity walls.
BS 5618: 1978 - Code of Practice for the thermal insulation of cavity walls (with masonry inner and outer leaves) by filling with urea formaldehyde foam.

BRE Digests
125 Colourless treatments for masonry.
127 An index of exposure to driving rain.
197 Painting walls: Part 1: Choice of paint.
198 Painting walls: Part 2: Failures and remedies.
224 Cellular plastics for building.
233 Fire hazard from insulating materials.

Strength of brickwork and blockwork walls: design for vertical load

The Code of Practice for the structural use of masonry, BS 5628 : Part 1 : 1978, deals with unreinforced masonry assembled from bricks or blocks mortared together; it is written in terms of limit state design and is intended to supersede CP 111 which used the permissible stress concept. Other important differences are the inclusion of sections dealing with laterally loaded masonry and design for accidental damage.

BS 5628 has been written for use by chartered structural and civil engineers or other appropriately qualified persons. This digest gives some background to the main recommendations in respect of the vertical loading and replaces Digest 61 which is now withdrawn. The design of concrete walls is covered by CP 110.

Design approach

The basis of limit state design is that the designer should consider all the likely ways in which a structure or element could fail to perform its required function and should then design against such failures. The design must take into account therefore the factors conferring stability to the whole of a masonry structure, even though the detailed approach is to break the structure down into walls and other elements partially or totally bounded by lateral supports and to design each element so that there is a reasonable margin of safety against the ultimate limit state (collapse) being reached. Using BS 5628, the designer must determine, either intuitively or by calculation, whether the critical design condition for any wall is compressive, shear (in or out of plane), tensile or flexural (in or out of plane), (Fig 1). The wall is then designed to meet the assumed critical load condition, and checked for the assumed non-critical conditions. The criterion on which a wall is adjudged to be satisfactory or not is the relationship:

Design resistance ⩾ design load.

Design for vertical load

Calculation of the design strength and load is based on characteristic values and a partial safety factor format in which the following concepts are required:

Characteristic compressive strength f_k: the ultimate compressive strength of brickwork as measured in the laboratory and taking into account laboratory sample to sample variability.

Characteristic load S_k: the weight of the finished construction in the case of dead load, or a statistical estimation of the likely load in the case of loads due to occupancy, snow or wind. In practice the loads will be obtained from CP3 Ch V or by calculation using BS 648.

Materials partial safety factor, γ_m: a number by which the characteristic strength is divided to allow for the possible difference in quality of materials and workmanship between laboratory test walls and a wall on site.

Load partial safety factor, γ_f: a factor by which the characteristic load is increased to allow for uncertainty in the data on which it is based, eg the variability of the actual density of materials, the uncertainty of wind data and snow data, beyond those considered in deriving the characteristic values.

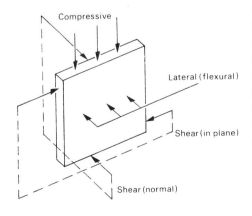

Fig 1 Different loadings on a wall

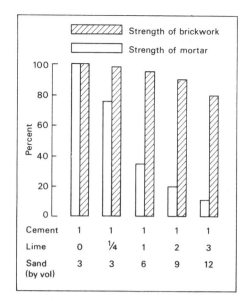

Fig 2 Effects of mortar mix proportions on the crushing strengths of mortar and brickwork built with medium-strength bricks. Strengths are shown relative to the strength of a 1:3 cement-sand mortar and the brickwork built with it.

For the simple, vertical load case (axially loaded squat solid wall):

Design resistance =

$$\frac{\text{Characteristic strength} \quad (f_k)}{\text{Materials partial safety factor} \quad (\gamma_m)} \times \text{area (Length} \times \text{thickness)}$$

Design Load = Characteristic load x load partial safety factor

BS 5628 gives values of f_k for common materials and values of γ_m which allow for the difference between laboratory and site-constructed masonry. A range of values is suggested depending on the degree of quality control in the manufacturing and construction processes. It also lists γ_f for various combinations of dead, imposed and wind load. The magnitudes of the various partial factors have been chosen to reflect explicitly the relative likelihood of extreme values of load and strength. In combination they correspond broadly to the overall factor of safety implicit in the permissible stress approach of CP 111 but offer the flexibility to consider individual areas of uncertainty.

Further considerations must be taken into account when designing slender walls, walls stiffened by piers, eccentrically loaded walls, cavity walls, walls with complex plan shapes and walls subject to concentrated loads or to significant lateral or shear forces.

BS 5628 gives characteristic strengths of brick and block masonry; guidance is also given on the values appropriate to other types of masonry, such as hollow blockwork filled with concrete, dressed natural stone and random rubble walls. The design stresses can be derived by dividing these values by the appropriate material safety factor γ_m, and the load capacity of an axially loaded squat wall can be calculated using the equation given above. In domestic buildings, where lower strength materials may be used in narrow walls between large openings in the front and rear elevations, wall thickness may be governed only by vertical stresses. However, more frequently the critical requirement will be the design for lateral load.

Strength relationships between walls and mortars

The underlying data and relationships in BS 5628 are the same as in CP 111. Generally, the maximum strength of brickwork is obtained with mortar mix proportions of (cement and lime) to sand of 1:3 by volume. There is however, little advantage in using a very strong cement-sand mortar in most brickwork and blockwork walls. Digest 160 discusses the factors, in addition to strength, which affect the choice of mortars.

Figure 2 compares the strengths of mortar and brickwork for a number of mortar mixes when a medium-strength brick is used. The mortar loses strength as the proportion of lime in the mortar is increased, although the effect on the brickwork is not nearly so marked.

For brickwork with high-strength bricks, the fall in strength of the brickwork is much more pronounced as progressively weaker mortars are used. Thus, in order to utilise the full capacity of high-strength bricks (70 N/mm² or more), a 1:3 cement-sand mix is needed. For lower strength bricks or blocks, mortars with an increased proportion of lime can be used without any great loss in masonry strength (Table 1).

For walls loaded vertically, BS 5628 also recognises correctly proportioned mortars based on masonry cement mixes, and aerated cement-sand mixes, as equivalent to the weaker cement-lime-sand mixes.

Strength relationships between walls and building units

The relationships in BS 5628 between strengths of masonry, structural unit and mortar are essentially similar to those on which CP 111 is based although detailed changes have been made in the light of more test results, particularly on high-strength brickwork and low-strength blockwork.

Table 1 Suitable mortar mixes for various unit strengths

Unit strength (N/mm²)	Mortar mix (by vol)	Designation in BS 5628
10	1:2:9	(iv)
20-35	1:1:6	(iii)
48-62	1:¼:3	(i)
70 or more	1:0:3	(i)

Note: The weaker cement-lime-sand mixes may be replaced by masonry cement-sand or plasticised cement-sand mixes of equivalent strength.

Strength relationships are shown in Fig 3; the walls were tested in the air-dry condition but the crushing strengths of the units were taken as the wet strengths, as required by the British Standards dealing with testing building units, ie BS 187, 3921 and 6073.

Brickwork

The strength ratio for brickwork:brick varies from slightly less than half to slightly less than one-fifth, the latter being sometimes found for high-strength (Class A) bricks used with a weak mortar. The trends indicated in Figs 2 and 3 are of particular importance for brickwork designed to BS 5628. In the Code, the characteristic compressive strengths of walls made of various bricks and mortar mixes are based on relationships of this kind, taking variability into account. The actual values of f_k allowed by the Code for brick-shaped units are given in Table 2. They represent the ultimate strengths of brickwork and generally are about 4.5 times the basic stresses given in CP 111.

Blockwork

Loading tests on one-block thick walls built with low to medium strength blocks of normal proportions (ie height exceeding thickness by a factor of two or more) give ratios of wall strength to block strength of between 0.5 and 1. This apparent enhancement in relation to 'brick-shaped' units (height less than thickness) occurs because the crushing strength test under-estimates the strength of the more slender block-shaped units when tested in isolation; there is, however, limited effect on the strength of the wall which has the same slenderness ratio for brick or block-shaped units. This apparent enhancement does not apply to the higher strength hollow or cellular units which behave much as bricks. The characteristic strength values given in Table 2 reflect these trends by incorporating ratios of characteristic strength of walls to block strength in the range one to one-fifth as appropriate. Other tables are given for squat form blocks when ratio of height to least horizontal dimension is 0.6 and for hollow blocks. For the purposes of the Code, cellular blocks should be

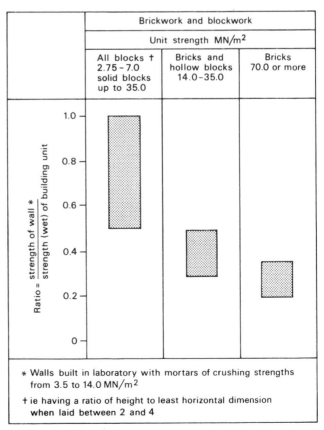

Fig 3 Ratio of strength of storey-high wall to strength of building unit (block, brick or cube specimen)

Table 2 Characteristic compressive strength of masonry, f_k
Constructed with standard format bricks

Mortar Designation	Compressive strength of unit (N/mm^2)								
	5	10	15	20	27.5	35	50	70	100
(i)	2.5	4.4	6.0	7.4	9.2	11.4	15.0	19.2	24.0
(ii)	2.5	4.2	5.3	6.4	7.9	9.4	12.2	15.1	18.3
(iii)	2.5	4.1	5.0	5.8	7.1	8.5	10.6	13.1	15.5
(iv)	2.2	3.5	4.4	5.2	6.2	7.3	9.0	10.8	12.6

Constructed from solid concrete blocks having a ratio of height to least horizontal dimension of between 2.0 and 4.0

Mortar designation	Compressive strength of unit (N/mm^2)							
	2.8	3.5	5.0	7.0	10	15	20	35 or greater
(i)	2.8	3.5	5.0	6.8	8.8	12.0	14.8	22.8
(ii)	2.8	3.5	5.0	6.4	8.4	10.6	12.8	18.8
(iii)	2.8	3.5	5.0	6.4	8.2	10.0	11.6	17.0
(iv)	2.8	3.5	4.4	5.6	7.0	8.8	10.4	14.6

treated as hollow blocks. The tables in BS 5628 avoid the need to apply separate factors to allow for the shape of the units as required in CP 111. Interpolation between values given in Table 2 is allowed and is facilitated by graphs corresponding to each subtable.

Slenderness ratio

Brickwork and blockwork walls of a given thickness and material strength tend to fail at lower loads as their height increases. This is caused primarily by elastic instability, ie a tendency to buckle, initiated by differences of the stiffness from one side of the wall to the other due to variations of materials and workmanship. In design, therefore, the slenderness is important; for most purposes, it is defined as the ratio of effective height to effective thickness. These 'effective dimensions' are used to take into account other features that affect the behaviour and load-bearing capacity of the member.

BS 5628 recommends, as in CP 111, that for walls set in Portland cement mortars, the slenderness ratio should not exceed 20 for walls less than 90 mm thick in buildings of more than two storeys, and 27 in all other cases. The design strengths of walls having slenderness ratios in excess of 8 are reduced on a sliding scale up to the maximum permitted slenderness ratio of 27, Column 1 of Table 3.

Effective height and lateral support

The effective height is related to the support provided to restrict lateral movement in the member. Rules governing the effective height to be assumed under various conditions of support are set out in BS 5628. For example, for a simple column member supported top and bottom, the effective height is the actual height between the lateral supports. For columns supported only at the bottom, an effective height of twice the actual height must be used. Walls are similarly regarded but it is accepted that the factors responsible for loss of strength with increasing slender-

Table 3 Capacity reduction factor, ß

Slenderness ratio h_{ef}/t_{ef}	Eccentricity at top of wall			
	Up to 0.05t (see note 1)	0.1t	0.2t	0.3t
0	1.00	0.88	0.66	0.44
6	1.00	0.88	0.66	0.44
8	1.00	0.88	0.66	0.44
10	0.97	0.88	0.66	0.44
12	0.93	0.87	0.66	0.44
14	0.89	0.83	0.66	0.44
16	0.83	0.77	0.64	0.44
18	0.77	0.70	0.57	0.44
20	0.70	0.64	0.51	0.37
22	0.62	0.56	0.43	0.30
24	0.53	0.47	0.34	
26	0.45	0.38		
27	0.40	0.33		

Note 1. It is not necessary to consider the effects of eccentricities up to and including $0.05t$.

Note 2. Linear interpolation between eccentricities and slenderness ratios is permitted.

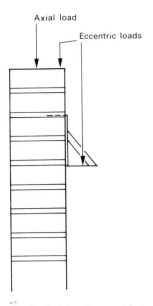

Fig 4 Axial and eccentric loads

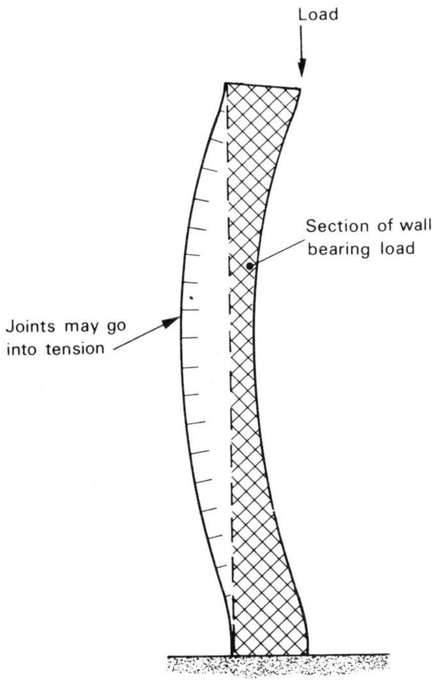

Load

Section of wall
bearing load

Joints may go
into tension

Fig 5 Exaggerated effect of eccentric load

ness are less serious for walls than columns. A distinction is also made in the effective heights to take account of the lateral support provided by different forms of floor or roof system at the boundaries of the wall. In normal domestic dwellings of up to three storeys, it is not necessary to use straps in cases where timber or concrete floors have a reasonable bearing (greater than 90 mm) on the loadbearing wall and these structures are deemed to provide enhanced resistance to lateral movement of a member. In cases where joist hangers are used instead (eg on party-walls to reduce sound transmission), straps must be used and the resultant connection is deemed to provide only simple resistance against lateral movement.

Where walls are bounded by lateral supports giving only simple resistance to lateral movement, the effective height is taken to be the actual height; where enhanced resistance is provided, the effective height is reduced to 0.75 of the actual height.

Where floors and roofs span parallel to a wall it is essential to provide straps or ties if the floor is to act as a lateral support. Where straps are not used the walls should be designed on the assumption that the horizontal support is not present.

Appendix C of BS 5628 lists a range of connections which will provide simple resistance to lateral movement, although in housing up to three storeys some connections may afford enhanced resistance.

Effective thickness

Normally the effective thickness assumed for calculating the slenderness ratio is the actual thickness of the member but there are two exceptions:

(a) A loadbearing wall bonded into piers or intersecting walls. The wall is stiffened by the additional features and an allowance for this is made by taking an effective thickness greater than the actual thickness. With suitably spaced and sized piers, an effective thickness can be used of up to a maximum of twice the actual thickness. However, where a load-bearing pier is bonded into adjacent walling, any beneficial interaction is usually small so that no increase in the effective pier dimension can be assumed. In such cases it is preferable to assume that the load is applied centrally on the pier and to ignore the presence of the walling.

(b) A cavity wall, as discussed later.

Effective length

As an alternative in walls where there are frequent piers or bonded intersecting walls, the slenderness ratio of a loadbearing wall can be based on an effective length between vertical supports (ie return walls and piers, into which the wall is bonded) instead of an effective height. This design method is based on the assumption that instability due to the normal form of buckling will be prevented by the vertical supports. When this concept is used the designer must carefully consider the adequacy of these lateral supports for the particular wall. In many practical cases vertical support in the form of piers could not be considered to have sufficient stiffness to allow the loadbearing wall to be carried to any height. Rules for determining the value of effective length are similar to that of height, ie length x 1.0 for simple lateral support and length x 0.75 for enhanced support; values for walls having one free edge are, respectively, length x 2.5 and length x 2.

Eccentricity and effect of eccentric loading

Eccentricity of vertical loading arises where the line of action of the load on a wall is not in the centre of the wall (Fig 4). In Table 3, which reproduces Table 7 from BS 5628, it is expressed as a fraction of the wall thickness. The effect is to cause the side of the wall on which the load is acting to suffer a greater compressive shortening than the other side, which can, under certain combinations of load and eccentricity, go into

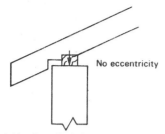

(a) load applied via centred wall plate

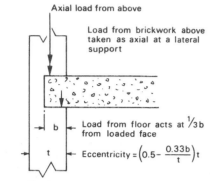

Axial load from above

Load from brickwork above taken as axial at a lateral support

Load from floor acts at $\frac{1}{3}b$ from loaded face

Eccentricity $= \left(0.5 - \dfrac{0.33b}{t}\right)t$

(b) generalised case

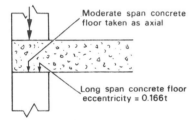

Moderate span concrete floor taken as axial

Long span concrete floor eccentricity = 0.166t

(c) Concrete floor spanning full width

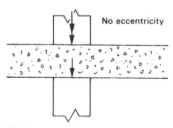

No eccentricity

(d) Continous floor load axial

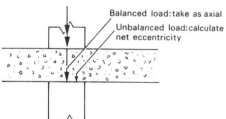

Balanced load: take as axial

Unbalanced load: calculate net eccentricity

(e) Non continous concrete floors or timber floors spanning from both sides

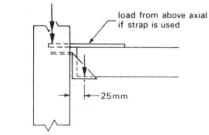

load from above axial if strap is used

25mm

(f) Corbel or joist hanger

Fig 6 Assessment of eccentricity

tension. Since walls of brickwork and blockwork have a low tensile strength they are particularly sensitive to eccentric loads. Table 3 illustrates the reduction in usable strength that occurs as a result of increasing the eccentricity of the load, according to the theoretical method used in BS 5628. In this method, assumptions about the distribution of eccentricity in a loaded wall are combined with a rectangular stress block to derive capacity reduction factors. When applied to characteristic strengths they give directly the load capacity of walls or columns without the need for intermediate calculation as in CP 111. Even for squat walls the capacity of the wall will be reduced because the effective cross section of brickwork bearing the load (the working thickness) is reduced, Fig 5. As the slenderness ratio increases the combined effect of slenderness and eccentricity reduces the stability of the wall and further reductions in design capacity are required to maintain safety. Table 3 gives the capacity reduction factor for the range of eccentricities and slenderness ratios which have been checked by experiment. Eccentricities of up to 1/20th (0.05) of the thickness of the wall may be disregarded as they are included in the value of ß in Table 3. Use of eccentricities or slenderness ratios outside the values in Table 3 are not considered wise. Although values for the capacity reduction could be calculated using Appendix B of the Code they are likely to be too small to be of value in design.

For axially loaded walls BS 5628 gives load capacities similar to CP 111 but for eccentrically loaded walls the capacity is enhanced, often considerably. It should be emphasised that the margins of safety for slender walls with highly eccentric loads are especially likely to be reduced where the workmanship is poor and that in these circumstances the supervision of the work is particularly important. It should also be noted that because 'capacity reduction factors' for very eccentric loads are numerically small walls designed for such loads may be uneconomic.

Assessment of eccentricity

The assessment of eccentricity of vertical loading at a particular junction eg between a wall and a floor, in a brickwork or blockwork wall is made complex by the many possible combinations of wall and floor systems. The structural behaviour of the junction will be affected by the magnitude of the loads, the rigidity of the inter-connected members and the geometry of the junction. It is seldom possible to determine the eccentricity of load at a junction by calculation alone, and the designer's experience must be his guide. Some help in assessing the eccentricity of loading on walls in domestic constructions is given below.

The primary assumption is that the load transmitted to a wall by a single floor or roof acts at one-third of the depth of the bearing area from the loaded face of the wall or loadbearing leaf (Fig 6b). Thus, in cases where concrete floors bear over the full width of the wall (Fig 6c), the centre of action should normally be taken as $\frac{1}{6}$ of the thickness of the wall from the centre in the direction of the load. However, in cases where the floor or roof is of very short span or very stiff, or if the load is applied via a centred wall plate (Fig 6a), it may be reasonable to regard the load as axial. In cases where a continuous stiff (eg concrete) floor spans over a wall (Fig 6d) the load can be considered to be axial provided the loads and spans on each side are not greatly different. In similar structures with more flexible floors or roofs, or structures where independent floors or roofs span on to each side of a wall, the load may be assumed to be axial provided that the span of the floor or roof on one side does not exceed the other by more than about 50 per cent. In cases where the difference is greater or two different types of floor are used, the net eccentricity should be assessed using the 'one-third of bearing area' rule (Fig 6e).

For a wall corbelled out to support a floor or roof, or where metal joist hangers are used, the load may be assumed to act at a distance of 25mm from the face of the wall, as in Fig 6f.

The other important assumption in the Code is that all vertical loads transmitted from above a lateral support act axially. Thus, in assessing the resultant eccentricity at a wall/floor junction in a multi-storey building, the loads transmitted to walls from the structure above by axially aligned masonry walls may be assumed to be axial.

Concentrated loading

Where floors or roofs are supported without interruption along the whole length of a wall, it is assumed that the load is uniformly distributed on the wall. Although not strictly in this category, floor and roof joists, filler joists and ribs of hollow tile floors are regarded similarly.

In practice, design calculations for loadbearing walls must also be capable of dealing with concentrated loads imposed, for example, by roof trusses, spine beams or lintels, in order to prevent failure from crushing or splitting under localised loading. Typical cases are shown in Fig 7.

It is well known that allowable bearing stresses for concentrated loads can safely exceed the design stress allowed for uniformly distributed loading. This is because of both the strengthening effect provided by the lateral restraint of material directly under the local load, and the distribution of the load throughout the depth of the wall.

The new guidance is much more detailed than in CP 111. In BS 5628 there are three types of concentrated load application. For detailed guidance users should consult the Code but briefly the types are:

Type 1 Concentrated loads from floors, lintels etc bearing over substantial areas of the loaded wall where stresses may be up to 1.25 times the normal design stress.

Type 2 Concentrated loads from floors, lintels etc bearing over very limited areas of the loaded wall where stresses may be up to 1.5 times the normal design stress.

Type 3 The special case of a concentrated load borne by a properly designed spreader or pad located at the end of a wall where stresses may be up to twice the normal design stress.

It should be emphasised that all other loading on the same area as the concentrated load must also be taken into account in the design.

Occasionally, concentrated loads cause high local stresses and for very weak solid and some hollow brick or block walls it may be necessary to increase bearing areas or to use padstones or spreaders. The latter may also be needed for any type of wall where indeterminate but very high local stresses occur, eg at the outer edge of a wall supporting a cantilever.

Cavity walls

The most common loading case for cavity walls is where only the inner leaf acts as the loadbearing leaf. In this case only the cross section of the loadbearing leaf may be used for supporting the load from above. It is reasonable however to accept that the stiffening and propping action of the other leaf is taken into account and this is done by adjusting the effective thickness; this is taken to be two-thirds of the combined thickness of the two leaves or the actual thickness of the loaded leaf, whichever is the greater. Since for most cavity walls with two 100 mm leaves the effective thickness $= \frac{2(100 + 100)}{3} = 133$ mm, the slenderness ratio will be reduced pro rata and the 'capacity reduction factor' will be increased accordingly in comparison with a 100 mm single leaf wall.

A comparison of wall strengths is given in Fig 8. It will be noted that the strength of 260 mm cavity construction with both leaves loaded is 16 per cent less than that of the 220 mm thick solid wall. When the load is carried concentrically on one leaf only, the cavity construction is 22 per cent stronger than a loaded leaf standing alone, because of the stiffening provided by the other leaf tied to it.

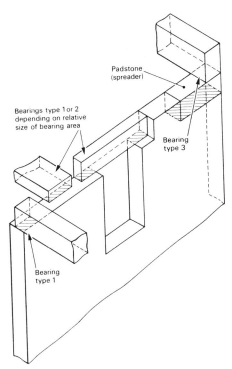

Fig 7 Where concentrated load should be taken into account - loaded areas hatched.

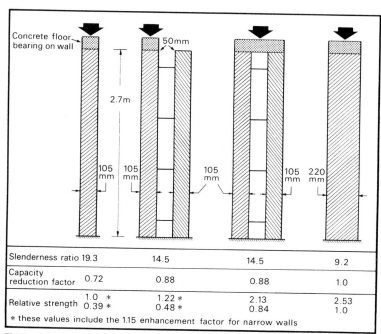

Slenderness ratio 19.3	14.5	14.5	9.2
Capacity reduction factor 0.72	0.88	0.88	1.0
Relative strength 1.0 * 0.39 *	1.22 * 0.48 *	2.13 0.84	2.53 1.0
* these values include the 1.15 enhancement factor for narrow walls			

Fig 8 Design strengths of solid and cavity brickwork walls

Wall ties are intended to share lateral forces and deflections between the two leaves. BS 5628 allows cavities of between 50 and 150 mm and specifies the spacing and type of ties suitable for the different widths. It should be emphasised that butterfly ties are not, under any circumstances, suitable for cavities wider than 75 mm because their axial compressive strength and stiffness are not great enough to ensure proper transfer of any lateral force; also they should not be used in walls above two storeys in height. Double triangle and vertical twist ties may be used in circumstances where butterfly ties are unsuitable and some designs of plastic tie may also be a suitable alternative.

Further reading

British Standards
BS 187:1978 Specification for calcium silicate (sandlime and flintlime) bricks
BS 648:1964 Schedule of weights of building materials
BS 3921:1974 Clay bricks and blocks
BS 5628 Code of practice for the structural use of masonry.
      Part 1:1978 Unreinforced masonry
BS 6073 Precast concrete masonry units.
BS CP3 Code of basic data for the design of buildings Chapter V Loading
BRE Digest
160 Mortars for bricklaying

Installation of wall ties in existing construction

Techniques have been developed in recent years for the reinstatement of cavity walls by insertion of new wall ties without recourse to demolition and reconstruction; this digest describes the range of techniques currently available. It deals particularly with cavity walls that have either been damaged or have lost their connection between the leaves as a result of the corrosion of steel wall ties. The methods described are also applicable to a range of related situations where the insertion of ties may be required; for example, the tying back of new walls to cross walls, the repair of subsidence damage, the stabilisation of collar jointed (faced) walls, the tying back of cladding walls to frame structures and tying back walls that have been cut for openings or movement joints.

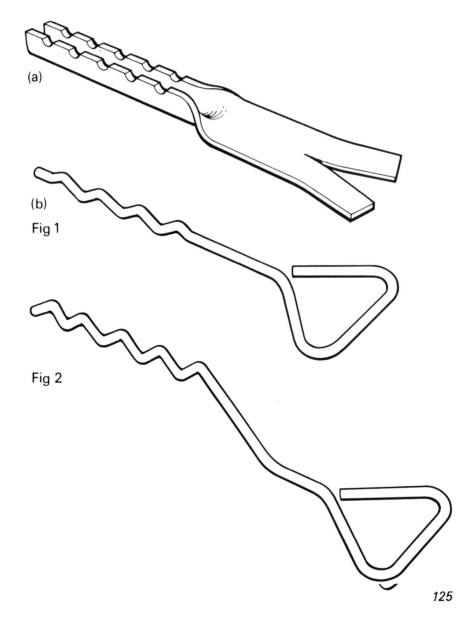

(a)

(b)

Fig 1

Fig 2

Installation of wall ties in existing construction may be needed to:

Reinstate masonry cavity walls damaged by expansive corrosion of vertical twist steel wall ties;

reinstate cavity walls rendered unsafe or unstable through loss of wire ties by corrosion;

increase the number of ties in walls built with insufficient ties connecting the leaves;

tie back existing cladding walls to concrete, steel and timber frame structures;

stabilise faced or collar jointed walls in cases where the outer layer is becoming detached from the backing;

tie new walls or bulging walls back to existing cross walls;

tie back walls on either side of cracks caused by subsidence or other damage;

tie back walls on either side of deliberate cuts made for insertion of openings or movement joints.

Appraisal of existing construction

Before decisions can be made on the need for the addition of wall ties and other repair work, the condition of the existing construction must be appraised. Whilst a full description of the appraisal process is beyond the scope of this digest, the following notes may be helpful.

Inspection of existing ties

The most satisfactory method is the removal of bricks or other units from the outer leaf overlying suspect ties so that the ties can be inspected for corrosion. Ties within a cavity can often be inspected by removing bricks at returns or by use of an endoscope (a fibre optic device for remote inspection). However, whilst the part of the tie in the cavity may appear to be unaffected, it could be severely corroded where it is buried in the outer leaf; such inspection may not, therefore, reveal a loss of connection between leaves.

Detection of ties

A large number of metal detectors and cover meters are on the market and many of the more sensitive types will locate ties to within about 50 mm. It is advisable before purchasing such equipment to have it demonstrated on a wall in which tie positions are known or can be verified. Some instruments will detect only ferro-magnetic materials. If the equipment is required to detect stainless steel or non-ferrous ties, it should be made clear to the supplier and tested in the appropriate situation. Some instruments are unable to discriminate between different metals or depths and it is rarely possible to get totally unambiguous indications. The weight and shape of the instrument are important because it will have to be carried on ladders or scaffolding for use on vertical walls. Ideally, detection instruments should be waterproof and have their own internal power supply.

Choice of repair method

Solutions to a retying or reinstatement problem range from merely repointing any cracks to the demolition and replacement of the whole cavity wall. The latter is a drastic step which is rarely economic but it is technically feasible. Table 1 presents the range of options in relation to the various applications and comments on the techniques. Table 2 lists suitable tying systems for the repair methods described and typical commercially available devices are shown in the illustrations. The devices shown may be the subjects of patents or design copyrights. Ties should be fabricated from stainless steel or suitable non-ferrous metals except where their design ensures that the metal rod is totally encapsulated with a compatible resin. It is stressed that where thick metal ties are present the best methods are those where the ties are removed completely to avoid the possibility of further cracking of the walls. Where wire ties are corroding, it is not normally necessary to remove them. If wall tie corrosion has led to substantial damage to the inner leaf, cracking of adjacent walls or movement of roof timbers, additional repairs will be necessary and appropriate advice should be sought.

Table 1 Repair methods

	Method	Comments	Tying system *(see Table 2)*
(i) (ii) (iii) (iv) (v)	Removal of single bricks. Complete removal of old corroded ties. Replacement of bricks. Retying. Repointing of cracks.	Best and cheapest where there is cracking damage from corroding ties. Can be used if there is damage to inner leaf. More difficult, and therefore more expensive, with hard mortars.	1 – 5, 7
(i) (ii) (iii) (iv) (v)	Removal of single bricks. Cropping off or bending back of corroded ties. Replacement of bricks. Retying. Repointing of cracks.	Should not be used if there is any sign of damage to the inner leaf due to tie corrosion. The cut stubs of ties may corrode in the inner leaf and, if vertical twist ties, may cause damage in the long term. More difficult, and therefore more expensive, with hard mortars.	2 – 5, 7
(i) (ii)	Retying without removal of corroded ties. Repointing as required.	Most appropriate for walls tied with corroded wire ties or for walls with zero or too few ties when constructed. If a wall is tied with corroding flat twisted ties there is a high probability of subsequent unsightly cracking caused by the continuation of corrosion of partly corroded ties. This factor should be weighed as a maintenance problem when considering this method. Wire and thin strip ties are unlikely to cause cracking when they corrode. Also appropriate to timber frame structures tied with the thin strip ties.	3 – 7
(i) (ii) (iii) (iv)	Demolition of outer leaf. Removal of corroded ties. Reconstruction of outer leaf. Retying.	Most appropriate for walls which are suffering from other forms of degradation in addition to tie corrosion such as sulphate attack of mortar, frost erosion of bricks, etc, or where it is desired to change the appearance of a building. Care should be taken to ensure that *all* the roof load is borne by the inner leaf and that the lintels pose no problem before attempting this technique. In some structures the roof load is shared. The method should be considered only where there are other problems or some tangible advantage.	1 – 5, 7
(i) (ii) (ii)	Propping of floors. Demolition of both leaves. Complete reconstruction of wall.	May be considered where the rest of the building is in very good condition but both leaves are damaged. A last resort option. Method is, however, technically feasible.	Techniques not relevant except to tie to party and partition walls, for which 1 – 5 and 7 are suitable.

Table 2 Tying systems

No.	Description	Diagrams of typical devices	Applications and restrictions	Comments
1	Simple replacement with standard double-triangle or special stainless steel ties resin-grouted into inner leaf and re-bedded in outer leaf when the brick is replaced.	Figure 1	Suitable for a wide range of applications. May be difficult if coursing height is not matched between outer and inner leaf. Also useful for concrete frame structures.	Versatile. Hollow units no problem because tie is replaced in original bed joint.
2	Special offset tie which grouts into the units in the inner leaf and can then be bedded in the outer leaf when the brick is replaced.	Figure 2	Suitable for a wide range of applications. Variations in coursing height present no problems. The grout fixing may not work if the inner leaf is of hollow or perforated units.	Versatile. Durability limited only by the grout used. Resin grouts should not be placed in water-saturated walls. (This applies to all grouted ties).
3	Replacement tie grouted into both leaves but staggered from the original tie position. Inner leaf grouted with resin capsule or by thixotropic resins placed with extension nozzles or via hollow ties, or sealed system with liquid resin. Outer leaf normally gun-grouted with thixotropic resin or liquid resin.	Figure 3	Suitable for most brick/brick walls but may be too stiff for some brick/block walls. Not reliable in perforated/hollow units. Should be satisfactory for concrete frames and cross walls.	Durability limited only by the grouts used. Could be carried out in reverse order if the wall was thought to be unstable. Some types have no drip.
4	All-metal expanding type tie in staggered positions.	Figure 4	As 3 but in some cases may function in hollow units. May not be suitable for units with low tensile strength. Special ties may be devised to fix to steelwork and concrete.	Durability is likely to be very good. Some types have no drip. Over-torquing can split the units. Reverse order possible.
5	Metal/plastics expanding type tie in staggered positions.	Figure 5	As 4.	Durability dependent on the plastics expanders. Other remarks as 4.
6	Special screw-in ties which can then be grouted to the outer leaf.	Figure 6	Could be used for timber frames or some types of low-strength concrete blocks.	In timber frame construction, ties must be positioned so that they screw into studs (old ties should provide guidance).
7	Partially tie using one of systems 1 to 6 and fill with heavy-duty polyurethane foam.	–	Suitable for most domestic cavity walls. Not affected by coursing height or perforations in the units. Unlikely to give satisfactory bond if wall is saturated with water.	Durability of the foam and of the bond is an unknown in this situation. Could encourage water leaks if the foam cracks. Improves the U-value of the wall and probably also the flexural strength.

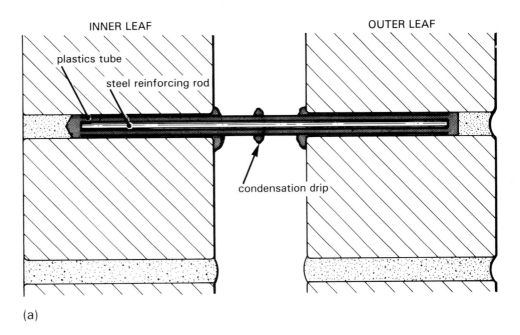

INNER LEAF OUTER LEAF

plastics tube

steel reinforcing rod

condensation drip

(a)

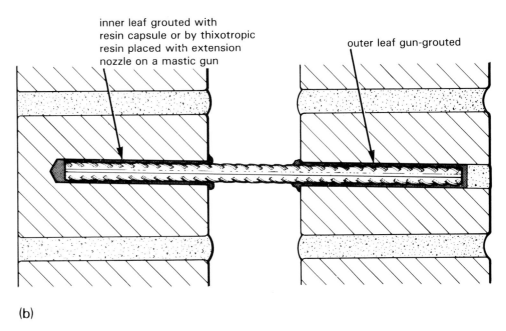

inner leaf grouted with
resin capsule or by thixotropic
resin placed with extension
nozzle on a mastic gun

outer leaf gun-grouted

(b)

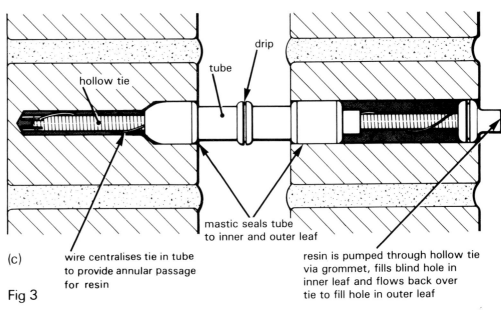

hollow tie

tube

drip

mastic seals tube
to inner and outer leaf

wire centralises tie in tube
to provide annular passage
for resin

resin is pumped through hollow tie
via grommet, fills blind hole in
inner leaf and flows back over
tie to fill hole in outer leaf

(c)

Fig 3

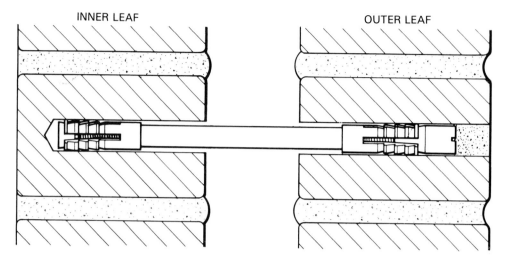

INNER LEAF   OUTER LEAF

Fig 4

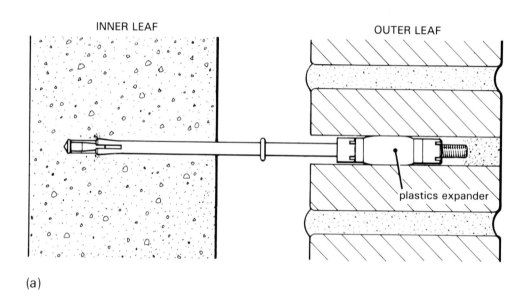

INNER LEAF   OUTER LEAF

plastics expander

(a)

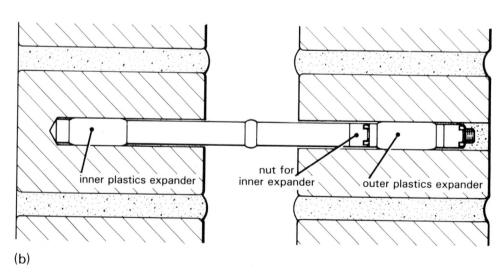

inner plastics expander

nut for
inner expander

outer plastics expander

(b)

Fig 5

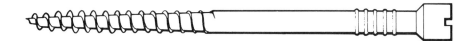

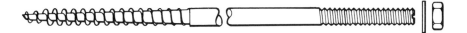

Fig 6

Repair techniques

Removal of bricks

This is not normally a problem with older lime or black ash mortars but the process can be speeded up considerably over hammer and chisel techiques by the use of power chisels attached to hammer drills or pneumatic hammers. Where vibration might cause damage, bed joints can be cut using a small portable dry carborundum disc saw, chain saw or angle grinder but great care is needed if the bricks are to be salvaged. Because perpends are short, they have to be cut by drilling and chiselling. Bed joints made with stronger cement mortars will need power cutting to obtain a satisfactory rate of progress. Care needs to be taken so that the equipment is not damaged or the operator endangered if pieces of steel are struck.

Removal of vertical twist ties

Ties can usually be removed fairly easily from the inner leaf by loosening the mortar on each side of the tie body to free the two fishtail splines and then working the tie loose. The mortar can be loosened using a power chisel or a masonry drill. Power devices or levers that either work the tie from side to side or grip and pull it may speed up this operation. At least one contractor has developed special tools to carry out this task.

Bending back or cropping vertical twist ties

Although this is probably less satisfactory than removal, it will be adequate in many cases. Bending back can usually be done with a hammer but cropping will probably require a power or lever cutter because the steel can be up to 5 mm thick.

Inserting resin grouted ties

Resin grouted ties can usually be installed using standard tools, such as a masonry drill, together with a few simple special tools, such as a driving attachment, alignment aid, a capsule insertion guide and a resin injection gun. Ties having no drip collar should be installed at an angle sloping down from inner to outer leaf. Some specialist contractors have their own tie system which should normally be placed only by a trained operative. Resin systems (especially the capsule type) are unreliable in very porous or perforated masonry units because the resin is lost into the holes. In some cases the problem can be by-passed by inserting the ties into mortar beds but this will not be possible in remote leaves of cavity walls. The inner fixing can be checked in doubtful cases by applying a torque test before grouting the outer fixing. It is not advisable to use perpend joints in modern brickwork for fixings because these are often only facades unfilled at the rear.

Resin systems should never be placed in rain-saturated brickwork but most will function in damp brickwork provided the drilling dust is cleared away. Grouts based on mixtures of Portland cement, fillers and water-based polymers or other proprietry inorganic formulations may also be suitable and may perform better than resin grouts in damp or wet walls.

Inserting expansion grip fixings

Installation of expansion grip fixings requires only a masonry drill and a controlled torque or pressure device. Cavity wall fixings should ideally have independently lockable ends so that the inner fixing can be tested before the outer fixing is locked. Simultaneous operation devices may function satisfactorily in a wall with leaves of similar strength and density but cannot be tested in situ. Experience has indicated that typical screw/cone or screw/expander-plug devices need to be tightened to a torque of up to 3 to 7 Nm: bricks may split if higher torques are used. Manufacturers' advice should be followed.

Damp or even saturated walls probably pose no problem but large perforations or voids of similar size to the expander collar may prevent the device functioning; they may not, be suitable for use with some hand-made or soft mud bricks, or with aerated concrete blocks which have insufficient resistance to the expander.

As with resin grouted ties, expansion devices without drip collars should be angled downwards towards the outer leaf and they should not be placed in perpend joints.

Inserting urethane foam

A heavy-duty polyurethane foam can be injected into the cavity to 'glue' the two leaves together and obviate the need for metal ties. It is a specialist operation not available to the general contractor. Some mechanical fixings are usually placed to prevent the walls bulging as a result of pressure build-up during the foaming process.

Replacing bricks, repointing, making good

Standard building techniques are used; mortar should, if possible, be of similar strength to the existing mortar. If the old mortar is very weak or friable, a low-strength but durable mortar may be formulated using one of the resin-in-water type additives such as are used to improve adhesion and waterproof floor screeds.

Further guidance is given in the items listed under *Further reading*.

Further reading

IP 28/79   Corrosion of steel wall ties: recognition, assessment and appropriate
           action
IP 29/79   Replacement of cavity wall ties using resin-grouted stainless steel
           rods
The following Digests include details on repair and repointing
157   Calcium silicate brickwork
160   Mortars for bricklaying
164   Clay brickwork: Part 1
165   Clay brickwork: Part 2
177   Decay and conservation of stone masonry
178   Autoclaved aerated concrete
200   Repairing brickwork

Cavity barriers and ventilation in flat and low-pitched roofs

Cavity barriers restrict the spread of smoke and flame; they are required by Building Regulations in certain types and sizes of new building and have been installed in some existing buildings. In flat and low-pitched roofs with a continuous weatherproof layer problems do not normally arise if cavity barriers are used in warm roof deck designs, but in cold roof deck designs care must be taken to ensure that there is adequate ventilation of the roof cavities. A total clear opening area of not less than 0.3 per cent of the plan area of the cavity should be used.

The practical problems of choosing appropriate materials and methods of fabrication and erection of cavity barriers and fire stops are discussed in Digests 214 and 215. This digest assesses the implications for ventilation of using cavity barriers and examines, where necessary, how adequate air movement can be provided in both new and existing flat roof voids, designed with or having installed cavity barriers.

This digest does not purport to be an authoritative interpretation of the legal requirements of the Building Regulations but has been produced as an aid to understanding their technical intention.

Voids often occur in flat and low pitched roof construction, particularly those with suspended or separate ceilings. Their presence has many advantages such as providing a space to contain pipework and other services. Ceilings can be constructed to resist the passage of fire but inadequacy of design and construction, the presence of openings or failure in fire are liable to allow smoke and hot gas to enter the void and spread rapidly through the horizontal plane. Following a number of fire incidents and fatalities particularly in institutional types of building, the Building Regulations, 1976, introduced requirements for the provision of cavity barriers and for fire stopping to restrict the unseen spread of fire and smoke.

The requirements to restrict the spread of smoke and flame, however, do not negate the need for providing ventilation in the cavities of certain forms of roof construction and particularly those with a continuous waterproof layer. The installation of cavity barriers and fire stopping without appreciating the implications for ventilation could seriously impair the efficiency of air movement. This could lead to a build up of moisture within the roof construction which can cause deterioration of many building materials resulting in the possibility of structural collapse.

Cavity barriers

A cavity barrier is defined in the 1976 Building Regulations (Part E, Safety in Fire, Regulation E14) as a construction to restrict movement of smoke or flame within a cavity, including a construction provided for another purpose if it conforms with the criteria required of a cavity barrier. The requirement for the installation of cavity barriers and the maximum permitted distance between cavity barriers are related to the Purpose Group of the building and are set out in the table to Regulation E14(4), the relevant part of which is given below.

Table 1 Maximum distance between cavity barriers in a roof void.
Based on the table to Regulation E14(4) of the Building Regulations 1976 and irrespective of the class of exposed surface within the cavity (excluding pipes, cables or conduit).

Purpose group of building or compartment	Maximum distance
I and flats or maisonettes within III	No limit (Cavity barriers not required)
II and III except flats and maisonettes	15 m with area limited to 100 m²
Any other	20 m

Purpose group I covers private dwelling houses, PG II institutional and PG III other residential buildings. Purpose groups IV, V and VI cover offices, shops and factories, respectively, VII embraces other places of assembly and finally, VIII is for storage and other general buildings.

It should be noted that cavity barriers are not required by E14(4) to subdivide roof voids in purpose group I buildings or for flats and maisonettes in purpose group III, although some barriers in and at the perimeter of voids may nonetheless be required by E14(2) and (3). In all other purpose groups, cavity barriers may be required in roof voids by E14(4) as well as by E14(2) and (3).

Digests 214 and 215 examine in detail appropriate materials and methods of fabricating suitable cavity barriers. Building Regulations and the Digests seek to achieve, in the materials and constructions they describe, a close fit of the barrier in the cavity and at the joint between the barrier and any through-going services. Thus the passage of air is restricted and any requirements for ventilation must be met within the permitted maximum distances and areas that result from the sub-division of roof space by the cavity barriers.

Flat roof design

The detail and construction of flat roofs varies greatly but currently it is common practice to classify them according to the location of the insulation in relation to the deck as being of warm or of cold roof deck design, see Digest 180.

Warm roof deck

In warm roof deck design the insulation is placed immediately below the waterproof layer with a vapour barrier beneath the insulation and on the upper side of the roof deck. The ceiling may be independently suspended at a lower level providing a cavity between the ceiling and the roof which is not ventilated with outside air. The roof deck is consequently warm and the insulation is protected from reaching dew point conditions by the vapour barrier on its warm side.

Since any cavity formed between the roof deck and the ceiling does not require ventilating this method of construction is not affected by the installation of cavity barriers. However, a warm roof deck design does not necessarily provide the best design solution for buildings requiring cavity barriers, particularly as other problems must be considered, for example the movement of the thermal insulation and its effect on the integrity of the water-proof layer and the costs incurred in the future for the replacement of the water-proof layer.

Cold roof deck

In cold roof deck design the insulation is placed immediately above the ceiling, usually with a vapour barrier interposed. A cold void is thus created between the insulation and the roof-deck, which supports directly the water-proof layer. Outside air is allowed to pass through this cavity helping to clear any build-up of moisture which could result from the percolation of interior air from beneath the ceiling (see Fig. 1). In addition, as the waterproof layer and supporting upper deck approach the outside temperature, the ventilation minimises the risk of condensation occurring on the deck. It is possible, however, by the use or installation of cavity barriers to interrupt or impair the efficiency of the ventilation, and it is this form of roof deck design, or variations of it, that are mostly affected by the use of cavity barriers in both new and existing buildings.

Existing roof decks

In view of recent experiences and legislation it may be considered necessary to install cavity barriers in certain existing buildings. In such cases the roof structure should be carefully examined and classified either as warm or as cold roof deck design. If warm, no problems should arise; if cold, then the implications for ventilation must be considered. If for some reason cavity barriers have already been installed in an existing cold roof without considering the implications for ventilation then the roof structure should be examined immediately and the necessary provision made for ventilation.

It is clearly possible to provide the ventilation needed between cavity barriers by roof cowl ventilators. However, it would be an advantage to have the additional facility of being able to use eaves or perimeter ventilation. At present it is necessary to obtain a relaxation of Regulation E14(2)(a) for this purpose; however, there are proposals to amend the regulation in order to permit generally in external walls the use of eaves ventilation openings to the adjacent sub-divided roof cavities. An additional advantage of providing roof ventilation is to assist with the clearance of smoke which may enter the void. However, the size of ventilation openings normally provided may be inadequate for complete smoke clearance.

If an existing building has little thermal insulation then the question of upgrading may occur at the same time as the installation of cavity barriers. Great care must be exercised in this situation. A complex solution combining cold and warm roof deck design should be avoided as should any possible duplication of vapour barriers, as experience has shown that these types of solution are often unsatisfactory.

Methods of ventilation

In most cases ventilation in flat and low-pitched roofs relies on intermittent winds of varying direction and intensity. For the ingress and exhaustion of air it is, therefore, necessary to arrange ventilators at least at both ends of a cavity avoiding the occurrence of any dead pockets of static air. Openings at one end of a cavity will not provide sufficient movement of air. A flow of air may be induced thermally where a deep roof zone is available by providing ingress at the lower eaves and escape at the high point of the roof or ridge. Apertures may be arranged in the form of cowls through the weatherproof layer or, in cases where the local authority agrees to relaxation of E14(2)(a), of openings either on the facade of the building within the roof zone, or at the underside of any roof overhang. In some forms of construction it is possible to provide ventilation at the base of a flush fascia detail, but care must be taken not to infringe the integrity of any required cavity barrier or to impede the flow of air by other construction materials such as insulation or rendering (Fig 1). In order to provide adequate ventilation within the voids between cavity barriers, it may be necessary to combine alternative types of aperture, particularly with large complex roof areas (Fig. 2).

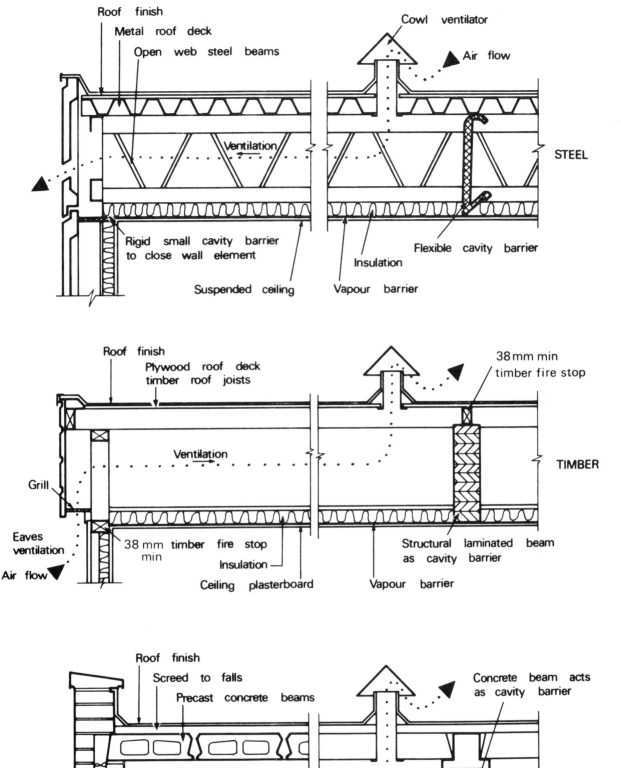

Fig. 1 Typical cold roof deck construction showing ventilation detail

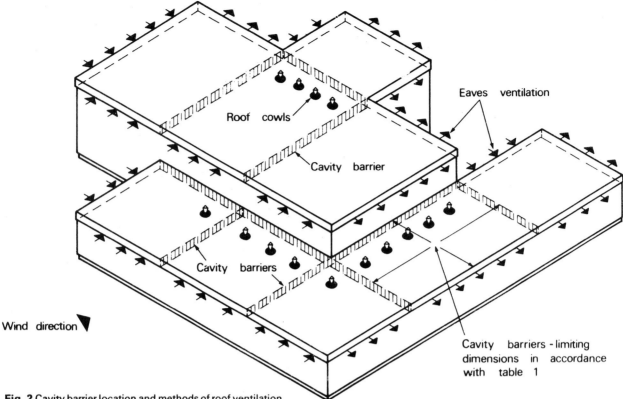

Roof cowls

Cavity barrier

Eaves ventilation

Cavity barriers

Wind direction ▼

Cavity barriers - limiting dimensions in accordance with table 1

Fig. 2 Cavity barrier location and methods of roof ventilation

The amount of clear aperture area required to give adequate ventilation will vary according to location, and the efficiency of the air movement. Since, however, material degradation does not occur, and performance of cold roof construction is not affected by an excess of ventilation it would seem appropriate to use a minimum distributed clear aperture opening area of not less than 0.3 per cent of the total plan area of the cavity, increasing this figure extensively wherever possible and especially when achieving satisfactory distribution within the cavity becomes difficult because of plan configuration. Thus a roof with a span of 30 m and with a cavity barrier at mid-span will require an aperture area of 0.023 m^2 for each metre of width and at each end of the two cavities formed. This could be met by a continuous 23 mm wide slot or by air grates or ventilators each having a clear aperture of 0.023 m^2 and spaced at 1 metre intervals.

Unusually-high relative humidities may occur in certain buildings such as those associated with swimming pools, service kitchens and some industrial processes. In these cases special arrangements should be made to exhaust the wet air from the building using fans and in the case of cold roof deck design a similar approach should be taken with the roof voids. Attention also needs to be paid to the selection and location of the materials used in the

roof construction to ensure that any damp conditions that may arise do not cause deterioration.

Ventilator design
Many types of ventilators, including louvres and cowls, both directional and non-directional are available and some are designed to ventilate the cavities in cold roof deck design. In some cases the ventilation can be incorporated as part of the construction detail. Where ventilators penetrate the waterproof layer care must be taken in detailing to ensure that there is no possibility of water ingress *around* the ventilating device into the roof space. Ventilators should be selected and sited to achieve the following:
induce maximum air flow throughout the full length of a cavity without infringing cavity barrier requirements;
be of sufficient clear opening area to provide the required ventilation rate;
prevent the ingress of snow, rain, insects, birds and leaves;
be sited to facilitate inspection;
be located so that there is no danger of obstruction in the void by loose materials, such as insulation;
be of maintenance-free materials and constructed to avoid the occurrence of condensation within the ventilator.

Condensation in roofs

Although most roofs perform well, problems of condensation are increasing. The risk is greatest in roofs that have impermeable sheet coverings, and flat roofs in particular have frequently given rise to problems. With newer forms of construction, lower roof pitches, and changes in standards and forms of heating, similar problems are now being met in pitched roofs.

This digest discusses design principles for minimising the risk of condensation and consequential damage to decorations or structure.

Design principles

The simplest roof is no more than a rain shield but many designs include a lining or a ceiling, separated from the rain shield or cladding by an air space and insulation. If warm moist air from the building can enter the air space, it will condense on any surface whose temperature is below its dewpoint. This is most likely to be the underside of the cladding, from which moisture can drip on to the ceiling or damage the roof structure. The design should therefore aim to balance temperatures and humidities so that the surface temperatures of critical component parts of the roof remain above the dewpoint of the surrounding air for most of the time. Practical measures that can be taken are:

a provide a vapour barrier at the warm side of the roof structure to prevent the entry of moisture from the building.
b provide a rain shield that is permeable to water vapour, to allow for the transfer of moisture to the outside.
c ventilate the roof space to the outside air.
d blow 'dry' air into the roof space under pressure and thus prevent moist air from entering it.

The practical difficulties of achieving these measures vary from one type of roof to another, and methods appropriate to different roof types are discussed later. For instance, it is very much easier to achieve a permeable rain shield on a pitched roof than on a flat one; it is also easier to form an impermeable membrane above a flat roof deck than below it.

Digest 110 *Condensation* sets out procedures for steady-state calculation of internal temperatures and dewpoints in roofs which do not incorporate ventilated air spaces, and these procedures enable the risk of steady deposition to be assessed for lightweight (low thermal capacity) roofs. An estimate has to be made of the most adverse external and internal temperatures and humidities that will occur at any time.

Such calculations cannot be made for heavyweight (high thermal capacity) roofs such as concrete roofs, which take some time to warm up and cool down, but it is possible to assess whether a steady deposition in concrete roofs is likely by making steady-state calculations based on the most adverse *daily mean* temperatures and humidities.

It is not generally possible to calculate with certainty the risk of condensation in roofs with ventilated air spaces.

Even if there is no steady deposition of water, intermittent condensation can occur. If the roof incorporates absorbent materials that are unaffected by moisture, small amounts of moisture may be deposited for short periods and can later evaporate without causing trouble. Care must be taken to avoid situations where water might drain to where it can cause damage and the ventilation must be good enough to encourage drying during favourable atmospheric conditions.

Condensation is not necessarily troublesome; on the upper side of undertiling felt it is usually harmless as it can normally drain away, but on the underside it is likely to cause trouble either by dripping on to the ceiling below or by draining to a point where it can wet the structure.

Particular attention has to be paid to the possibility of condensation on cellulosic materials such as flaxboard, strawboard, fibreboard or chipboard, which permanently lose mechanical strength or rot when they become wet. Untreated timber is susceptible to fungal attack when its moisture content exceeds 20 per cent by weight. Where there is any risk that it might reach this condition, it should be pressure impregnated with preservative, but timber that has been treated with preservation salts may, when it gets wet, cause corrosion of metal fastenings.

Types of roof

Various forms of roof are now discussed to bring out the factors affecting condensation. The order of presentation is not related to the frequency of occurrence of the roofs, but is chosen to illustrate the principles in a convenient manner.

Sheeted roofs (Fig 1)

Sheeted roofs, which are commonly used in factories, consist of an outer cladding of, say, corrugated metal or asbestos-cement and an inner lining, often fibreboard or plasterboard, with an air space between cladding and lining which may incorporate some additional thermal insulation. In adverse conditions, moisture can enter the air space from the building through gaps between the lining boards or by diffusion through the lining itself, condense on the underside of the cladding and drip on to the insulation or the lining. The problem is reduced if air can flow through gaps between the cladding sheets; spacers can sometimes be used to increase the size of the gaps. Ventilation of the air space can reduce the moisture content of the air within it, and hence the risk of condensation and dripping; it also promotes drying during favourable conditions.

Though sheeted roofs with ventilated air spaces are suitable for most factories, there can be problems in factories where high humidities occur, eg breweries, dye-houses, etc. These can sometimes be overcome by providing a vapour check at the inside of the structure. The best available method of forming a vapour barrier at ceiling level is to spray the underside of the lining with a suitable plastics coating. This treatment is, however, expensive and the film might be ruptured by roof movements. Nevertheless, some form of vapour barrier should be provided as it will reduce the amount of water vapour entering the roof.

Lightweight flat roofs (Fig 2)

Lightweight flat roofs comprise a waterproof membrane covering a structural deck, an air space and a lining or ceiling; they may also incorporate insulation. The air space cannot be ventilated through gaps in the cladding, neither can water vapour diffuse through the waterproof covering which is usually bitumen felt, asphalt or sheet metal. Moist air which finds its way into the air space therefore condenses on a metal deck, or diffuses through a timber roof deck, wetting the deck and condensing on the underside of the waterproof covering. The condensation risk depends on the roof design and because of this all timber used in flat roofs should be pressure impregnated with preservative.

Cold roof

In the roof illustrated in Fig 2a, the insulation is placed on top of the plasterboard; this will prevent surface condensation on the ceiling but there is a risk of condensation on the underside of the waterproof covering. This type of construction is

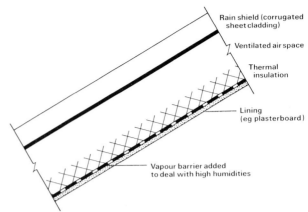

Fig 1 Sheeted roofs

commonly referred to as a 'cold' roof, because for much of the year the temperature of the air within the roof space is lower than the temperature inside the building. The amount of water vapour entering the roof structure can be restricted by a vapour check, eg sheet polythene at ceiling level.

The only way in which the air spaces in a lightweight flat roof can be ventilated is through gaps or grilles at each end of every air space but there is a fairly high resistance to the flow of air in these long narrow air spaces, particularly if they are partially obstructed by stiffeners. If the roof overhangs the external walls, ventilation openings can be provided in the soffit but if the roof finishes flush with the external walls, grilles have to be built into the walls. Neither the air flow through the roof spaces nor the moisture flow into the roof can be estimated with any accuracy. Furthermore, if water is trapped between the timber deck and the waterproof covering, one cannot rely on this being removed by evaporation. Experience has shown that there is a relatively high risk of condensation in this type of roof.

Warm roof (Fig 2b) The behaviour of a lightweight flat roof in respect of condensation is improved if the insulation is placed above the deck and a vapour barrier added between the deck and

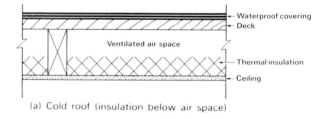

(a) Cold roof (insulation below air space)

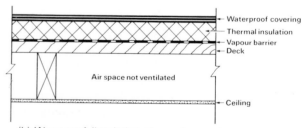

(b) Warm roof (insulation above air space)

Fig 2 Lightweight flat roofs

the insulation. The air in the deck spaces is warmer than the outside air and this type of roof is commonly referred to as a 'warm' roof. In this form of construction with overdeck insulation, no attempt is made to ventilate the roof spaces. If the temperature of the vapour barrier is kept above the dewpoint of the air, condensation will not occur within the roof structure. When it is possible to specify the most adverse temperatures and humidities both inside and outside, the amount of insulation required above the vapour barrier can be calculated.

In housing, the internal conditions are not known but experience has shown that if the roof insulation meets the requirements of the Building Regulations, with most of it located above the vapour barrier, the risk of condensation within the structure is small.

The vapour barrier normally consists of bitumen felt (not less than 13 kg/10 m²) well lapped at joints and nailed or spot bonded to the structural deck in compliance with BS CP 144. An all-over coat of hot bitumen mopped on to the top of the bitumen felt completes the vapour barrier and also provides a means of sticking down the thermal insulation. With this form of construction it is essential that the insulation is kept dry. The insulation boards must also be closely butted since there is a high risk that coverings like bitumen felt or asphalt will fail over gaps. At the perimeter of the roof the vapour barrier must be turned up and sealed to the rain shield to prevent ingress of moisture at the edges of the insulation boards. Similar measures are needed at any breaks in the roof such as at roof lights, around pipes, etc. On large roofs it is also advisable to divide the insulation into sealed compartments.

Lightweight pitched roofs (Fig 3)

Lightweight pitched roofs can be constructed in a similar way to lightweight flat roofs, with a sloping waterproofed deck, a ventilated roof space and a ceiling. Fig 3 illustrates a typical construction with a timber deck and insulation between joists. The roof space can be ventilated by suitable openings at eaves or gables.

The roof illustrated in Fig 3 is a 'cold' roof; the insulation is at ceiling level and the roof space is cold. As with the similar flat roof there is a high risk of condensation on the underside of the water-proof covering. It is more satisfactory to fix the insulation on the slope of the roof, as in the 'warm' flat roof. There is then little risk of condensation if a vapour barrier is placed below the insulation.

Tiled or slated roofs (Fig 4)

The tiles or slates of traditional pitched roofs were often laid only on battens on rafters, or fixed direct to timber sarking, so that the roof space was freely ventilated through gaps between the tiles or slates. It is now usual to provide an underlay to the tiles or

slates, usually of bitumen felt. If the underlay is permeable, either because it is not saturated with bitumen or because of gaps at the lapped joints, there is little risk of trouble from condensation. Moist air which enters the roof space can escape through the permeable covering, and any intermittent condensation in the roof is absorbed by the timber or felt and later re evaporated. If timber sarking is used above the rafters it provides further absorbent material.

However, impermeable materials such as saturated bitumen felt, PVC and polythene are now extensively used for underlays. These reduce the rate at which moist air can escape from the roof space so that condensation problems are becoming more common. Water condensing on the underside of an impermeable underlay may drip on to the ceiling or drain down the roof slope, wetting timbers at the eaves and causing damage to the structure. If timber, chipboard or other organic material used as sarking has an impermeable underlay above it, the

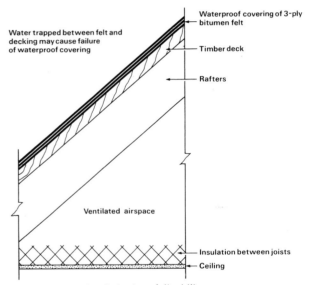

Fig 3 Lightweight pitched roof ('cold')

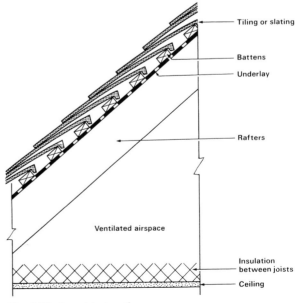

Fig 4 Tiled or slated roof

sarking material may be damaged by condensation; this could be avoided by increasing the ventilation of the roof space.

Concrete roofs

Concrete, either cast in situ or precast, can be used as a structural deck. A lightweight screed is sometimes used to provide falls (though these are better formed in the structural deck) and additional insulation. The deck is usually covered with an impermeable waterproof covering, such as bitumen felt or asphalt.

In wet districts it is not easy to dry out the construction water or to prevent further wetting before the waterproof covering is laid. Moisture can diffuse through the concrete or any cracks in it and condense on the underside of the waterproof covering. Condensed water may flow between the waterproof covering and the concrete to drip down through joints or cracks in the concrete deck. The condensed water may also saturate any insulating screed, thus greatly reducing its value as insulation. These roofs can, nevertheless, perform satisfactorily if the concrete is dry before they are covered and if the internal humidity in the building is low.

The waterproof covering may also be damaged by blisters caused by vaporisation of water entrapped below it. Properly designed breather vents, in conjunction with a pressure-releasing layer beneath the rain shield, can overcome this problem but they are not very effective in preventing trouble from condensation.

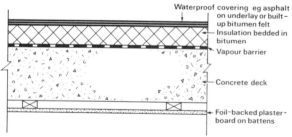

Fig 5 Conventional concrete roof

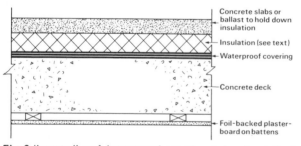

Fig 6 'Inverted' roof (waterproof covering *below* insulation)

An effective method of avoiding condensation, at least in continuously heated buildings, is to provide overdeck insulation as shown in Fig 5. There may be some temporary condensation on the underside of such concrete roofs in intermittently heated buildings, but this can usually be avoided by using a lightweight battened out ceiling, preferably using foil-backed plasterboard, to avoid staining during the drying-out period.

The 'inverted roof' (Fig 6) operates on the same principle as overdeck insulation but uses materials that are unaffected by moisture, such as foamed glass or extruded polystyrene, above the waterproof covering. The insulation is not covered with a waterproof layer as with overdeck insulation, but simply weighted down by gravel of a suitable size or concrete paving slabs.

Pressurised roof space

A suspended ceiling may be used to provide a roof space to accommodate machinery, or for appearance, or for acoustic absorption (Fig 7). This introduces an air space which must be taken into account in assessing the condensation risk. For instance, the thermal insulation of an acoustic ceiling may be high enough to reduce temperatures within the structure below the dewpoint of the air within the building.

In such cases, warm 'dry' air can be blown into the roof space to ensure that the dewpoint of the air within it is kept below the temperature of any part of the structure. The air pressure in the roof space has to be high enough to prevent the entry of water vapour from the building, and to ensure a downward flow of air through gaps. It is desirable to incorporate a vapour check at ceiling level to reduce the diffusion of water vapour into the roof space and to reduce the gaps through which air is lost. The excess pressure can then be kept to a minimum, to save on the cost of fans and energy.

This technique is normally justifiable only for buildings with abnormally high internal humidities, such as swimming pools.

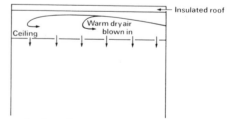

Fig 7 Pressurised roof space

Condensation in insulated domestic roofs

Thermal insulation laid on top of the ceiling in the roof space is one of the most cost-effective methods of energy conservation. But increasing the amount of insulation in a domestic pitched roof increases the risk of condensation in the roof. This digest describes the types of damage that condensation can cause and outlines the design options available to reduce the risk of condensation.

Most of the water vapour comes from within the house, both by movement of air through gaps in the ceiling and, to a much lesser extent, by diffusion through the plasterboard. The type of damage depends on the structure of the roof. If there is a non-absorbent lining, such as sarking felt or plastics sheet, water can condense on the lining and subsequently run or drip on to the timbers and ceiling. Absorbent linings, such as sarking boards, are then wetted and may rot.

The importance of adequate ventilation of the roof is emphasised. Openings in the eaves on opposite sides of the roof are recommended where possible; other methods of ventilating are discussed.

Thermal insulation laid on the ceiling is one of the most cost-effective methods of conserving energy but inadequate precautions may result in an increase in the risk of condensation in roofs for two reasons. Firstly, the insulation reduces the amount of heat entering the roof from the house below but generally has very little effect on the amount of water vapour transferred. Consequently the air temperature in the roof will drop while the vapour pressure remains constant. This leads to a rise in the relative humidity. The moisture content of wood and other hygroscopic materials depends on the relative humidity of the surrounding air; therefore the roof timbers with insulation at ceiling level will be wetter than those without. Secondly, unless care is taken during installation, it is possible for the ventilation gaps in the eaves to be blocked.

Damage caused by condensation in pitched roofs has increased in recent years. As problems within the loft are often not noticed until they have reached an advanced state, structural damage can result. The type of damage that occurs depends upon the construction of the roof.

Roofs with a non-absorbent lining

These types of roof include conventional constructions with a sarking felt or plastics sheeting under the tiles or slates, and constructions with metal or asbestos decks. Condensation can occur on the underside of the sheeting. This is not damaged itself, but the condensed water can then wet rafters in contact with the sheet (Fig 1), increasing the risk of rot, and drip and soak any insulation ultimately damaging the plasterboard; electrical services on the ceiling may be wetted causing shorting. The water can also run into the eaves to soak wallhead plates and might cause corrosion to punched metal plate fasteners in trussed rafter roofs (especially in CCA treated timbers).

These problems may be especially severe during a thaw after large amounts of ice have built up on the sheeting during a prolonged cold spell. Volumes of water released may be large enough to give the impression of a major leak in the roof.

Roofs with an absorbent lining

Included in these types are roofs with timber or timber-based sarking boards under the tiles or slates or roofs with sarking boards covered with impermeable waterproofing materials. In these cases, any water condensing on the underside of the roof covering may be absorbed by the board. This may either cause moisture-swelling in materials such as chipboard or may result in rot (Fig 2). Under such conditions the boards may lose their strength and fall into the roof space.

If the relative humidity in the roof is persistently high, mould and mildew can grow on furniture, clothes, luggage or other materials stored in the roof. This is often the first sign of the problem and the first cause of complaint by the occupants.

Fig 1

Fig 2

Sources of water vapour

Within the roof space Insulation at ceiling level in the roof space should be carried over and around (but not below) water tanks to prevent freezing. However, this leaves the water warm enough to evaporate into a cold roof space if the top is open. It is essential, therefore, that all water tanks are covered. Occasionally, central heating systems pump steam or hot water into the expansion tank. Some of this water also evaporates into the roof space. If water is discharging from the expansion pipe in the roof space while the central heating pump is running, appropriate steps to modify the system should be taken.

From within the house Water vapour is generated in the dwelling space by the normal activities of the occupants, particularly the washing and drying of clothes and cooking. In recent years, greater use of unflued paraffin and bottled gas heaters has added to the amount of water vapour produced. BS 5250 gives 7–14 litres per day as typical of a house with five occupants. Most of the vapour is carried out by ventilation and some condenses in the house; however, a proportion enters the roof space. More water vapour is likely to enter the roof if fireplace openings have been blanked off and if occupants have attempted to conserve energy by sealing cracks around doors and windows.

Routes of water vapour transfer

Water vapour enters the roof from the dwelling space by two means. Vapour pressure difference between the house and roof causes water vapour to diffuse through the plasterboard of the ceiling. The published diffusion coefficients of plasterboard indicate that, for a typical house, about 10 grams/hr of water pass into the roof by this means. However, there is evidence to show that in practice the plasterboard absorbs large amounts of water resulting in slower rates of transfer than expected from calculations.

Secondly, and more importantly, the water vapour enters the roof by air movement. When wind blows through cracks around doors and windows on the windward side of the house, the air pressure in the dwelling space is raised above that in the roof and air carrying water vapour is forced through gaps in the ceiling. For a typical semi-detached house with all the windows closed, about 20–30 per cent of the air which enters the house leaves via the loft. In doing so, it carries water vapour into the roof void. With windows open on the windward side of the house and shut on the leeward side, substantially more than the 20–30 per cent of air will enter the roof. This is similar to the case of single-aspect, top-floor flats which have only a door to an access corridor on one side; as much as 60 per cent of the air entering this type of flat has been shown to leave via the roof. From measured air flow rates and the vapour pressure difference between the house and roof, it is possible to estimate that for a typical two-storey house about 40 grams per hour of water enters the roof by this means (over 100 gm/hour in the case of single aspect flats). These values are much larger than the amounts that are diffused through the ceiling (Fig 3).

Tests have shown that the relative contributions of the different air paths through the ceiling vary greatly from house to house. However, typically, 50 per cent of the air passes around the hatch cover, 40 per cent through holes where pipes penetrate the ceiling (these holes can be large, especially when the pipes are concealed in cupboards), and the remaining 10 per cent through ceiling roses and cracks at the wallheads.

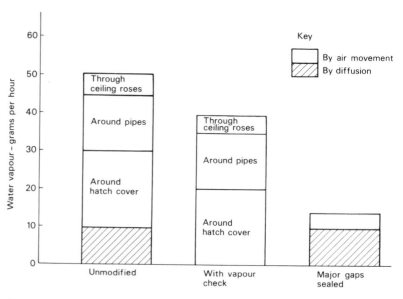

Fig 3 Relative importance of different routes for transfer of water vapour from a house to its roof.

Reducing moisture transfer into the roof

The risk of condensation causing damage in the roof will be greatly reduced if water vapour is prevented from passing from the house into the loft. As most of the moisture is carried into the roof by air movement, measures should concentrate on blocking the major gaps in the ceiling.

Weatherstripping, similar to that used to exclude draughts around doors and windows, should be fitted around the hatch cover. With very lightweight hatch covers, it may be necessary to increase their weight or provide some form of catch which compresses the weatherstripping and prevents the cover blowing up into the roof in high winds.

Where pipes pass through the ceiling, especially in airing cupboards, holes should be sealed. A flexible seal will allow for movement of hot water pipes.

The ceiling roses of all electric lights on the top floor should be screwed tightly to the ceiling. It may be necessary to include a rubber gasket if they are particularly ill-fitting.

Extractor fans help reduce water vapour transfer to roof spaces; when an extractor fan is turned on in the kitchen or bathroom, air is sucked out of the house, reducing the air pressure in the house relative to that in the roof. This reduces the air flow through the ceiling and at low wind speeds air can be drawn from the roof to the house. Therefore, not only does the extractor fan remove water vapour from the house at places where it is generated, thereby reducing the risk of condensation in the house, it also reduces the amount that enters the roof and assists in reducing the risk of condensation in the roof space.

The use of extractor fans and the blocking of holes at ceiling level may affect the ventilation rate within the dwelling. These modifications must not impair the safe operation of gas and oil heating systems by reducing the supply of air for combustion: Building Regulations require a minimum unobstructed area of vent for flued appliances.

Ventilation of the roof space

Ventilation of the roof space is very important and is the usual way of removing moisture from the roof. This can be achieved in a number of ways (Fig 4), for example by placing ventilation openings at the eaves, either in the fascia or the soffit boards, or at both eaves and ridges.

Eaves openings should be designed to prevent the ingress of rain and snow, birds and large insects such as wasps and bees, ie mesh smaller than 2–5 mm (see Digest 238). Ventilation openings located at irregular intervals are satisfactory, providing they are of equivalent area to the continuous openings recommended and avoid the risk of stagnant pockets of air in the roof space.

The location of eaves ventilation openings above windows might facilitate the spread of fire from the dwelling into the roof space. Naked flames must be used with care in the vicinity of such openings, eg when burning off old paint.

If ridge ventilators are installed, ventilation openings must also be fitted at or near eaves level or there may be an increase in moisture transfer from the dwelling into the roof space. This is because the air flow over the apex of the roof creates an air pressure drop from inside the roof space to outside which in turn increases the air flow from the dwelling space to the roof space. If it is not possible to provide ventilation openings as outlined above, ventilating tiles may be used on the roof or air bricks inserted in gable ends above the ceiling insulation. The ventilating tiles or air bricks must be located at both high and low level to provide air movement.

Where eaves ventilation alone is used, the ventilation openings should be provided along two opposite sides of the roof. British Standard 5250 recommends that roofs of more than 15° pitch should be provided with ventilation openings equivalent to a continuous opening of not less than 10 mm. For roofs of 15° pitch and lower, the ventilation should be increased to the equivalent of not less than 25 mm continuous opening. The Building Regulations (England and Wales) require the roof spaces above insulated ceilings to be ventilated either in accordance with BS 5250 or to be cross-ventilated by means of permanent vents not less than 0.3 per cent of the roof plan area.

Roofs covered with slates or tiles will have some fortuitous ventilation but this must be ignored when calculating ventilation openings. This fortuitous ventilation helps to disperse any moisture vapour that might otherwise be trapped between the undertiling membrane and the tiles; it is essential that membranes used in this position are waterproof but permit the transfer of water vapour. Thermal insulation at ceiling level must not block the eaves ventilation openings but should cover the wallhead to avoid cold bridging effects from a gap in the insulation envelope. In low-pitched roofs with high levels of insulation this may be difficult to achieve. Ducts are available which can be installed in the eaves to allow air to be brought into the roof over the insulation.

In some house designs, the horizontal ceiling may be omitted so that there is no loft. In that case, if insulation is located between the sloping

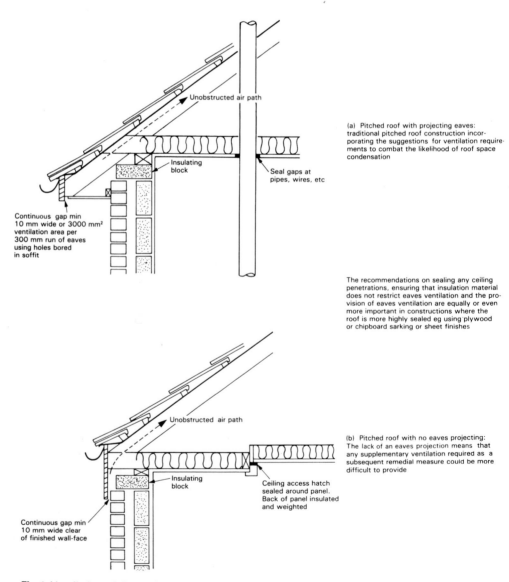

Unobstructed air path

Insulating block

Seal gaps at pipes, wires, etc

Continuous gap min 10 mm wide or 3000 mm² ventilation area per 300 mm run of eaves using holes bored in soffit

(a) Pitched roof with projecting eaves: traditional pitched roof construction incorporating the suggestions for ventilation requirements to combat the likelihood of roof space condensation

The recommendations on sealing any ceiling penetrations, ensuring that insulation material does not restrict eaves ventilation and the provision of eaves ventilation are equally or even more important in constructions where the roof is more highly sealed eg using plywood or chipboard sarking or sheet finishes

Unobstructed air path

Insulating block

Ceiling access hatch sealed around panel. Back of panel insulated and weighted

(b) Pitched roof with no eaves projecting: The lack of an eaves projection means that any supplementary ventilation required as a subsequent remedial measure could be more difficult to provide

Continuous gap min 10 mm wide clear of finished wall-face

Fig 4 Ventilation of the roof space

rafters, the construction should be regarded as a 'flat roof' and the relevant guidance followed.

It is possible that under extreme overnight conditions increased ventilation may lead to increased condensation in lightweight sheeted roofs. However, ventilation will allow any condensate to clear quickly when conditions improve and prevent any long-term build up of moisture. Tests have shown that, in conventional roof constructions with higher thermal mass, improved ventilation greatly reduces the risk of damage.

Effect of ventilation on fibrous insulation

Concern has been expressed that increased loft ventilation rates will cause a reduction in the performance of thermal insulation materials laid upon the ceiling. The thermal performance of fibrous or loose insulation at ceiling level can be reduced by excessive air velocities at the exposed surface of the insulation. However, the air speeds required to avoid condensation (0.1 m/s) are much lower than those which will cause deterioration of the performance of the insulation (1–2 m/s). The ventilation openings recommended above are not therefore sufficient to affect the performance of the insulating materials.

Checklist

The possible increased risk of condensation or other technical problems that might arise from the use of thermal insulation in the roof can be overcome by the measures outlined below and there is no reason for improved thermal insulation to be accompanied by condensation or mould in the roof space.

Ventilate the roof space as detailed under *Ventilation of the roof space.*

Ensure water tanks are covered.

Plug holes at ceiling level to prevent moisture transfer in roofs.

Weatherstrip and weight hatch cover to reduce moisture ingress from house.

Ensure insulation covers wallhead but does not block eaves ventilation.

Ensure that water pipes in the roof are insulated to avoid freezing in winter (ideally, locate pipes below the over-ceiling insulation).

Ensure joists are visible so they can be used to locate foot-holds where roof is used for storage or for access to water and electrical services.

Ensure electric cables are above the insulation (except for access to luminaires) to avoid overheating, or derate the cable performance.

Keep pvc cables out of contact with expanded polystyrene. There can be an interaction between the pvc sheathing and the expanded polystyrene; whilst not likely to cause a serious problem if the degraded sheathing is left undisturbed, the two materials are best kept apart by appropriate siting of the cables or the use of conduit.

Ensure that all insulating materials are used in conformity with relevant British Standards and Agrément Certificates. These documents may lay down conditions of use to avoid impairing the performance of other components.

Further reading

For designers:

BS 5250:1975 Code of basic data for the design of buildings: the control of condensation in dwellings.

Condensation and mould growth. Domestic Energy Note No 4; DOE, HMSO, 1979.

Condensation in domestic roof spaces. Domestic Energy Note No 2; DOE, HMSO, 1978.

Slated or tiled pitched roofs: ventilation to outside air. Defect Action Sheet (Design) 1; BRE Housing Defects Prevention Unit.

Slated or tiled pitched roofs: restricting the entry of water vapour from the house. Defect Action Sheet (Design) 3; BRE Housing Defects Prevention Unit.

Pitched roofs: thermal insulation near eaves. Defect Action Sheet (Site) 4; BRE Housing Defects Prevention Unit.

For occupants and housing managers:

Appendix B to BS 5250.

Condensation and mould growth in your home. Leaflet to Domestic Energy Note No 4; DOE, HMSO, 1979.

Condensation in domestic tiled pitched roofs – Advice to householders. BRE Technical Information Leaflet No 59.

Treatment of mould – advise to householders. BRE Technical Information Leaflet No 66.

BRE Digests

110 Condensation
180 Condensation in roofs
221 Flat roof design: the technical options
233 Fire hazard from insulating materials
238 Reducing the risk of pest infestation

Flat roof design: the technical options

The term flat roof is commonly used in Codes and Standards to denote a roof which can be horizontal or which can have a fall of up to 8°, or even 10°, to provide drainage. At the upper end of this range the term low pitched is also used. However, whatever the actual definition and slope limitation, flat roofs are characterized by having a continuous waterproof layer. In some cases such roofs are used in situations where traditional pitched roof designs with a discontinuous waterproof layer could have been used. In other cases, especially on large buildings of irregular plan, they provide the only feasible solution. Experience suggests that high maintenance costs can occur with flat roofs. However, many of the problems that arise could have been avoided at the design and construction stages if designers and constructors had appreciated fully the limitations of the various design options, and had selected and applied correctly the one most suitable for their particular building taking into account the consequences and implications of failure and the costs of maintenance and replacement.

Roof requirements

Among the prime requirements for a roof is that, in conjunction with other relevant building elements, it should protect the occupants and if necessary the structure of the building it covers from the external environment. In practice, the roof designer usually has to provide a rainproof layer, means of excluding wind and snow, sufficient thermal insulation and a supporting structure. The structure must be able to resist wind and snow loads which can be more severe on flat than on pitched roofs. In the case of wind the uplift forces increase with decreasing roof pitch *(Digest 119)*. With snow the downward loading will tend to increase with decreasing pitch. The risk of high snow loading will also increase with higher thermal insulation. In addition the designer has to recognize the implication for his design arising from the activities of the occupants. Most activities generate moisture to some degree which increases the vapour pressure of the interior air over that surrounding the building. There can also be an air pressure excess at ceiling level due to stack effect and to wind movement around the building. Thus, unless prevented, there is a movement of the usually wetter interior air through the fabric of the building, including the roof, with the danger of condensation occurring on the colder parts of the construction. The roof designer has also to acknowledge the risk of failure of the waterproof layer itself or of leakage from some detail associated with it. Finally, the designer has to recognize not only that roofs have often to be completed in other than ideal weather conditions, so that the subsequent weathertightness performance may be affected, but also that poor workmanship can occur during construction which can result in the entry of water. Whether from condensation or leakage such wetting, especially if entrapped, can affect the properties of many

materials involved in roof construction and indeed can result in actual deterioration, ie an irreversible change in properties. The implications of water ingress are, therefore, a major consideration in the design.

In meeting the requirements for a roof, the designer initially has a number of choices available to him. He can decide on a pitched roof with a discontinuous waterproof layer such as tiles, slates or profiled sheeting attached to a supporting structure or he can consider a horizontal or low-pitched roof with a continuous fully supported waterproof layer such as asphalt or multi or single-layer roofing membranes of bituminous felt, metal or plastics. If the decision is for a continuous, fully supported waterproof layer, then he has available to him a number of technical options for the design depending on the relative positions of the waterproof layer, the deck and the thermal insulation. This digest seeks to present in broad terms the advantages and disadvantages of the various arrangements for the three constituent parts.

The technical options

There are a number of possibilities for the arrangement of the three constituent parts of a roof with a fully supported continuous waterproof layer. However, there are only three arrangements for the relative positions of the deck, the insulation and the waterproof layer that are believed to be both practical and technically acceptable. These are known as the cold deck and the warm deck types of design, the latter having two variations usually referred to as sandwich and upside down (or inverted) construction. The choice of the arrangement for a particular building involves many considerations but it can be approached systematically through two options

FIRST OPTION

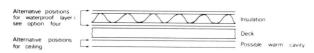

Warm deck design	OR	**Cold deck design**

(Thermal insulation over deck)   **(Thermal insulation below deck)**

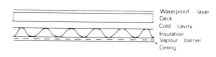

Alternative positions for waterproof layer: see option four

Alternative positions for ceiling

Insulation
Deck
Possible warm cavity

Waterproof layer
Deck
Cold cavity
Insulation
Vapour barrier
Ceiling

Advantages
(a) Roof cavities not necessary unless required for services or provided with separate ceiling
(b) No ventilation required of any cavity (1)
(c) If fire barriers required (2) in any cavity then they can be readily accommodated without making special provisions for ventilation
(d) Continuous vapour barrier readily provided on flat decks to avoid condensation occurring in the insulation. On troughed decks more care is necessary to achieve a continuous vapour barrier.
(e) Structural deck protected from extremes of temperature
(1) In hazard conditions, ie swimming pools, any cavity can be pressurized with fresh ventilation air to prevent the ingress of wet air from the building interior which can degrade some materials.
(2) See BRE Digest 218

Disadvantages
(a) The waterproof layer and insulation has to be securely held to the deck against wind suction forces
(b) Replacement of waterproof layer may involve sacrificing insulation
(c) Insulation has to support maintenance traffic and equipment
(d) Failures in waterproof layer may be difficult to locate and repair.

Advantages
(a) Waterproof layer directly supported by deck
(b) Waterproof layer readily repaired
(c) Waterproof layer readily replaced without sacrificing insulation
(d) Non-rigid insulation can be laid in position (1)
(e) Water vapour leaks from occupied spaces can be ventilated from cavity.
(1) With high ventilation rates fibrous and loose fill insulation may need some securing.

Disadvantages
(a) Efficient ventilation of cavity to outside required (1)
(b) Ventilation of cavity difficult to achieve if solid strutting or fire barriers required (2)
(c) Air barrier/vapour check required at ceiling level and not readily installed without immediate or subsequent damage or puncturing
(d) Irregular roof shapes and abutting roofs difficult to ventilate (3)
(e) Care required to prevent ingress of snow and vermin through ventilation apertures.
(1) A clear aperture of at least 0.3% of plan area should be allowed. With this aperture area sufficient ventilation is normally provided by the pressure difference around buildings caused by wind. In hazard conditions, ie swimming pools, any cavity can be pressurized with fresh unheated air to prevent the build-up of wet air from the building interior which can degrade some materials.
(2) See BRE Digest 218
(3) Ventilation apertures required at least at each end of each cavity if necessary using through roof ventilators.

Proceed to Second Option   **Proceed to Third Option**

SECOND OPTION

Warm deck design - sandwich construction	OR	**Warm deck design - 'upside down' construction**

(Thermal insulation between deck and waterproof layer)   **(Thermal insulation over waterproof layer)**

Waterproof layer
Insulation
Vapour barrier
Deck

Insulation
Waterproof layer
Deck

Advantages
(a) Waterproof layer readily accessible for inspection and repair
(b) Insulation can be secured by bonding or by mechanical fasteners. These latter do not penetrate waterproof layer.
(c) Structural deck protected from extremes of temperature

Disadvantages
(a) Continuous vapour barrier required on decks to avoid condensation in insulation (1)
(b) Water from leaks or rain falling during construction trapped in insulation
(c) Insulation has to support waterproof layer against maintenance traffic and equipment
(d) The large differential thermal movements between the waterproof layer and some plastic insulants has to be accommodated or a suitable thermally stable layer interposed (2)
(e) Because of the low thermal capacity of most insulants the temperature range of the waterproof layer in the service will be greater. Therefore faster ageing will occur at the higher temperatures and increased brittleness at lower.
(1) A continuous membrane is required. Joints should be bonded and flanking paths between the interior and the insulation avoided
(2) The daily thermal movement of polyurethane and isocyanurate based materials is less than that of polystyrene but can be greater than the seasonal moisture movement of fibre insulation board. However the risk to this latter material of any moisture ingress should be recognized.

Advantages
(a) Waterproof layer protected from sunlight from maintenance traffic and equipment and from extremes of temperature
(b) No separate vapour barrier required.

Disadvantages
(a) Waterproof layer not immediately accessible for inspection and repair
(b) Insulation has to be securely held against wind suction forces without puncturing the waterproof layer (1). When ballast is used the additional loading must be recognized in design and usually will result in higher costs
(c) Drainage can be more difficult and channels can become blocked
(d) Closed cell insulation required to maintain optimum thermal characteristics and to avoid frost attack
(e) Some loss of heat to rain water and to water from melting snow since this percolates under insulation and comes into contact with the warm waterproof layer; increased thickness of insulation therefore required.
(1) Usually the insulation can be secured by the weight of gravel or concrete slabs, which also help to protect it from mechanical damage and will improve sound insulation. However, the occurence of high wind suction forces and their effects should be considered.

Proceed to Third Option

Roof slope

Having decided on the relative positions of the deck the insulation and the waterproof layer the designer now has to consider whether the roof should be horizontal or low pitched. The advantages and disadvantages of the alternatives provide a third option in the development of the outline design.

THIRD OPTION

Constructed to falls or low pitched	Horizontal

Waterproof layer
Deck

Waterproof layer
Deck

Advantages
(a) Drainage positively controlled
(b) No retained water to feed small leaks[1]
(c) Scouring by rain provides cleaning action
(1) Slopes should be sufficient to accommodate irregularities in the surface due to movement of the constructional materials and to inaccuracies in the building process. Falls of not less than 1:40 are recommended if acceptable to waterproof layer.

Disadvantages
(a) Can be difficult to accommodate on a large and irregular plan
(b) Gravel or other granules can be washed to gutter unless bonded
(c) Parapet may be required aesthetically, concealed gutters are prone to leak.

Advantages
(a) No need to construct to falls
(b) Gravel or other granules which may be used, eg for fire protection, is retained provided that the design and exposure are such that the risk of wind scour is obviated.

Disadvantages
(a) In practice water will be retained on uneven surface increasing loading and providing a continuous feed for leaks
(b) Dirt is not readily washed away

Proceed to outline design

Having reached this stage, the major technical decisions have been made and the designer can proceed to the detailed design and to the selection of materials for deck insulation and waterproof layer.

Costs

This digest is concerned primarily with the technical options available to the designer of horizontal and low-pitched roofs and not with the relative costs of the various solutions although these will often be very relevant not only in reaching the outline design stage but also in selecting from the wide variety of materials available. While some information is available or can be obtained readily on the initial costs of construction it should be emphasized that these data on their own provide only limited guidance to the designer as subsequent maintenance and replacement costs must also be recognized in assessing comparable solutions. At present little authoritative and sufficiently well-documented information is available on maintenance costs and on time to replacement, though BRE is trying to obtain such data. In the future, when this information becomes available, more precise guidance will be possible on the costs inherent in the alternative technical options.

Conclusions

When a designer needs to use a horizontal or low-pitched roof with a fully supported continuous waterproof layer on a building he has a number of choices available to him both in the type of design (warm or cold deck) and in the constructional arrangement he can use. Both design types have advantages and disadvantages; which should be employed in a particular situation will depend on a number of factors, such as whether or not cavity barriers for fire stopping have to be incorporated, whether in a cold deck design sufficient ventilation can be assured and whether in a warm deck the problems of insulation movement can be overcome. Above all, the degree of confidence in the design detail (eg parapets, upstands and edge trim) and in the quality of workmanship, particularly in avoiding leaks and in installing a continuous and effective vapour barrier, must be considered realistically. In assessing alternative designs both initial and maintenance costs and the life to replacement must be considered. Finally the need for regular inspections of roofs in service must be recognized. Only with a realistic and careful consideration of these factors will an effective design be evolved and the number and cost of problems associated at present with the use of horizontal and low-pitched roofs be reduced.

Further reading
BS CP 144 Roof coverings: Part 3:1970 Built-up bitumen felt
                              Part 4:1970 Mastic asphalt
BRE News, No 49; Autumn 1979; Survey of the falls of flat roofs
Cornish, JP and Hendry, IWL; Avoidance of condensation in roofs. BRE Current Paper CP1/75
Hide, WT; Inspection and maintenance of flat and low-pitched timber roofs, BRE Information Sheet IS 26/76
McIntyre, IS and Birch, DP; Considerations in the design of timber flat roofs. BRE Information Sheet IS 6/78
McIntyre, IS; Moisture in a timber-based flat roof of cold deck construction. BRE Information Paper IP 35/79

Other BRE Digests
8   Built-up felt roofs
110 Condensation
119 The assessment of wind loads
144 Asphalt and built-up felt roofings: durability
180 Condensation in roofs
188 Roof drainage: 1
189 Roof drainage: 2
218 Cavity barriers and ventilation in low-pitched roofs

Built-up felt roofs

Built-up bitumen felt roofing is an efficient and durable form of roof covering provided it is properly laid. Many roofs of this kind have remained serviceable for 20 years or more with little need for maintenance or repairs. There are others, though, which for a variety of reasons, have become defective, sometimes quite early in their life, causing leakage and other troubles.

With due care, difficulties can be avoided; this digest explains the reasons for the defects and shows how they can be overcome. The recommended precautions are included in British Standard Code of Practice CP144 Roof coverings, Part 3:1970, Built-up bitumen felt.

Roofing felt may be used as a single thickness for temporary structures, such as sheds, but for permanent construction three layers of felt are usually bonded together on site with hot bitumen to form 'built-up' felt roofs.

Types of felt

Roofing felt consists of a mat of organic or inorganic fibres impregnated and usually coated with bitumen. BS 747 Roofing felts Part 2:1970 groups the felts into four classes, sub-divided as follows:

Class 1. Bitumen felts (fibre base)
  1A Saturated
  1B Fine sand surfaced
  1C Self-finished
  1D Coarse sand surfaced
  1E Mineral surfaced
  1F Reinforced

Class 2. Bitumen felts (asbestos base)
  2A Saturated
  2B Fine sand surfaced
  2C Self-finished
  2E Mineral surfaced

Class 3. Bitumen felts (glass fibre base)
  3B Fine sand surfaced
  3E Mineral surfaced
  3G Venting base layer

Class 4. Sheathing felts and hair felts
  4A(i)   Black sheathing (pitch)
          Black sheathing (bitumen)
  4A(ii) Brown sheathing
  4B(i)   Black hair
  4B(ii) Brown hair

Durability

As already stated, built-up bitumen felt roofing of reputable quality, when properly used, can be expected to last for many years. Some of the felts made under the 'austerity' conditions of the last war gave poor service, but these are not representative of the general run of production before or since.

When felt roofing fails to give satisfactory service, the failure is generally due to incorrect use of the material, or neglect of the necessary precautions, rather than to poor quality felt. If, for example, no suitable provision is made against the movements of the sub-structure of the roof that result from drying shrinkage or thermal changes, the felt may be stretched beyond its capacity, and crack or tear.

Again, defects may arise through the entrapment of large amounts of water under the felt, or through excessive condensation on the underside. Effects such as these usually occur long before the felt shows any serious deterioration as a direct result of exposure to the weather.

The long-term effect of exposure is to cause a gradual loss of bitumen from the surface; crazing and pitting may eventually occur, allowing access of moisture to the fibre, and deterioration may then be accelerated. The felt also loses flexibility on exposure and so becomes more liable to crack. Walking on old felt that has become blistered or wrinkled may cause cracking and subsequent leakage.

Organic fibre felts can be used on dry roof decks and insulation, but are not recommended as the first layers on concrete or screeds. Felts based on asbestos or glass have better dimensional stability than those based on organic fibres, and so are less liable to cockle where the felt is not fully bonded to the roof.

Choice of felt

Built-up felt roofing will generally consist of three layers of felt bonded with hot bitumen.

If self-finished felt is used, some roofing contractors prefer to use a felt coated with a light dusting of sand instead of the talc normally used to prevent sticking in the roll, because they consider that the sand coating gives a better bond to the roof deck and so helps to avoid blistering. In that event, allowance of 0·35 kg/m² for fine sand and 1·1 kg/m² for coarse sand should be made for the additional weight of the sand in specifying the weight of the roll. Saturated felts, particularly those based on organic fibres, are not recommended for the lower layers of a built-up roof in damp climates, because they tend to hold moisture and may cause blistering.

The type of felt for the top layer depends to some extent on the slope of the roof. On roofs with a slope of not less than 10 degrees, mineral-surfaced felt type 1E can be used, whilst types 2E and 3E are suitable for slopes not less than 5 degrees. On slopes less than 5 degrees the protective mineral chippings should be applied *in situ*, secured with an adhesive of 'cut-back' bitumen (a solution of bitumen in a volatile solvent), blinded with 5 or 10 mm mineral chippings. The chippings should preferably be white or light in colour, so as to keep the felt and the underlying structure cool in sunny weather and so minimise thermal movements.

Fire protection

Although bitumen felt is a combustible material, the degree of fire protection afforded by a built-up roof depends upon the roof structure as a whole. Requirements relating to the ability of a roof covering to afford protection against the spread of fire into the building or to adjoining buildings are laid down in both the English and the Scottish Building Regulations, and examples are quoted of various felt-covered roofings that would be deemed to satisfy these regulations.

The requirements are two-fold:

   (1) The roof shall resist penetration of fire.

   (2) The roof shall not encourage the spread of flame.

Each requirement is classified from A to D, representing minimum to maximum hazard; thus an 'AA' roof resists penetration of fire for one hour and the flames will not spread. Details of fire resistance for pitched and flat roofs will be found in Table A3 of CP144 and in the Building Regulations.

Felt roofs must not be laid without falls

Roof construction

The various kinds of roof decks on which built-up roofing can be laid are listed in **Table 1** with the appropriate methods of treatment. For example, some that are thermally insulating in themselves require a topping of cement and sand, and the felt is laid on this; with others, the thermal insulation, where necessary, is provided on to which the felt can be laid direct.

In the construction of roof decks, the following three points call for special consideration since they have an important bearing on the performance of the felt covering and the efficiency of the roof as a whole.

Moisture and thermal movement

It was mentioned earlier that tearing of the felt can be caused by movement of the underlying structure, especially drying shrinkage and thermal movements. Since these cannot be eliminated entirely, special precautions are necessary in laying the felt to minimise their effect and these are indicated under **Preparation for fixing**; in addition, everything practicable should be done to ensure that the movements themselves are kept to a minimum. To control the drying shrinkage in screeds or topping the mix should not be richer than 1 : 4 and it is important that the sand should be clean, well graded and fairly coarse. The water content of the mixes should be no more than is necessary for placing, compacting and finishing. The laying of screeds over weak insulating materials supported on roof decks is not recommended. Drying shrinkage of the screed is unrestrained and the screed is liable to crack and curl during drying, and the screed and the insulating material can become waterlogged during the hardening period for the screed.

Thermal movements of a concrete decking or topping are best controlled by a white or light-coloured treatment applied to the felt after it is laid, e.g. a layer of light-coloured grit or stone chippings, or decking slabs; movement joints should also be provided in large areas of concrete decking.

Constructional and rain-water

The average weekly rainfall in the driest part of the United Kingdom is approximately 12 mm; an evaporation rate of 12 mm per week is achieved only in fine summer weather. Porous decking or screed exposed to the weather is more likely therefore to increase its moisture content than it is to dry out.

Once felt has been applied the entrapped water, whatever its origin, can escape only very slowly, and its effects may continue for many months or even years. Apart from any visible effect, moisture retained in the structure reduces the thermal insulation and so encourages condensation, thus defeating the purpose of the insulation. It may, moreover, create a serious nuisance by causing stains, or even

appearing as drips, on the ceiling below; also, in sunny weather, the pressure of water vapour may cause the felt to blister. Every practicable step should therefore be taken to reduce the water content. Drainage tubes, inserted in the structural roof and left open until the ceiling is plastered, are of great benefit in reducing the amount of water retained.

A practice known to have given satisfactory results is as follows. The structural deck is drained so that no ponds can form on it. This may be done by inserting drainage tubes at the time of construction; alternatively, the roof may be flooded and the deck punctured at the centre of all ponds. An insulating screed consisting of cement and no-fines lightweight aggregate (e.g. sintered pulverised-fuel ash) is then laid, followed by a thin 1 : 4 cement/sand topping, just sufficient to bring the screed to a fair face. The screed can then be allowed to mature until conditions are suitable for the roofing felt covering to be laid.

Although most of the rain penetrating the screed will drain away, even a drained screed will retain some moisture, and provision must be made for its escape. Small pressure release vents can be provided every 20 m^2, or when a lot of moisture is trapped brick box ventilators as shown in **Fig. 5** can be used. The use of a spot-bonded ventilating felt as the first layer of built-up roofing will also encourage evaporation.

A system of sucking air through porous screeds using a vacuum pump has been developed in the last few years. Some success has been reported, but it cannot be expected to dry out in a few weeks a screed that may contain 1000 kg of water.

Lightweight concrete slabs, insulating boards, compressed straw panels, wood-wool slabs and other absorptive materials intended to be incorporated in the roof structure should be stored under cover and should be fixed in sections as the roof covering is proceeded with, so that each section may be covered without delay. Wherever possible, tarpaulins or polythene sheets should be used to protect uncovered sections in wet weather.

Condensation

Moisture condensing within the thickness of a roof structure under built-up roofing can, if the condensation is heavy and long-continued, produce the same effects as entrapped construction or rainwater. This is not confined to high humidity buildings such as mills or laundries, it is common in dwellings. Two methods of preventing trouble are possible; to fit a true vapour barrier over the structural roof covered by thermal insulating material and waterproof covering. The vapour barrier should consist of one layer of bitumen felt fixed with hot bitumen using the 'pour and roll' technique, with the insulating material stuck to the vapour barrier with more hot bitumen. The whole job, from vapour barrier to covering, should be completed at one time, with precautions taken to protect raw edges overnight. The other technique is to use a vapour check at ceiling level combined with ventilation of the roof space. The ventilation of the roof is necessary because it is impossible to make a true vapour barrier at ceiling level, but the ceiling should be as free as possible from gaps and holes, and should have a low vapour permeability. A ceiling could, for example, be constructed of foil-backed plasterboard, or have a polythene membrane immediately above it. The minimum ventilation is given in BS 5250. Air must have a free passage from one side to the other, and if the roof is wider than 12 m, the size of the openings should be doubled. With some types of roof slab, especially those of cellular concrete, these precautions can be relaxed. The slabs give satisfactory service in most situations without a vapour barrier beneath them.

Preparation for fixing

Splitting of the covering can be avoided by careful design. Research into the behaviour of bitumen felt in tension has indicated that it will tear at about 5 per cent extension, so if in the design a limit of 2 per cent is adopted, the risk of tearing would be avoided. Thus, if a crack or joint is likely to open 2 mm, the width of felt left unbonded over the crack or joint should be 100 mm.

Recommended preparatory measures for roofs of different kinds are outlined in **Table 1** and particular attention is directed to those relating to lightweight concrete screeds and woodwool slabs.

Observations on roofing felt laid on these materials demonstrate that the practice of bonding the felt to a blinding coat of slurry often leads to cracking of the felt in places where shrinkage cracks develop in

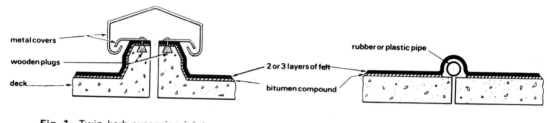

Fig. 1. Twin-kerb expansion joint for major movement

Fig. 2. Expansion joint for moderate movement

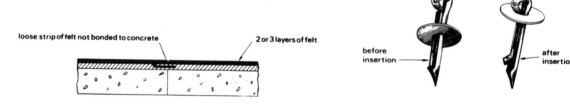

Fig. 3. Flat expansion joint for minor movement

Fig. 4. Expanding nail

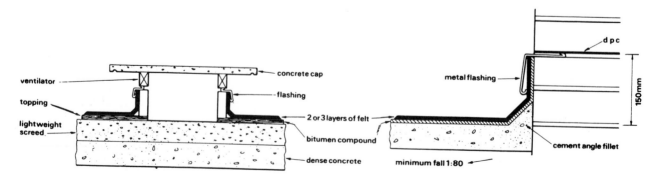

Fig. 5. Brick box ventilator

Fig. 6. Treatment of upstand

the roof structure. Felt laid directly on aerated concrete is sometimes prone to blister.

For these reasons it is recommended that a 12 mm topping of one part of cement to four parts of clean coarse sand should be used, and that this should be laid in alternate bays, each of not more than 10m². For aerated concrete screeds, however, some contractors prefer to prime the surface with a bitumen primer instead of using the topping, and this is permissible.

Since shrinkage cracks often develop along the line separating two areas of roofing of different widths, or at junctions between lengths of roof, or in places where the run of the roof is interrupted by roof-lights, it is further recommended that cuts should be made in the topping and preferably through the full depth of the screed along the lines of such junctions and along lines joining the adjacent corners of roof lights, and that any large areas of topping should be similarly subdivided at junctions between the bays.

Apart from providing a fair surface for adhesion of the felt and facility for correcting any inadequacy in fall, the purpose of the topping is two-fold. It aims to restrain the drying shrinkage of the woodwool slab or lightweight concrete screed and also to

encourage any cracking of the topping to occur along the lines of the cuts rather than in random directions across the slab. Subsequently, loose strips of felt should be laid along the lines of the cuts, **Fig. 3,** to prevent adhesion of the overlying felt for a distance of about 100 mm on either side. The aim here is to allow the felt to stretch rather than tear in response to any small movements that may occur in the topping. The method illustrated in **Fig. 2** is better where considerable movement is likely. Expansion joints in the roof structure should preferably be of the twin-kerb type, **Fig. 1.**

Fixing

Methods of fixing are also set out in **Table 1.** The surface should be clean, free from dust or debris, and at least surface-dry at the time of laying. Except for wooden boarded roofs, where the first layer is nailed and should not be bonded to the boards, roofing felt is customarily bonded to the roof with hot bitumen spread at the rate of about 1·5 kg/m². On highly absorptive surfaces, this is preceded by an application of a bitumen primer to reduce frothing of the bitumen and assist adhesion. The primer must be allowed to dry before proceeding.

Table 1   Recommended constructions

Roof decks	Treatment before laying felt	Method of fixing first layer
Aerated concrete screeds, or lightweight aggregate concrete screeds, on dense concrete slabs, precast concrete beams, hollow pots, etc.	12 mm topping of 1 : 4 cement : clean coarse sand, laid in alternate bays not exceeding 10 m²*. Drain tubes through the deck and ventilators may also be required.	Partial bonding. Where cuts are made in the topping (see text), strips of felt to be laid along the cuts.
Asbestos-cement	Insulation board, laid to break joint, bonded with hot bitumen to a vapour barrier	Bonding overall
Dense concrete, shell roofs, etc.	Nailing battens should be provided at the top of steep slopes. Insulation board may, if required, be bonded to the roof over a vapour barrier	Bonding overall, unless cracking is expected
Metal deck	Fibre insulation board, laid to break joint, bonded with hot bitumen to a vapour barrier	Bonding overall
Wood boards	If additional insulation is needed, insulation board, laid to break joint, may be fixed	Nailing
Woodwool slabs	12 mm topping of 1 : 4 cement : clean coarse sand, laid in alternate bays not exceeding 10 m²	Partial bonding. Where cuts are made in the topping strips of felt to be laid along the cuts.

*With aerated concrete screeds, some manufacturers recommend priming the surface in preference to a cement : sand topping; either is permissible.

It is seldom necessary to bond the felt overall, but there should be sufficient bonding to prevent lifting and tearing of the felt in high winds. Where there is a substantial loading of tiles or stone chippings, it may be enough to bond the edges of the strips of felt. For fixing to the cement/sand topping recommended for use over lightweight concrete screeds or woodwool slabs, partial bonding at the edges and in strips or spots elsewhere is preferable to overall bonding, since this gives the felt more scope for stretching in response to any differential movement in the roof slabs.

The suggestion for partial bonding applies only to the first layer of felt. Partial bonding is essentially a precautionary measure imposed by the impossibility of predicting precisely where cracking may occur. It is not necessary or desirable to use partial bonding where the felt is laid on fibre insulating board, cork or compressed straw slabs.

Table 2 Defects in built-up felt roofs

Defect	Cause	Remedial treatment
Tearing or cracking	1. Differential movement at cracks or joints in the substructure	1. Adopt details shown in Figs. 1, 2 or 3. If defects extensive, re-lay over fibre insulating board
	2. Perforation of unsupported felt	2. Provide a supporting fillet and patch with felt
	3. Perforation of blisters by traffic	3. Cut, bond down and patch over blister
	4. Sharp bends in felt	4. Round off and patch, or use a metal flashing
Pimpling on top layer of felt, eventually breaking open and exposing fibres	Expansion of more volatile fractions of bitumen, or of air or water, in sunny weather. May occur with self-finished felt, particularly where pools of water can stand on it, or with mineral-surfaced felt laid at too low a pitch	In serious cases on felt roofs, dress with cut-back bitumen and grit
Blisters between layers of felt	Expansion, in sunny weather, of entrapped air or water	Cut the blister, re-bond and patch. If the trouble is persistent, a heat-reflecting treatment, or the weight of a heavy dressing, may help
Blisters between felt and deck	Expansion in sunny weather, of entrapped air or water. Particularly liable to occur on surfaces such as lightweight concrete screeds or asbestos cement, if not dealt with as in Table 1	
Cockling and rippling	Moisture movement of either felt or roof, especially where felt is not bonded	Little can be done, except to relay. Site dressing, using a fair weight of grit, may make the defects less conspicuous
Lifting of laps	1. Bad bonding initially 2. Pulling as a result of formation of blisters	1. Re-bond 2. Cut, bond down and patch
Local deterioration associated with ponding	Inadequate fall, or obstruction of outfall	Clear outfalls. Site dressing with cut-back bitumen and coarse grit may limit further damage
Arching of tiles, screeds, etc.	Inadequate allowance for thermal or moisture movement	Provide 25 mm gaps around bays of about 9 m² and fill with a bitumen compound. If necessary, rake out old compound and re-point
General deterioration and embrittlement	Premature deterioration indicates inadequate falls, wrong choice of felt, neglect of any recommended surface dressing, or wrong laying	Re-lay if deterioration is far advanced; if not, site dress with cut-back bitumen and grit
Loss of grit	1. Site dressing in adverse weather conditions 2. Use of hot bitumen or emulsion instead of cut-back bitumen 3. Inadequate fall	Site dress, using cut-back bitumen and fairly coarse grit

Partial bonding may also be achieved by using a proprietary underlay perforated with holes about 12 mm in diameter and gritted on the undersurface. Hot bitumen is spread over this so that the bonding of the felt to the roof is restricted to the areas of the holes in the underlay. The gritted under-surface provides a continuous air space through which vapour can escape at the verges, thus preventing a build-up of pressure beneath the felt.

A form of expanding nail, **Fig. 4,** has been introduced for nailing felt to lightweight concrete of medium strength without a topping, but there has not yet been much experience of its use. Because of the alkaline character of concrete, nails in an aluminium alloy would be unsuitable for this purpose.

Upstands at parapet walls, etc., need careful detailing to exclude rain. The upstand, which should be at least 150 mm high, should preferably be covered with a metal flashing as shown in **Fig. 6.** Where there is a damp-proof course in the wall, the flashing should be made continuous with it. Bends in the felt in these or similar circumstances should be supported, preferably with a wood or mortar fillet.

Where the edges of a roof are finished with a kerbing under the felt, the development of shrinkage cracks in the joints of the kerb may lead to tearing of the felt. Laying a loose strip of felt over each joint, **Fig. 3,** to break the bond with the overlying felt will reduce this risk. A metal trim should be firmly anchored at close centres to a substantial member in the roof deck.

Roof paving

Where a built-up roof has to carry much traffic, a more substantial surface is needed. This may be of tiles bedded in bitumen, or a topping of bitumen macadam not less than 12 mm thick or a mortar screed not less than 25 mm thick. Since there must be enough freedom of movement in tiling or screed to prevent lifting or arching under the combined effects of thermal and moisture movement of the roof structure, tiling or screed should be laid in areas of not more than 10m² and these areas should be separated by 25 mm joints. Tiles should be butt-jointed. Each area of mortar screed should be subdivided into units not larger than 0·6 m by 0·6 m by

cutting through the full thickness of the screed before it has set and hardened. Subsequently these cuts and the joints between the separate areas should be filled with a bitumen jointing compound.

Treatment of defects

The appearance of dampness, or even of water drips below a built-up roof does not necessarily mean that the roof covering is leaking, for these defects can also be produced, as already explained, by construction water, by rainwater or by heavy condensation within the roof structure. If, therefore, on careful inspection, the felt covering appears to be intact, these possibilities should be considered, remembering that water can remain entrapped for many months after the covering has been laid.

There is no quick way of drying out a roof that, from any cause, has become waterlogged. If water is dripping from points in the ceiling or, as often happens, from electric conduits, holes may be bored near the places affected to assist drainage. Drying can also be assisted by building brick box ventilators, **Fig. 5,** on the roof at appropriate places, or by the other methods already described.

If the conditions within the building are warm and humid, condensation may be suspected; if it is in fact the cause of the dampness, the only remedy, in severe cases, may be to provide more thermal insulation over an effective vapour barrier. In milder cases it may be sufficient, if practicable, to improve the ventilation of the building.

Sources of dampness caused by cracking or deterioration of the felt or failure to cover upstands with flashings can usually be traced by inspection. Where the felt has become torn or cracked but is otherwise in good condition, patching on the lines indicated in **Figs. 2** or **3** will be well worth trying; it can best be undertaken by a specialist contractor. Other defects can be dealt with by the methods given in **Table 2.** If there is reason to think that thermal movement of the roof has been a contributory factor in damaging the felt, it may help to prevent a recurrence if, after repair, the felt is covered with a layer of light-coloured grit to reflect solar heat.

Further reading

BS 747 Roofing felts Part 2: 1970
BS 5250 The control of condensation in dwellings
BS CP 144 Roof covering Part 3: 1970 Built-up bitumen felt
Built-up roofing; Felt Roofing Contractors Advisory Board: 1966

Asphalt and built-up felt roofings: durability

A study of flat roofs covered with mastic asphalt and built-up bitumen felt roofing has disclosed the most common causes of failure and made possible an assessment of these roofings when properly designed and laid. It is suggested that they should be inspected at least annually so that action can be taken to deal with defects early enough to prevent their leading to failure.

Although many complaints are made about leakage and maintenance costs of flat roofs, these still remain popular with designers. A survey of flat roofs on Crown buildings covered with mastic asphalt and built-up bitumen felt was therefore mounted by the Building Research Station at Garston in order to provide more detailed information about the frequency and causes of failure and success. Figures 1 and 2 show the number of examples studied and the age and performance of each up to the date of the survey. The failures recorded could all be attributed to failure to comply with published recommendations for design and installation (*see* 'Further reading'). A study of similar roofings on local authority dwellings in Scotland is also nearing completion. Failure to comply with published recommendations, particularly in regard to edge details, at verges, curbs and parapets was also noted.

General characteristics

A flat roof is normally a composite structure. Its functional requirements are met partly by the load-bearing deck and insulation, partly by the covering and, where appropriate, by a vapour barrier under the insulation. Only the covering is considered here.

Mastic asphalt Asphalt to BS 1162 tends to develop a grey appearance when weathered whereas the BS 988 material remains dark in colour, though finishing by sand rubbing lightens its appearance; the two are visually indistinguishable when given a solar reflective treatment. In direct sunshine, both types harden gradually and shrink slightly; this causes shallow surface crazing which does not usually develop into cracks. Cracking from other causes, such as the drying shrinkage of a coating of unsuitable paint or the differential movements of paving tiles not laid on a separating layer, may progress through the full thickness of the asphalt.

Asphalt being, in effect, a stiff liquid can tolerate slow movement involving the full thickness of the material, but otherwise it behaves as a brittle solid and is liable to crack under any suddenly applied strain, particularly under impact and in cold weather. Because of its high coefficient of thermal expansion, and because partial bonding to a roof deck of 'wet' construction tends to cause blistering due to concentrated vapour pressure, it is now usual to separate the asphalt from any substrate, except bitumen-bonded lightweight aggregate screeds, by an isolating membrane of sheathing felt. The purpose of this is to avoid blistering or cracking and to bridge discontinuities, but where significant movement may occur, for example at a butt joint in the deck, it is desirable to break the continuity of the asphalt by means of a movement joint. The dead weight of the roofing, including sheathing felt, is about 40 kg/m^2, and this, with proper edge detailing, is usually sufficient to prevent uplift by wind suction in the UK.

Built-up bitumen felt roofing The early felts were based wholly on organic fibres which were very strong when new but dimensionally unstable, and could rot, when moisture eventually penetrated the bitumen coating. The asbestos-based felts are more stable but they may still include up to 20 per cent of organic fibre. Bitumen felt based on glass fibre is stable and rot-proof but the glass fibre is in the form of a bonded tissue, not a woven fabric, and does not provide very high strength, so that the felt needs careful handling. The merits of each type can be exploited by correct design, often using two or more types in the same system. None of these three standard types can be stretched, before splitting, more than about 5 per cent (say 2 per cent for design purposes) and if fully bonded to a substrate which subsequently cracks they will split. On concrete and screeded surfaces, it is now usual to fix the first layer by only partial bonding to a pattern that allows the escape of water vapour, during drying, and reduces the risk of splitting. The felt can be fully bonded to dry insulation materials; on a wooden deck, the first layer is fixed by nailing.

If exposed to the weather, a bitumen surface is gradually attacked by solar radiation, both ultra-violet and heat-producing, and by atmospheric oxidation; the effects are increasing embrittlement and crazing, or superficial pimpling, leading to exposure of the fibres and progressive attack of the bitumen underlying them. Some form of surface protection is therefore necessary. Unless a special finish for solar reflection or foot traffic is required, the roofing should be given a surface dressing of bitumen compound and mineral chippings; in the Scottish study it was found that stone chippings smaller than 25–32 mm grade are liable to be scoured by the winds to expose the bitumen surface below. By its added weight this dressing reduces the risk of lift by the wind; it also contributes to the fire grading of the roof. To reflect solar heat, white chippings may be used. The weight of built-up felt roofing varies with the nature of the surface dressing and the risk of uplift by wind suction may limit the proportion in area that can be safely left unbonded.

For more detailed recommendations for built-up felt roofs, see Digest No 8 (1970 edition).

Performance

Not all of the sites were visited and though a great deal of information was obtained by technical questionnaires some of the detail requested, particularly as to falls, was not provided. Official records of minor repairs (under £100) are almost non-existent and some reliance had to be placed on the memories or personal notes of the maintenance personnel. Published guidance has undergone some changes, for example in the revision of Codes of Practice, the effects of which could not in all cases be isolated.

About one-third of the roofs studied from Garston had 'failed', this being defined as a roof, or its weathering detailing, that has permitted water to penetrate at some time. The roofs shown in Figs 1 and 2 to be 'defective' exhibit visible imperfections such as blisters, cockling and ponding which could lead to failure though this has not yet occurred.

The incidence of failure seems to vary between the two types of roofing mainly in that the probability of failure remains practically constant throughout the life of an asphalt roof but increases steadily during the life of a built-up felt roof.

Asphalt roofing, properly designed and laid, should prove capable of lasting 50–60 years; the natural ageing of bitumen felt is likely to limit its life to about 20 years.

Mastic asphalt Of 123 coverings, 34 were classified as having failed: 20 by splitting, cracking or tearing under strain, as by differential movement of a deck from which the covering was not properly isolated; 14 due to disruption of associated weathering, skirtings or flashings, at parapet walls, roof lights or around rainwater outlets. After repair, none of these failed coverings had needed to be replaced.

Built-up bitumen felt Of 200 coverings, 77 had failed. Most of these were due to the same causes that damaged the asphalt roofs, inability to accommodate movements in the roof decks (37 roofs) or disruption of weathering (26 roofs). A few failures attributable to entrapped moisture or condensation had also resulted from avoidable inadequacies in design or workmanship. A single instance of wind damage could be ascribed either to inadequate fixing or to a gale of abnormal severity. Five of the roof coverings had been replaced after 20–30 years of service (see Fig 2) because of deterioration by natural ageing.

Findings common to both types

Use and location of building No correlation was found between the performance of the roof covering and the function or structural type or form of the building, or with the exposure and topography of the site.

Falls There was no evidence that the provision of falls had any effect on the life of the coverings. But a truly flat surface is unlikely to be achieved in practice, and ponding is likely to occur unless a fall sufficient to drain depressions is provided. Ponding is less harmful to the covering than was at one time supposed but if a leakage occurs in a ponded area water will enter the building in greater quantity than through an effectively drained surface.

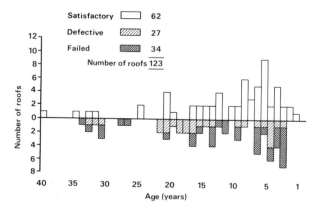

Fig 1 Mastic asphalt coverings

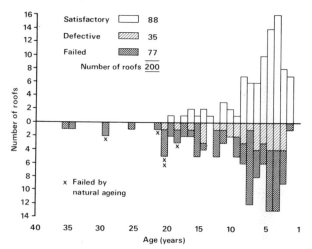

Fig 2 Built-up bitumen felt coverings

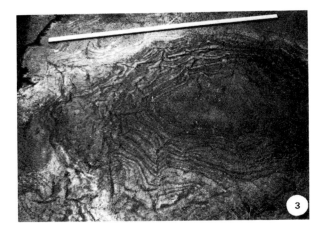

Visual appraisal of defects

Roofings should be inspected at least annually by a maintenance surveyor to ensure that rainwater outlets are kept clear and to decide on any action necessary to prevent defects from becoming failures. The photographs (3–9) may assist in identifying defects.

Mastic asphalt

Ponding: Slight localised deflections below the general plane of the drainage falls can result in ponding. In asphalt roofing, this can cause crazing which may be only shallow and in the condition illustrated (3) does not warrant the cost of remedial measures on technical grounds alone though it might do so on grounds of appearance.

Cracking: Differential movement between precast concrete roofing units can cause cracking (4). This might have been avoided had the perimeter of the asphalt not been bonded directly to the concrete beyond the edges of the sheathing felt, which stops short as can be seen from the change in level of the surface. Rain has not yet penetrated but it could do so by capillary action. Repair is desirable, but not urgent.

Blistering: (5) shows a combination of blistering and sagging in an asphalt skirting. The most likely sequence of events was that, during hot weather, vapour pressure from water leaking into the parapet wall produced the large blister and in so doing either fractured the tucked-in portion above the blister or pulled it out of its chase. The detached portion of the asphalt when warmed by the sun would tend increasingly to sag under its own weight and so produce the fold seen below the blister. If not arrested the sagging will progress and rainwater will enter the building. The damaged area should be cut away and made good without delay.

Built-up bitumen felt covering

Splitting: Tearing (6) occurred over an edge or verge curb, the capping of which is of plywood; the plywood has delaminated as a result of entrapped moisture and as it distorted it imposed sufficient tensile forces to split the felt. Adherence to recommended details would avoid this defect. Metal edge trims were found also to split the felt at or about the butt joints in the trims.

Cracking: A portion of replacement felt at the northeast corner of a roof (7) shows cracking of the type sometimes called 'crocodiling'. The horizontal area of felt is protected by mineral aggregate dressing but on the fillet at the base of the upstand to the parapet wall the felt suffers maximum exposure to the sun. The combination of solar heating, ultra-violet radiation and atmospheric oxidation has crazed the coating of bitumen, applied generally to the area to stick down the mineral aggregate and then cracked the top layer of self-finished felt. Further progress of the

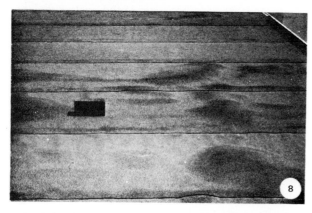

Further reading

Mastic asphalt:

> BS 988 Mastic asphalt for roofing (limestone aggregate)
> BS 1162 Mastic asphalt for roofing (natural rock asphalt)
> BS CP 144 Roof coverings Part 4:1970 Mastic asphalt (metric units)
> Application of mastic asphalt; Mastic Asphalt Advisory Council:1967

Built-up bitumen felt:

> BS 747 Roofing felts Part 2:1970
> BS CP 144 Roof covering Part 3:1970 Built-up bitumen felt
> Built-up roofing; Felt Roofing Contractors Advisory Board: 1966

cracking into the underlying layers of felt can be arrested by a reflective treatment, and as the roofing is laid on insulation of vegetable origin this should be done immediately.

Blistering: The brick indicates the size of the blisters (**8**)—up to about 1 m long and 75 mm high. The top layer of the three-layer roofing is mineral-finished. Cutting open a blister revealed that the bottom layer of felt is adhering firmly to the base and the middle layer is firmly bonded to the top; the blisters have developed between the middle and bottom layers. This could result from insufficient pressure when rolling the middle layer into the hot bitumen bonding compound, or from moisture entrapped between the two layers (either rain or dew). As none of the blisters shows signs of bursting, and the bottom layer of felt will still provide cover if they do, repair can be delayed. Meantime, the alternating expansion and contraction of the blisters resulting from thermal variations, particularly in sunny weather, can be reduced by the application of a lime/tallow wash, taking care not to tread on the blisters during application.

Ruckling, rippling, cockling: Undulations (**9**) to which these descriptions have variously been applied can result from inadequate pressure on the roll or insufficient or badly distributed bitumen compound. It is particularly important to avoid these faults in the intentional partial bonding of the first layer. But this did not apply to the present case in which the bottom layer of felt was fully bonded to a fibreboard underlay. Asbestos-based felt type 2A was specified for the bottom and middle layers, but type 1C, which can contain a considerable proportion of vegetable fibre, for the top layer. The vegetable fibre in the top layer of felt could, therefore, have been exposed to the ingress of moisture and the resulting dimensional changes would then aggravate the effects of vapour pressure corresponding to variations in ambient temperature. However, the regular, parallel pattern of the undulations suggested that most, if not all, of the blame stemmed from not allowing the top layer of felt to flatten before fixing.

Except in one case where an undulation is associated with partial lifting of a lapped bond in the felt, which needs to be re-sealed, no immediate repairs are considered necessary so long as the undulations are not likely to be trodden on by maintenance staff servicing plant on the roof.

Selection of windows by performance

Poor or inadequate specification of components is a common cause of unsatisfactory building performance. Reliance can be placed on the claims of sales literature or on British Standards or other procurement documents without appreciating their limitations. The initial cost can be made the controlling factor so that the performance achieved and the subsequent maintenance costs become only minor considerations in the selection process.

This digest provides the basis for a more informed approach to the selection of windows. It reviews the available information and provides a basis from which a performance profile can be developed. The relevant primary attributes are identified and for each in turn the requirements are stated and the range of performance levels that have been proposed are listed against the relevant test methodology.

The specifier of windows for new buildings or for replacement purposes has a wide choice. Windows are available in softwood or hardwood, some intended for painting or clear finishing on site, others prefinished with a paint or a similar coating or with a plastics skin. Steel windows can be supplied galvanised for painting on site or coated with a finish which requires little maintenance for a number of years. Stainless steel windows, which do not require a protective coating, and bronze windows are also available for special applications. Aluminium windows, with a variety of finishes, can be fixed direct or supplied for use in a wood frame. Aluminium and plastics combinations can provide a 'thermal break', that is, an interruption in the thermally conductive path between the heated inside environment and the outside. Finally, an increasing range of unplasticised PVC windows is becoming available. This digest provides guidance on the selection by performance of windows from this wide choice.

In selecting a window some specifiers may require a particular material for its aesthetic appeal: for example, the grain and colour variation of clear finished wood. The size and configuration (the arrangement of the opening and fixed lights) and perhaps the operational type may also be important considerations. However, a major factor in selection should always be the achievement of the required performance at the minimum total cost, ie the initial installed cost and the maintenance costs over the life of the building.

Window size

Most manufacturers list a standard range of metric sizes; some are equivalents of the established imperial dimensions but others are based on a metric module, usually in 100 mm increments from 300 mm to 2400 mm. Aluminium and plastics windows are usually made to order and non-standard sizes can be produced readily, for example, for replacement purposes in non-standard openings. Wood and steel windows are usually made in a standard range although non-standard sizes can often be produced by specialist manufacturers. The price of specially made wood windows is considerably higher than those from standard ranges and the installed cost may approach that for the equivalent aluminium and plastics products.

Window configuration and operational type

Many types are available. Opening lights can slide vertically or horizontally or be hinged at the side, the top or the bottom and special hinges are available to allow the window to project out either from the top or the side. These sliding axis windows can usually be reversed for cleaning from inside. Opening lights can be centre pivoted in a horizontal plane, or centre or off-centre pivoted in a vertical plane, when they are usually also reversible for easy cleaning. Some windows incorporate small hand controlled ventilators in the frame.

Most windows can be double glazed with sealed units or can have separate secondary windows to increase thermal insulation and a few manufacturers produce windows, usually of the horizontal sliding type, which incorporate double, independently moveable glass panes separated by a substantial air gap.

Window performance

There are British Standards which define sizes, configurations, operational types and some construction details for wood, steel and aluminium windows, but there are none based to any extent on the concept of specifying by performance. However, Draft for Development 4 does suggest performance levels for resistance to wind loading, air infiltration and water penetration for each of three classes of exposure which are linked to the expected wind pressure derived from the BS Code of Practice on wind loading. Only one level of air infiltration is given for opening lights irrespective of the exposure and only one level of water penetration is listed for each exposure. Thus, the suggested levels of DD 4 for any one location are minimum levels which do not allow the specifier to select for higher performance, except perhaps by increasing the exposure rating. Other procurement and similar documents have been produced by PSA[1] and the Agrément Board[2].

DD4 superseded by BS 6375 Part 1

Wind resistance

As indicated in DD4, the required wind resistance should be based on the design wind pressure that the window is expected to resist. For the UK, this can be calculated from the wind loading code, CP3: Chapter V.

A method of test for determining if the window can withstand this pressure is described in BS 5368 Part 3: this is a European Standard which has been adopted in the UK. The window is mounted with its weather side facing inwards in one side of a pressure box and the air pressure in the box is increased to simulate the wind pressure. The basis for wind loading calculations in the UK is the three-second gust; as this is more severe than the basis used in other European countries, it is considered that the procedure of BS 5368 can be simplified for use in the UK. The deformation test can be omitted as deformation is included in the definition of the criteria used in the UK for assessing the performance. The positive and negative pulses which are intended to assess the window 'durability' and which, it is suggested, should be repeated five times, should be at the required design wind pressure or at the level for the designated window grade; the safety test in BS 5368 is then not required.

For the tests the minimum glass thickness and type should be selected in accordance with CP 152 to withstand the design wind pressure. During the wind resistance test:

(a) The deflection of any member, such as couplings, glazing bars or meeting rails should not exceed $^1/_{125}$ of the span (or $^1/_{175}$ over the length and width of an insulating glass unit).

(b) The air permeability and the watertightness should not increase significantly. In effect those tests described later are carried out before and after the wind resistance test when:

    i(i)   the air permeability and watertightness performance level should not fall below that specified;

    (ii)   the air permeability should not increase by more than 1 $m^3/h/m$, ie per metre length of joint in the opening light for initial values up to 5 $m^3/h/m$ or 2 $m^3/h/m$ for initial values over 5 $m^3/h/m$.

As an aid for the designer and to simplify the marketing of standard ranges of window components it is convenient to recognise performance bands of wind resistance; proposals that have been advocated are in Table 1.

Table 1 Performance bands for wind resistance that have been suggested for use in the UK. *Comparisons should not be attempted between similarly designated bands from each source.*

Performance band designation	Source		
	DD 4:1971 N/m^2	AB-MOAT 1 1974 Safety test Pa	PSA/DHSS MOB 3rd Prog 1979 Pa
1	Sheltered – up to 1500	V_1 – up to 1000	not less than 1200
2	Moderate 1500 – 1900	V_2 1000 – 2000	not less than 1500*
3	Severe (a) 1900 – 2300	V_3 2000 – 3000	not less than 2000
4	Severe (b) 2300 – 2800	–	not less than 2400
5	–	–	not less than 2800

* For PSA buildings a minimum level of 1500 Pa is required.

Air permeability and watertightness

To reduce energy waste and prevent draughts, the penetration of outside air to the interior of a building should be minimised either by ensuring that opening joints are close fitting or by the use of separate weather-stripping seals. Some windows are now supplied with seals already fitted but there are a variety of seals available for windows which have been installed without them[3]. Because of their sliding action, it may be difficult to ensure a good seal with sliding windows without impairing their operation.

It must be emphasised that some ventilation is essential for comfort. While this can be provided by air-conditioning systems, in most dwellings the ventilation requirement is met fortuitously, and closed windows can provide a convenient low volume feed of air to the interior. While it is usually accepted that the requirement for air permeability must be for as low a value as can be achieved economically, it could be argued that it is only in air-conditioned and special purpose buildings that the minimum achievable should be needed.

In contrast, water penetration through joints in windows is always undesirable but it would be unrealistic to require that windows should never leak. Little data exists on the levels of water leakage which building occupants will tolerate but it is suggested that while most occupiers will probably accept the need to mop up leakage which remains on a sill and which occurs, say, once a year, few will accept leakage which frequently runs off a sill and down the wall. This is, therefore, used as the criterion for failure.

For air permeability the windows can be tested by the methods described in BS 5368: Pt 1. For watertightness, the spraying method (No. 2) of BS 5368: Pt 2 should be used; this can be more demanding with certain types of window than the water spraying method described in BS 4315: Pt 1, which was the method previously established for use in the UK and which has not yet been withdrawn.

For air permeability the amount of air leakage is plotted against the test pressure, usually up to about 600 Pa. Two methods are used for expressing the air leakage, either as cubic metres per hour per metre length of opening joint (m³/h/m) or as cubic metres per hour per square metre of window (m³/h/m²). In this digest, the first method is used.

Figure 1 shows the four performance levels required in Ref[1]. For a window to satisfy the requirements of a particular graph, its performance over the indicated test pressures must remain below the line. In each case, the line against the logarithmic scales can be characterised by the leakage at a specific pressure, say 100 Pa, and by the maximum test pressure. On this basis, the ranges of performance bands suggested by the various documents are shown in Table 2.

Table 2 Performance bands for air permeability of opening lights. *Comparisons should not be attempted between similarly designated bands from each source*

Performance band designation	Source					
	DD4: 1974		AB MOAT 1 1974		PSA/DHSS MOB 3rd Prog. 1979[1]	
	Maximum air permeability					
	m³/h/m at 100 Pa	Max test Pa	m³/h/m at 100 Pa	Max test Pa	m³/h/m at 100 Pa	Max test Pa
1	12[2]	100	12	150	12	150
2	12[2]	150	6	300	9.5	200
3	12[2]	200	2	600	7.5	300[3]
4	–	–	–	–	2	600[3]

(1) For fixed lights the air permeability should not exceed 1m³/h/m at 300 Pa on PSA buildings
(2) 12m³/h/m should not be exceeded at the maximum test pressure
(3) Only these grades acceptable for PSA buildings

During the test for air permeability, the pressure at which significant water leakage occurs becomes the rating for the window. The performance bands for watertightness recognised in the various documents are shown in Table 3.

Table 3 Performance bands for watertightness. *Comparisons should not be attempted between similarly designated bands from each source*

	Maximum test pressure without 'leakage' Pa		
	DD4: 1971	AB-MOAT 1 1974	PSA/DHSS MOB 3rd Prog 1979
1	50*	50 to 150	100
2	150*	150 to 300	200
3	300*	300 to 500	300
4	–	over 500	–

* Linked to the design wind pressure

Strength (other than for wind loading)

A window has to resist three types of loading from occupants; firstly, the operating forces applied to fasten or to unfasten an opening light and to move it to the desired position. Secondly, abusive forces: for example, the forces used to move a jammed window. These are applied to effect the normal operation of the opening lights in the plane of the window with sliding windows and at right angles to the plane of the window and often through the latch with hinged and pivoted windows. Thirdly, accidental loading: for example, the load generated when a person falling on a step ladder partially supports himself on the top of the window or when he grabs the top of an open window to regain balance or to break his fall. Safety stays also have to resist the accidental forces likely to be applied to them. Stays are often hidden within the construction and, therefore, can be unintentionally loaded by those not familiar with the window.

Deliberate actions, when the aim is to cause permanent damage, vandalism for example, are not considered here.

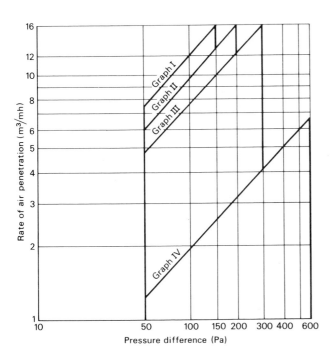

fig 1 performance levels for air permeability.

Operating forces

For convenient operation, window latches should be within easy reach, ie below, say, 1600 mm if the space at the window is unobstructed. Also, the effort required to operate the latches and to open or close the window should be within the capability of the weaker groups of people, ie the elderly and, in particular, women over 60. Maximum sustained forces which can be applied are listed in Table 4 to provide a basis for defining the operating requirements of a window.

Table 4 Suggested maximum operating forces for the opening and closing of windows[4]

| Movement | Hinged or pivoted | Sliding | |
	Push/pull (One hand)	Horizontal Lateral movement (One hand)	Vertical Depress/lift (Two hands)
Sustained:	55 N	25 N	60 N
Jerk:	65 N	30 N	70 N

Table 5 Maximum operating forces required by specification documents in UK *See Table 4 for suggested requirements*

| Source | Hinged or pivoted | Sliding | |
	Push/pull	Horizontal Lateral movement	Vertical Depress/lift
AB-MOAT 1 1974			
To initiate:	80 N[1]	5 kg × 50 mm[2]	5 kg × 200 mm[2]
Sustained:	80 N[1]	60 N	100 N
PSA/DHSS MOB 3rd Prog 1979			
To initiate:	80 N	120 N[3]	180 N[3]
Sustained:	80 N	80 N[3]	120 N[3]
BS 4873: 1972			
The greater of:			
To initiate:	–	120 N or 120 N/m² [4]	180 N or 180 N/m² [4]
Sustained:	–	80 N or 80 N/m² [4]	120 N or 120 N/m² [4]

(1) 130 N if two hands can be used

(2) ie an impact provided by the weight falling through the stated distance

(3) For windows greater than 1 m² this force should be multiplied by the window area

(4) ie N per square metre of sash

The maximum sustained forces in Table 4 were obtained by applying a gradually increasing force to a handle. However, in practice, movement might be initiated by a jerk and so the 'sustained' forces have been increased by about 20 per cent to give the 'jerk' values listed[5]. It has also been assumed that for lift and depress actions the total force applied with two hands is 50 per cent greater than that applied with one. With some latches on horizontal sliding windows, a push or a pull can be applied after turning the body sideways to the window; in this case the push-pull values can be used.

In addition to moving a window the user has to be able to fasten and unfasten it from a closed position, usually by rotating a handle. Assuming that the torque is applied within the limits at which the operating handle of a window is mounted ie, 1000 mm to 1600 mm, it appears that a window latch must not require a torque of greater than 5 Nm for its operation.

For comparison with these measured requirements for elderly women, the operating forces that have been suggested by various specification documents in use in the UK are listed in Table 5. It is evident that for sliding windows higher forces are allowed than can be applied by elderly women standing facing the window; therefore if the elderly need to operate windows either the operating forces from Table 4 should be specified or, to satisfy this requirement, hinged or pivoted windows should be fitted.

Resistance to abuse

The first tests to simulate the abuse of windows and the associated performance levels were suggested in 1974[2]; in subsequent documents [1] [6] these tests have been modified and the performance levels altered. Indeed, it could be argued that in some cases the original concept which provided the basis for the development of the tests has become less apparent. There is, therefore, a need to re-appraise the abuse factor in window performance and a systematic approach is now suggested.

Abuse, as distinct from the accidental loading of windows, results for example from attempts to open or to close a jammed window. The potential loads are therefore those that can be applied in a direction which would open or close a window either in a shut but unfastened, or in an open position. The maximum loads that can be applied are those from healthy males[4].

However, to provide windows capable of resisting the maximum forces would be uneconomic. It is also recognised that responsible people would realise that such forces could result in permanent damage to the window and so lower values have been assumed. These are given in Table 6 against window type and are compared with measured values[4].

If it is assumed that the maximum forces that responsible people will apply to release a jammed window are a proportion, say 40 per cent, of the maximum that can be applied with one hand, the excess operating forces that windows must withstand can be derived; these are given in Table 6 as 'adjusted values'. These relate to some degree with the forces used in the various performance documents and are suggested as providing a basis for the development of the performance requirements for window abuse.

With the abusive forces applied at a latch a number of test arrangements have to be considered. The first is when a corner of the window furthest from the latch is restrained in the direction of movement or, with side,

Table 6 Abusive forces which are considered to be applied to window handles in direction of movement

Source	Window type and method of operation		
		Sliding	
	Hinged or pivoted Push/pull	Horizontal Lateral movement	Vertical Depress/lift
PSA/DHSS MOB 3rd Prog 1979	400 N[2]	400 or 216 N[3]	400 or 216 N[3]
AB-MOAT 1971	400 N[2]	200 N	200 N
BS 4873: 1972	–	144 N[4]	216 N[5]
Measured values[1]	745 N	320 N	930 N
Adjusted values	300 N	130 N	370 N

(1) 95 per cent exclusion, ie force that can be exceeded by not more than five out of every 100 males (19 to 31 years)

(2) with also a dynamic test of 13 kg falling 100 mm

(3) ie initial force to operate + 20 per cent for windows less than 1 m² (above 1 m² × value by area)

(4) or 230 N per m² of sash + 20 per cent if greater

(5) or 180 N per m² of sash + 20 per cent if greater

top or bottom-hung windows a corner adjacent to the latch is restrained. The second is when the corners at each end of the rail or stile on which the latch is mounted are restrained in the direction of movement. These tests should be carried out with the window closed and open (but before a limiting position provided by any restrictor device is reached).

The criteria for acceptance at a particular test level are that no permanent deflection of members, permanent distortion of frames or lights, or damage should occur and both the glass and seal between the glass, and the members comprising the opening light should not be disturbed. With gasket glazing this final criterion may be difficult to assess but if the air penetration and watertightness tests are carried out after the abuse tests, any failure of gasket glazing will be apparent.

Resistance to accidental loading (including safety)

With sliding windows accidental loading can occur when a force is applied at right angles to the plane of the window and to the middle of a member when it is unsupported by the guides in which the window slides. Such a situation could occur if a person standing on steps or a ladder used the open window edges as a steadying anchorage. Although the horizontal force applied in this situation is not considered to be great (both 150 N[2] and 200 N[1] have been proposed) it is considered that the window rail should be able to withstand, without breakage or permanent deformation, the greater of these forces applied at mid-length.

Pivoted windows, hinged windows (except those hinged at the top rail) and open vertical sliding windows could also be used for support should, for example, a person standing on steps or a ladder start to fall and seek a steadying anchorage. The resulting loading applied in the most sensitive position (at a top corner furthest from the hinge or pivot or in the middle of the top rail on a vertical sliding window) is recognized[1][2]. It is considered that a window should

resist a vertical force of 500 N without breakage or permanent distortion when in a fully open position or against a restrictor device. The force should be applied without shock and held for 1 min. If a fall is not prevented an open window can be expected to support a person (a force of about 1000 N applied without shock and held for 1 min). With this load, however, a window should not be expected to survive undamaged and the criterion is simply that the window should not collapse and the restrictor device should not become detached.

A final consideration is that of a window being allowed to slam open against a restrictor device; to assess this dynamic condition, an impact energy of 13 kg falling 100 mm has been proposed[1].

Durability

It is usually expected that, properly maintained, a window will have the same life as the structure of the building. However, experience has shown that this expectation has rarely been fulfilled. Most windows can be replaced without disturbing the structure but this is usually a costly operation and the aim of the window specifier must be to ensure either that, with the required maintenance, the product installed has a potential life approaching that envisaged for the building, or that the design is such that replacement at intervals is facilitated and that the replacement costs are considered when making the initial selection.

There are three aspects that should be considered; firstly, the constructional material; secondly any finish applied to the constructional material and, thirdly, the associated hardware. Only the first and second will be considered here.

Materials and finishes

Wood

Traditionally, softwoods have been used in the UK for window construction but hardwoods have been introduced recently. Whichever is used must be a durable species[7] or a preservative treatment must be applied[8]. However, the influence of design on material durability is emphasised. The ability to shed water readily and an absence of water traps, particularly at the bottom corners of the frame, can reduce the risk of premature failure and especially important is the sealing of end grain at joints. Wood windows can be either painted or supplied with a natural finish or a factory-applied plastics skin. For painting, windows are usually supplied primed for building-in during construction or for insertion in prepared openings. Factory-finished windows are best installed in prepared openings because of the risk of damage during construction but some are supplied for building-in and have protective wrapping. Advice on good practice for the protection of windows on site is in CP 153, and guidance on the painting of windows is in Digest 261. Painted windows require regular maintenance at about five-year intervals depending on exposure.

The alternative to paint is the use of an exterior

natural finish: preservative stains are particularly suitable for hardwoods and good quality softwoods. Stains are easy to apply, but under comparable conditions these may require more frequent maintenance applications than paint. If stains are used, putty is not suitable for retaining the glass; either gaskets, or wood beads with neoprene tape or mastic, or a suitable sealant must be used. Guidance on sealants can be obtained from the manufacturers.

Wood windows are also available with a plastics skin, 1 to 1.5 mm thick. Although experience in the UK is limited, they should not require painting for at least 15 years and as long as the skin remains undamaged the wood core should not deteriorate. As an additional protection the wood core can be given a preservative treatment.

Steel

Steel windows can be secured direct to prepared openings but it is more usual, especially when building-in, to interpose a wood frame of adequate durability. Steel windows can be supplied galvanised for painting on site. As with wood, the paint has to be refurbished but usually only at five to seven-year intervals.

As an alternative to site painting, steel windows are available with factory-applied polyester coatings. They are claimed to have a potential life of 10 to 15 years but after this period normal painting at five to seven-year intervals will be necessary. Gaskets or glazing beads usually have to be used to retain the glass. Putty would have to be painted after glazing to avoid rapid deterioration and is not usually acceptable.

Aluminium

Aluminium windows can be installed direct in prepared openings but it is common to interpose a wood frame of adequate durability and this is usually considered essential for building-in during construction.

Unprotected aluminium with a mill finish should not be used other than, perhaps, in pollution-free environments as it rapidly loses its bright appearance and can become pitted by corrosion. However, if appearance is not important and provided corrosion does not affect the functional performance, unprotected aluminium can provide an economical option.

Apart from site-applied paint, a variety of finishes can be used. Anodising to a thickness of about 35 μm should have a life in excess of 15 years in other than polluted environments; the window can then be painted to provide protection to the exposed aluminium. In polluted atmospheres anodised surfaces require frequent washing to remove corrosion deposits and so in these environments alternative finishes should be considered. Organic coatings are available; acrylic types are well established and polyester types are now becoming more common. The acrylics have been in use for about 15 years and during that time there has been a gradual improvement in performance. Although the coatings are usually only 20 to 25 μm thick, they erode slowly and rarely peel or flake; they should have a life to half-thickness of about 10 years after which painting may be necessary. Most experience has been with white coatings, but the more recently introduced coloured coatings (especially black) may retain their initial colour better. In marine and industrially polluted environments, deterioration is more rapid and the occurrence of pin holes in the thin film can rapidly shorten the life to painting. Polyester coatings are thicker, up to 50 or 70 μm, and can be expected to have a life to painting of between fifteen and twenty years. A wide range of colours is available.

Silicone modified acrylics and polyesters have been used. The presence of silicone is claimed to increase the life to painting but there is little experience available. Fluoropolymers, principally polyvinylidene fluoride (PVDF) usually modified with an acrylic polymer, have also been introduced.

These are potentially very durable and light-fast, but as they are applied in films only about 25 μm thick, they are possibly more easily damaged than the polyesters.

Plastics

Although plastics windows have been used on the continent for a number of years, they have only recently been introduced on any scale in the UK market. Like aluminium, the impact modified unplasticised PVC sections can be readily fabricated to any required size and thus they are particularly suitable for replacement purposes. There are not yet any British Standards for plastics windows.

Plastics windows should not need painting to restore the surface for a number of years. White products should last 15 to 20 years, especially with regular washing to remove dirt but experience with the more recently introduced colour products is limited. Dark paints should be avoided on light-coloured plastics because distortion can result from the higher surface temperatures attained on exposure to the sun. Paint can impair the impact resistance of PVC and the material can be damaged by common paint stripping techniques.

Durability assessment

For the systematic assessment of the durability of finishes, performance bands can be used for the service life up to the first refurbishing; these are suggested in Table 7.

Certain stain finishes on wood would be classed as Band 1, paint on wood or metal as Band 2 and the various longer-life factory-applied finishes on metal or wood as Band 3, 4 or 5. The assumption is made that when these latter finishes are refurbished, site applied paint will be used at intervals until the life of the window, say 60 years, is attained or, for reasons other than durability, the window is replaced.

Table 7 Performance bands for the durability of finishes for windows

Performance band	Time to first refurbishing _years_	Time to second and subsequent refurbishing _years_
1	less than 3	less than 3
2	3–6	3–7
3	7–14	3–7
4	15–24	3–7
5	25 and over	

the way in which the sample is mounted for test and the test apparatus itself have been identified[9] as contributing to the variation in test results. To obtain a meaningful result it may, therefore, be necessary to test at least three samples, preferably of the larger sizes of each type of window produced and it may even be necessary to test up to seven windows if the performance levels attained are close to the minimum level of a band. The results should be assessed statistically to ensure that 95 per cent of the population of windows of the type tested will have a performance in excess of the minimum level required. Alternatively, a two-stage procedure can be used with a statistical assessment at each stage[9].

Secondary considerations

In addition to the primary attributes considered in this digest, there are some secondary ones which may require checking or which may become primary in special circumstances or at the wish of the specifier. They include thermal insulation and the risk of condensation, sound insulation and security. Thermal and sound insulation are very dependent on the glass infill and, if desired, significant improvements in window performance can be obtained either by the use of sealed, double glazed units in place of a single thickness of glass or by the installation of secondary windows. Condensation is likely to occur occasionally on most single-glazed windows depending largely on the moisture producing activities in the building and on the degree of ventilation. The risk of condensation occurring on the glass can be reduced by double glazing. Condensation is unlikely to occur on the members of a wood or plastics window but it is likely on metal members unless a thermal break is introduced. This interrupts the continuous metallic path between the inside and the outside environments.

Expressing window performance

There are a number of ways in which the performance of a window can be expressed. In this digest, the concept of developing a performance profile has been advocated. The primary attributes are identified and it is suggested the performance level required for each is placed in the context of a realistic scale of values. For wind resistance, air permeability, watertightness and durability of finish, a range of performance bands has been used. For operating forces, abusive and accidental loading and for material durability it is usually only necessary that a single level of performance (either a maximum or minimum as appropriate) be considered. The performance bands and levels that have been advocated are summarised in Table 8.

Finally, it is emphasised that there will inevitably be variation in the results of a test programme carried out to assess the performance of a window. This variation will be due not only to differences between windows of the same type and configuration caused, for example, by slight deviations in the manufacturing or assembly methods but also to the test procedure itself. Factors such as the experience of the operator,

Table 8 Performance bands for windows

Performance criteria	Performance bands			Test method	Acceptance criteria
	Number of bands	Reference in this digest			
Wind resistance	5	Table 1 as proposed for PSA/DHSS		BS 5368:Pt 3 modified	1/125 deflection limit on members. Air permeability and watertightness not significantly affected.
Air permeability	4	Table 2 as proposed for PSA/DHSS		BS 5368:Pt 1	Air leakage values for band not exceeded
Watertightness	3	Table 3 as proposed for PSA/DHSS**		BS 5368:Pt 2	No 'significant' leakage
Operating forces (a) Latch torque	1	5 Nm		Torque measured	Torques of 5 Nm not exceeded
(b) Movement of opening light	1	Table 4			Forces of Table 4 not exceeded
Abusive loading	1	Table 6			
Accidental loading (a) Horizontal (Sliding windows)	1	200N		Appropriate tests of PSA/DHSS[1] and EN 107[6]	No permanent deflection of member or distortion of opening lights or other damage
(b) Vertical (Hinged pivoted vertical sliding)	1	500N			
(c) Safety* (Hinged pivoted vertical sliding)	1	1000N			Window should not collapse
Durability (a) Material	1	Materials and finishes		Qualitative assessment	Expected life of not less than 60 years
(b) Finish	5	Table 7			Life to first refurbishing

* If a restrictor is fitted, an additional dynamic test should be carried out.
** With an additional level at 50 Pa and linked to the wind pressures. The 50 Pa level with that for Band 1 is for a wind resistance of up to 1200 Pa, Band 2 is for between 1200 and 2000 Pa and Band 3 is for over 2000 Pa.

References and further reading

1 PSA/DHSS Performance specification – Windows – Third Programme, Aug 1979. DOE Property Services Agency – Method of Building.

2 UEAtc Directive for the assessment of windows MOAT No 1. The Agrément Board; 1974.

3 The weatherstripping of windows and doors. BRE Information Paper IP 16/81.

4 COVINGTON, S A. Ergonomic requirements for building components and associated operating devices. BRE Current Paper CP 1/82.

5 Human strength – terminology measurement and interpretation of data Kroemer Human Factors 12, 3; 1970.

6 European Standard prEN107 (Final Draft) Methods of testing windows – Mechanical tests; Jan 1980.

7 WEBSTER, C. Timber selection by properties, Part 1. HMSO

8 Preservation treatments for exterior softwood joinery timber. BRE Technical Note No 24; Dec 1979.

9 CARRUTHERS, JFS and NEWMAN, C J. The repeatability and reproducibility of test results on windows and wall span elements and the expected results. BRE Current Paper CP 49/77.

British Standards Institution

BS Draft for Development 4:1971 Recommendations for the grading of windows. Resistance to wind loads, air infiltration and water penetration and notes on window security *(under revision).* BS 6375 PART 1

BS 644 Wood Windows
  Part 1: 1951 Wood casement windows
  Part 2: 1958 Wood double hung sash windows
  Part 3: 1951 Wood double hung sash and case windows (Scottish type)

BS 990 Steel windows generally for domestic and similar buildings
  Part 1: 1967 Imperial Units
  Part 2: 1972 Metric Units

BS 3987: 1974 Anodic oxide coatings on wrought aluminium for external architectural applications.

BS 4315 Methods of test for resistance to air and water penetration
  Part 1: 1968 Windows and structural gasket glazing systems.

BS 4842: 1972 Stoving organic finishes on aluminium extrusions and preformed sections for external architectural application.

BS 5368 Methods of testing windows
  Part 1: 1976 Air permeability test (EN 44).
  Part 2: 1980 (EN 46) Watertightness test under static pressure.
  Part 3: 1978 Wind resistance tests (EN 77).

BS 5589: 1978 Preservation of timber.

CP3 Basic data for the design of buildings; Chapter V Loading
  Part 2: 1972 Wind loads

CP 152: 1972 Glazing and fixing of glass for buildings.

CP 153 Windows and rooflights Part 2: 1970 Durability and maintenance.

BRE Digests

71 Painting: non-ferrous metals and coatings.
73 Prevention of decay in external joinery.
140 Double windows and double glazing
206 Ventilation requirements
210 Principles of natural ventilation
261 Painting woodwork.

Double glazing and double windows

Two diverse environmental requirements—one, a desire for improved heat insulation, the other, the need for protection against external noise—have stimulated the production and use of various forms of double glazing.

The essential difference between double glazing designs to meet these two needs lies in the width of the air space. For heat insulation, air-space widths as small as 6 mm are of some value; for sound insulation, air-space widths of not less than 100 mm, and preferably more, are essential, but there are other factors which are also discussed in this digest.

Heat insulation

In response to the general desire for improved heat insulation in heated buildings, various double glazing and double window systems are available, ranging from simple 'do it yourself' sealed *in situ* systems to the more sophisticated factory produced hermetically sealed double-glazing units and from double-rebated frames to openable coupled casements and sashes or separate secondary windows (see Figs 1–5). Some of the practical considerations peculiar to the various types are discussed later.

Width of air space

For effective heat insulation, the optimum width of air space for vertical double glazing varies according to the mean temperature of the air space and the temperature difference across it, but it is usually taken as 20 mm. Figure 6 shows that, for all practical purposes, the optimum is maintained down to an air-space width of about 12 mm. Below this width, the heat transmission becomes progressively greater until it approaches the figure for single glazing. For air-space widths greater than 20 mm, the heat transmittance remains practically constant.

Table 1 Thermal transmittance (U) in W/m² °C through glazing (without frames)

Glazing system	Degree of exposure:		
	sheltered	normal	severe
Single	5·0	5·6	6·7
Double			
air space 3 mm wide	3·6	4·0	4·4
6 mm	3·2	3·4	3·8
12 mm	2·8	3·0	3·3
20 mm (or more)	2·8	2·9	3·2
Triple			
each air space 3 mm wide	2·8	3·0	3·3
6 mm	2·3	2·5	2·6
12 mm	2·0	2·1	2·2
20 mm (or more)	1·9	2·0	2·1

Comparative performance of double glazing

Given air-space widths of not less than about 12 mm, the heat insulation of single-glazed windows can be improved appreciably by double glazing; in general terms, an air-space between two layers of glass halves the thermal transmittance. Table 1 shows the comparative thermal transmittance ('U') values for double glazing for four widths of air-space and three grades of exposure. For comparison, the U-values for single glazing and triple glazing are included.

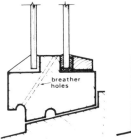

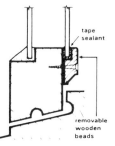

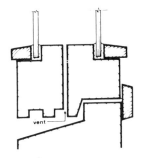

Fig 1 Typical factory-sealed double glazing units

Fig 2 Typical glazed *in situ* double glazing

Fig 3 Typical double windows, coupled type

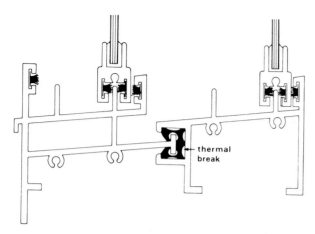

Fig 4 Horizontal sliding type, metal

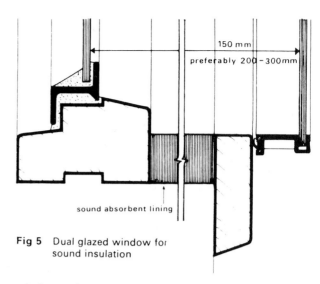

Fig 5 Dual glazed window for sound insulation

The above data relate to transparent and translucent glasses. For glazing systems using heat-reflecting glasses with metallic surface coatings (not laminates) of low heat emissivity, the metallic coating improves the insulation against heat loss For double-glazing units, the improvement in insulation provided by the unit may be as much as 30–40 per cent.

Effect of window frames

The U-values in Table 1 are for the glass only and do not allow for the effect of the surrounding frame and glazing bars. In wood windows, the thermal resistance of the frame can contribute usefully to the insulation value of the whole window but the reverse is true of metal windows (because of the relatively high conductance of the metal frame) unless thermal breaks are introduced to offset the 'cold bridge' effect. Some proprietary metal double windows now incorporate insulating plastic insets in the frame section to break the thermal continuity (Fig 4). For heat loss calculations, it is often useful to know the average U-value for the window as a whole, and unless the frame section is complex in profile, its effect on the average thermal transmittance can be worked out on a proportional area basis. Table 2 gives comparative U-values for a number of typical wood and metal windows.

Tables 1 and 2 are derived from the IHVE 'Guide'.[1] The three categories of exposure are defined as:

sheltered Up to third floor of buildings in city centres

normal   Most suburban and country premises: fourth to eighth floors of buildings in city centres

severe   Building on the coast or exposed on hill sites: floors above the fifth of buildings in suburban or country districts: floors above the ninth of buildings in city centres.

Loss through windows in relation to the whole

To assess the value of double glazing in terms only of heat saving under steady-state conditions, the heat losses through the glazing must be considered in relation to the overall heat losses. A broad comparison can be made by taking the average thermal transmittances for the different parts of the fabric, multiplying them by the appropriate areas to give the comparative rates of conduction heat loss per degree C difference of temperature between indoors and outdoors and then adding the ventilation heat loss. In a two-storey semi-detached house of 100 m² gross floor area, the component rates of heat loss might be:

Conduction heat loss	Average U-value W/m² °C	Area m²	Rate of heat loss W/°C
Roof	0·50	× 50 =	25
Ground floor	0·76	× 50 =	38
Unglazed walling	1·50	×100 =	150
Windows (single-glazed)	4·30	× 17 =	73

Total rate of conduction heat loss through fabric 286

Ventilation heat loss (assuming 1 air change/hour)

$$= 240 \text{ m}^3 \times \frac{\text{W/m}^3\ °\text{C}}{3} = 80$$

Total   366

Thus the single-glazed windows account for about 20 per cent of the total heat loss including ventilation, or about 50 per cent of the conduction loss through the unglazed external walls. If double-glazed windows with an average U-value of 2·5 W/m² °C are substituted for the single-glazed windows, the rate of heat loss through the windows would be reduced to about 42 W/°C, and the corresponding total rate to about 335 W/°C. The heat loss through the windows would thus be reduced to about 13 per cent of the total.

Table 2 Thermal transmittance (U) in W/m² °C through typical windows (including frames)

Window type	% total window area occupied by frame	Degree of exposure: sheltered	normal	severe
Single-glazed: metal casement*	20	5·0	5·6	6·7
wood casement	30	3·8	4·3	4·9
Double-glazed:† metal horizontal sliding window with thermal break	20	3·0	3·2	3·5
wood horizontal pivot window	30	2·3	2·5	2·7

* Metal frame assumed to have a similar thermal transmittance to that of the glass
† With 20 mm air space

Double glazing and comfort

Apart from the reduction in heat loss gained by using double glazing, the increase in surface temperature of the glass facing the room may improve the comfort particularly of persons sitting or working near the windows; the discomfort caused by radiation losses and cold convection currents from the cold surface of single glazing is well known. In general, the surface temperature of the glass facing a heated room in a double glazing system in winter will be some 4–7 °C higher than that of single glazing for the same internal and external temperature conditions (Fig 7).

Condensation

An explanation of the conditions which lead to condensation is given in Digest 110.[2] Condensation can occur on the surface of the glass and also on the frame, particularly if it is metal. The condensation on the glass is more troublesome because of the relatively large surface area and because it interferes with the view out. Where condensation on the glazing persists for long periods the run-off of excess moisture can lead to deterioration of the bottom member of the frame and spoil the appearance of the window reveals and areas of wall below the sill. Double

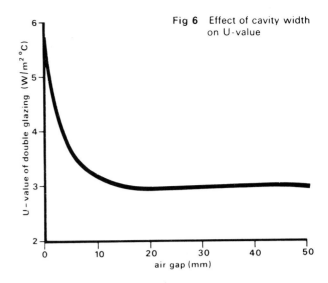

Fig 6   Effect of cavity width on U-value

glazing can reduce the risk of condensation on the glass because the surface exposed to the room is warmer than single glazing and has a better chance of being above the prevailing dew-point temperature. In practice, this will depend on the relative humidity, and in buildings where high humidities occur, coupled with low standards of heating, there is no guarantee that double or even triple glazing will

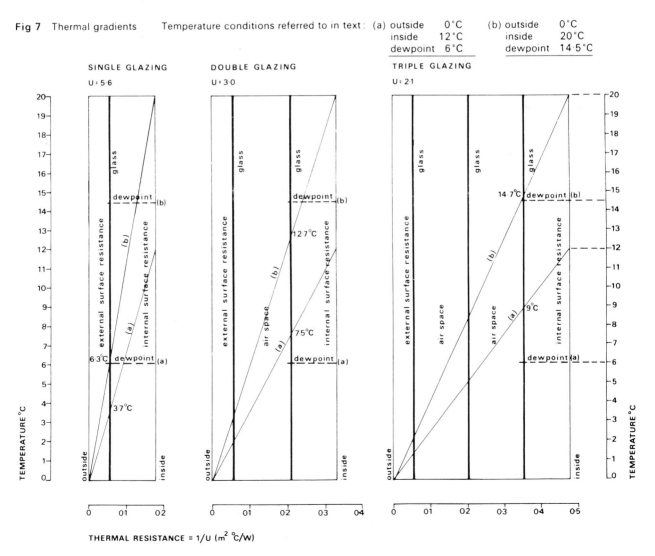

Fig 7   Thermal gradients   Temperature conditions referred to in text :   (a) outside   0 °C   (b) outside   0 °C
inside   12 °C   inside   20 °C
dewpoint   6 °C   dewpoint   14·5 °C

THERMAL RESISTANCE = 1/U (m² °C/W)

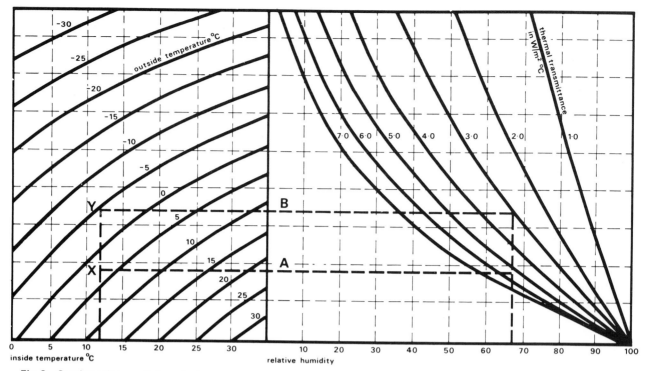

Fig 8 Condensation prediction chart

always avoid condensation on the glass. For instance, assuming an internal temperature of 12°C, an outside temperature of 0°C and a dew-point temperature of 6°C (typical of conditions in a bedroom), condensation would occur on the surface of single glazing, but not on double or triple glazing (see Fig 7). Raising the room temperature to 20°C and hence the glass surface temperature, for the same humidity conditions, there would still be a risk of condensation on single glazing. For conditions of high humidity, such as might occur in a domestic kitchen, assuming an internal temperature of 20°C, an outside temperature of 0°C and a dew-point temperature of 14·5°C, condensation would occur even on double glazing.

If the relative humidity and indoor and outdoor temperatures are known, the possibility of condensation on glazing can be predicted from Fig 8. This gives comparative dew-point curves for a range of U-values which embraces those given in Table 1 for single, double and triple glazing. The chart applies only to steady-state conditions but it can be used for a first check on the likelihood of condensation. As an example, the broken line **A** on the chart indicates the conditions of relative humidity 67 per cent, thermal transmittance 5·6 W/m²°C (for single glazing) and an inside temperature of 12°C; condensation is likely to occur when the outside temperature drops to about 3°C (point 'X' on the chart). The line **B** shows the same temperatures and relative humidity plotted against a thermal transmittance of 3·0 W/m² °C (for double glazing); the outside temperature must now drop to nearly −5°C (point 'Y') to cause condensation on the glass.

Sound insulation

The simplest way of increasing the sound insulation of an element of structure is to increase its mass; in a general sense this is true for windows, but with such lightweight components a substantial improvement can be obtained by double-leaf construction, as shown in Table 3 (taken from Digest 128[3]), provided that the windows are sealed, for example by weather-stripping, and that the air space is wide enough to give the required insulation at the lower frequencies.

Even small gaps in double windows can impair the sound insulation and, therefore, if at all possible, one leaf of a double window should be a fixed light system. If both leaves have openable lights in them, all the openable lights should be weather-stripped. For rooms subject to high humidity, it may be necessary to seal the inner leaf of glazing to prevent condensation in the air space as discussed on page 7.

Table 3 Sound insulation of windows

Description	Sound Reduction (av 100–3150 Hz)
Any type of window when open	about 10 dB
Ordinary single openable window closed but not weather-stripped, any glass	up to 20 dB
Single fixed or openable weather-stripped window, with 6 mm glass	up to 25 dB
Fixed single window with 12 mm glass	up to 30 dB
Fixed single window with 24 mm glass	up to 35 dB
Double window, openable but weather-stripped, 150–200 mm air space, any glass	up to 40 dB
Double window in separate frames, one frame fixed, 300–400 mm air space, 6–10 mm glass sound-absorbent reveals	up to 45 dB

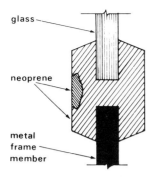

glass

neoprene

metal
frame
member

Fig 9 Flexible mounting of glass in neoprene gasket

Width of air space

The optimum air-space width for thermal insulation is about 20 mm, but this is too small to be of any practical advantage for sound insulation. For protection against road traffic noise, in which the low frequency components predominate, a minimum air-space width of 150 mm is recommended and preferably more—say 200–300 mm whenever it is economically obtainable. Unless an air space at least 100 mm wide can be provided, practical insulation against road traffic noise may well be obtained more effectively by heavy single glazing selected to give the same average performance.

Room ventilation

Table 3 shows that to obtain a useful improvement in sound insulation windows must be closed. A room with permanently closed double windows will usually need some form of mechanical ventilation through a duct system. The ducts should be lined with acoustic absorbent material to give sound attenuation comparable with that of the insulation provided by the building enclosure. For the ventilation of individual rooms there are fan-operated ventilating cabinets with sound attenuation designed to match the sound insulation provided by double windows.

Absorbent linings and flexible mountings

The provision of sound-absorbent linings, eg acoustic tiles, on the reveals between double windows can give marginal improvements in sound

insulation. Flexible edge-mounting of the glass, for instance in neoprene gaskets, see Fig 9, can also help by promoting resonance damping. Recent experiments have shown that the latter treatment can improve the performance of double windows by at least 5 dB over most of the frequency range 100–3150 Hz, but the extra sound insulation can only be realised if the windows are well sealed; air leakage would tend to mask any benefit from the use of flexible mountings.

Windows in relation to the whole building

The improvement in sound insulation obtainable from double windows depends to some extent on the standard of insulation of the rest of the fabric and on their respective areas, although there is no simple relationship. The net insulation for windows and wall for a range of relative areas is given in Table 4, taken from CP153: Part 3.[4] If the standard of the walling is of the same order as the windows, the percentage area of glazing will have no significant effect on the net sound insulation; if it is appreciably higher, the net insulation of the wall and windows will be less than the wall insulation. The converse is also true as the standard of insulation of the wall or other parts of the building fabric may be lower than that of the windows. For example, in an ordinary house, a tiled roof plus ceiling may have an average sound insulation of about 35 dB as against 40 dB or more for double windows. Thus if it is required to improve the protection against external noise the restricted performance of the roof could inhibit the improvement sought by double glazing.

Effect on light transmission

The transmission of light through glass varies with the angle of incidence and the properties of the glass, but for categorising different types of glazing, a percentage representing the light transmission at normal incidence is usually given by manufacturers. The light transmission through clear glass up to about 6 mm thick could be of the order of 85–90 per cent for single glazing, and about 70 per cent for double glazing. For daylight calculation purposes, it is usually convenient to calculate the daylight factor on the assumption of a single thickness of clear glass and then if necessary to apply a correction factor to allow for the reduced transmission of double glazing or other types of glazing material. Table 5 gives correction factors for a range of typical glazing materials in double glazing, the factor for single clear glass being taken as unity.

For comparison purposes, the transmission of radiant solar heat through various glasses is also given by manufacturers on a percentage basis assuming normal angles of incidence and taking into account the proportion of incident radiation reflected at the outer surface of the glass and the proportion absorbed by the glass and re-radiated.

Table 4 Effect of comparative area of window on the sound insulation of external walls rated at *40 dB and †50 dB respectively

| | Average sound insulation (dB) | | | |
| | 20 dB window | | 40 dB window | |
Percentage of glazing area to wall area	40 dB wall	50 dB wall	40 dB wall	50 dB wall
0 (windowless wall)	40	50	40	50
10	30	30	40	47
25	26	26	40	45
33	25	25	40	44
50	23	23	40	43
75	21	21	40	41
100 (fully glazed wall)	20	20	40	40

* Equivalent of walls weighing about 120 kg/m², for example, a 50 mm dense concrete composite panel backed with thermal insulation material
† Equivalent of walls weighing about 480 kg/m² for example, a 215 mm solid or a 255 mm cavity brick wall

Table 5 Recommended daylight correction factors and solar gain factors to allow for effect of various types of double glazing

Glasses	Recommended correction factor to apply in daylight calculations	Solar gain factor (S)	Alternating solar gain factor (Sa) Heavy-weight building	Light-weight building
4–6 mm clear single glazing	1·00	0·76	0·42	0·65
4–6 mm clear both panes	0·90	0·64	0·39	0·56
6 mm surface-tinted bronze outer pane 4–6 mm clear inner pane	0·45	0·47	0·32	0·44
6 mm selectively absorbing green outer pane 4–6 mm clear inner pane	0·70	0·42	0·30	0·40
6 mm body-tinted grey outer pane 4–6 mm clear inner pane	0·35	0·39	0·28	0·37
6 mm heat-reflecting laminate (gold) outer pane 4–6 mm clear inner pane	—	0·15	0·12	0·14

When calculating cooling loads in air-conditioned buildings or temperatures in uncooled buildings, it is necessary to know the solar gain through the windows; this varies with the angle of incidence and the properties of the glass. A simplifying concept, adopted in the IHVE Guide[1] allows for these varying characteristics under representative conditions and employs a *solar gain factor* to allow for the effect of a specified glass and any shading devices. In a broad sense, solar gain factors can be used as an approximate measure of the relative effectiveness of different types of glass and sun controls in combating solar gains. For calculating daily mean solar cooling loads or indoor temperatures, the solar gain factor **S** is used; for calculating the fluctuations of solar cooling load or indoor temperature about the mean, the factor S_a is used. Values of **S** and S_a for five types of double glazing and for single clear glazing are given in Table 5.

Practical considerations

Installation

Factory-sealed units Recommended glazing procedures for various types of factory-sealed double-glazing units are given in a booklet[5] issued by the Insulation Glazing Association. The booklet limits its advice to new work; for installing units in existing frames it recommends consultation with the manufacturer.

The glazing instructions relate to minimum depth and width of rebate to accommodate the thickness of the double-glazing unit, fixing of beads, type of bedding compounds, provision of setting blocks and distance pieces to ensure that the unit is correctly positioned in the frame and preparation of the frame. In addition, the booklet gives 'step by step' site glazing procedures appropriate to various kinds of bedding systems, and recommendations for the handling and

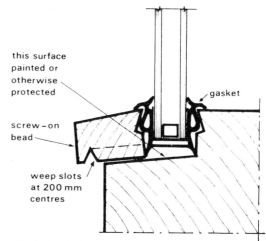

Fig 10 Drained glazing system

storage of units. Some manufacturers provide lists of approved glazing compounds.

Manufacturers' standard instructions are generally in line with the IGA recommendations, supplemented in some cases by additional guidance on the application of the bedding compounds and routine pre-glazing checks.

Failure to follow the glazing instructions of individual manufacturers may invalidate their warranty, which is usually for a period of ten years, but may be longer, and covers failure of the unit to function properly due to deterioration of the seal. If the seal fails, the unit cannot be repaired and can only be replaced by a new one.

Sealed units with fused all-glass edges are being increasingly used and a type using a welded glass-to-metal seal is also available, but there is still considerable use of the form in which flat sheets of glass are bonded to spacing strips and sealed. With the latter, it is important that the edges are kept dry, as continual wetting tends to destroy the bonded joints. For this reason, special care is needed to ensure that the glazing method and compound will protect the edges of the unit. The compound must also be compatible with the bonding materials of the unit. Attention has recently been directed to the value of drained glazing systems because of the difficulty of ensuring, particularly at the bottom edges, that no

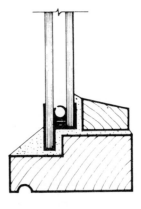

Fig 11 Typical stepped unit

crevices are formed where water may lodge between the unit and the bedding compound; a typical system is shown in Fig 10.

Some firms produce double-glazing units to fit into the rebates of standard sections, wood and metal, without the use of face beads. For frames that are too small, or unsuitable for enlarging to accept the thickness of standard units, stepped units are available (Fig 11).

Sealed double-glazing units with dark coloured, heat-absorbing or heat-reflecting glasses are liable to be heated strongly by the sun. If during a sunny spell the glass is put in partial shade, for example by other buildings or parts of the building, differential thermal movements may cause fracture. There is some evidence also of an increased likelihood of thermal stresses in double-glazed units when tinted glasses are backed by internal blinds of high reflectance. If these conditions are likely to arise the manufacturers should be consulted.

Single-frame double glazing systems sealed *in situ* Many attempts have been made to provide sealed double glazing by glazing to double rebated frames, or by fixing a second line of glazing with wood or plastic face beads, generally to existing frames (see Fig 2). Experience has shown that however well the glazing seals are made, the cavities cannot be expected to remain air-tight indefinitely; under the various movements and shrinkages that occur the seals may break down, water vapour (and dust) then finds its way into the air space and at some times condenses on the inside of the outer glazing.

If the inner panes are bead glazed it may be fairly easy to remove them for cleaning but it is often difficult to reseal the windows effectively and the 'slip-on' or 'press-on' type of added glazing, using proprietary compressible plastic edging strips, may be easier to reseal.

For wood windows, double-glazed *in situ*, the wood exposed to the air space should be painted or varnished to reduce the evaporation of moisture from the timber into the air space and breather holes to the outside should be provided on the basis of one 6 mm diameter hole for 0·5 m² of window. The holes should be plugged with material such as glass fibre insulation or nylon to exclude dust and insects. The frame material of metal or plastic windows will not contribute to a build-up of moisture in the air space. The double glazing should be completed under relatively dry conditions (preferably in cold weather) to prevent trapping humid air in the air space and the room-side glazing should be sealed as effectively as possible.

Coupled or sliding double sashes These may be pivoted, with openable coupled sashes, or they may slide, with pairs of sliders operating in the same frame; the former may be wood or metal but the latter

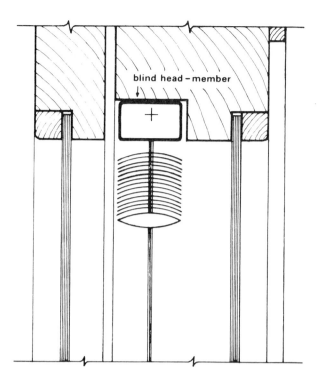

Fig 12   Coupled type double sash with venetian blind

are usually metal (Figs 3 and 4). To reduce the risk of condensation, the inner sashes should be well sealed when the sashes are closed together. For the same reason, in the coupled pivoted type a ventilating slot is commonly left round the periphery of the outer sash to ventilate the air space to outdoors when the sashes are closed. This does not seriously reduce the insulation of the window. In the sliding types, the air space is not usually ventilated because the inner surfaces are readily accessible for cleaning. The air space in the double-sash types is usually sufficient to allow retractable blinds to be installed between the inner and outer glazing (Fig 12). The blinds, usually venetian or pleated, are controlled by cords or rod action, but fully automatic control of the venetian types is available.

Double windows with separate frames When wide cavities are required for sound insulation, or it is not practicable to double glaze single-frame windows, secondary windows can be fixed to the existing frames or to ancillary frames. With the latter, a space can be left between the two panes, depending on the depth of the reveals, for fixing acoustic absorbent material to give additional sound insulation. There are proprietary secondary windows available in aluminium or PVC. They may be either hinged or sliding, to give access for cleaning; fixed lights can also be incorporated. Units can be supplied for screw fixing to the original window by householders, but specialist firms will supply and fix. The casement types usually have a compressible strip to provide a seal against the existing window or the ancillary frame; the sliding types usually have a wool pile seal in the track. Both types can be removed for cleaning or storage but large glazed units are awkward to handle. Where the secondary window has to provide access to the opening lights of the outer frame for cleaning it is necessary to ensure that the opening lights in both frames work conveniently together. In this respect, difficulties can arise with pivoted windows because of the unavoidable projection of their opening lights across the cavity.

If tinted glass is used to reduce solar heat gains, blinds of high reflectance in the inter-space may give rise to increased thermal stresses as already mentioned.

Maintenance

General recommendations on the durability and maintenance of windows are given in CP 153 : Pt 2.[6]

The glazing joints of factory-sealed double-glazing units should be checked at intervals recommended by the manufacturer and when repainting the window frames. For low-cost schemes using self-hardening compounds and without beads, a maintenance check every three years may be required; for silicone acrylic-based or polysulphide sealants a check every ten or twelve years may be sufficient. Where there are surface cracks, extrusion or retraction of the original compound, it should be raked out to a depth of 3 mm and replaced with a compound preferably of the same type. The joint should be shaped to direct water away from the glass on the outside and room side. Glazing beads should be re-secured as necessary and drainage holes in drained joint and gasket systems should be cleared of any dirt or other obstructions. For gasket glazing, maintenance checks at one-year intervals are recommended by specialist firms.

With sealed *in situ* systems it may be necessary to remove the glazing on the room side, clean the glass and reseal at intervals of two years or more depending on the effectiveness of the seal. The appearance of the inner surface of the outer glazing will show whether it is necessary to remove the inner glazing. The joints of wood frames, specially the bottom joints, should be checked for cracks, and when the glass is removed the opportunity should be taken to re-paint and re-varnish the wood exposed to the air space. The glass should be replaced under dry conditions, preferably a cold dry day, with the room amply ventilated to avoid entrapping warm moist air from the room.

For coupled or sliding double sashes or double windows with separate frames, maintenance will be

as required for single windows but the fit of the inner opening lights should be checked to ensure that the seal on the room side is maintained as effectively as possible and if necessary weather-strip or flexible seals replaced by new.

Tests

There are currently no British Standard tests that are specific to sealed double-glazing units or double windows, but the IGA booklet [5] includes performance tests for glazing compounds for use with double-glazing and multiple-glazing units. BS 4254[7] includes methods of test for two-part polysulphide-based sealing compounds.

In general, for glazed *in situ* double-glazed single-frame windows and coupled or sliding dual sashes, tests related to the performance requirements for single-glazed windows would apply. The provisional recommendations published by the British Standards Institution in DD4[8] for resistance to wind loads, air infiltration and water penetration are relevant.

The thermal transmission of double windows is usually calculated, taking into account the width of the air space, the type of frame and the proportional areas of frame and glazing. A description of the method of calculation and the concept of standardised U-values is given in the IHVE Guide.[1]

For sound insulation measurements of windows, the standard methods given in BS 2750[9] apply.

References

1 IHVE Guide: Book A, Design Data (1971); Institution of Heating and Ventilating Engineers, London

2 BRE Digest 110 Condensation

3 BRE Digest 128 Insulation against external noise—1

4 British Standard Code of Practice CP 153 Part 3 : 1971 Windows and roof lights—Sound Insulation

5 Glazing requirements and procedures for double glazing units; Insulation Glazing Association, London 1968

6 British Standard Code of Practice CP 153 Part 2 : 1970 Windows and roof lights—Durability and maintenance

7 British Standard BS 4254 : 1967 Two-part polysulphide-based sealing compounds for the building industry

8 British Standard Draft for Development DD4 : 1971 Recommendations for the grading of windows

9 British Standard BS 2750 : 1956 Recommendations for field and laboratory measurement of airborne and impact sound transmission in buildings

Further Reading

Beckett, H. E. and Godfrey, J. A.—*Windows*, Crosby Lockwood Staples : London (1974)

Prevention of decay in external joinery

Reports of 'wet rot' in external joinery, particularly in new houses, suggests that the factors responsible are not as widely understood as they should be. This Digest examines the causes of decay and makes recommendations as to its prevention.

Some progress has been made: window joinery should have been preservative treated in houses built privately since 1970 and preservative treatment has been recommended for external soft-wood panelled doors since 1975.

If mass-produced external joinery is used, preservative treatment should be part of the purchase specification.

Incidence

Decay in exterior windows and doors has always occurred sporadically, but the number of reported cases of decay has increased appreciably over the past few years and is found even in joinery complying with current Codes of Practice and Specifications. Window joinery in newly built houses has given most cause for complaint; decay has sometimes become a serious problem within five or six years from the time of construction. Usually, decay has been noted earlier in the wetter, western areas of the British Isles though it has by no means been confined to these regions. Recent surveys have also revealed a high incidence of decay in untreated, mass-produced, external panelled doors which are not fully protected from the weather by porches, etc.

While decay may occur anywhere in opening lights and in frames permanently in contact with brickwork or blockwork, it is particularly marked in ground floor windows, especially kitchen and bathroom windows. The lower parts of these windows, ie the cills, the bases of jambs and mullions and the lower rails of opening lights, are particularly susceptible.

Type and symptoms

Almost invariably decay is of the wet rot type. This means that the fungi responsible, unlike the dry rot fungus, will not spread the rot to other woodwork in the building. Discoloration of the paintwork and 'cupping', or softening of the underlying wood, are the usual first symptoms of decay. Later, cross-cracking and dark discoloration of the wood itself may be observed. Sometimes in the later stages the wood becomes soft and stringy. There is no evidence of Baltic redwood having been infected prior to manufacture by the fungi responsible for wet rot.

Causes and prevention

Decay is caused by timber of low natural resistance becoming sufficiently moist to allow wood-destroying fungi to grow. Prevention of decay therefore depends on the selection of timber which is either naturally resistant to decay or which is otherwise protected by preservative treatment. Only heartwood has natural resistance to decay; sapwood* *must* be excluded where preservative treatment is not used.

---

* Sapwood cannot economically be excluded from joinery grade redwood.

Moisture control

Irrespective of the species of timber employed, adequate seasoning to remove moisture is essential before manufacture as joinery. A low moisture content restricts dimensional changes, permits satisfactory painting and contributes generally towards decay prevention. After seasoning, further access of moisture should be restricted:

by good design and careful fabrication of the joinery itself, particularly of the joints;

by storage indoors or raised clear of the ground and covered with waterproof sheets to protect the woodwork from exposure to the weather prior to final installation and painting;

by good detailing at the window/wall joint;

by thorough painting and regular maintenance;

by prompt attention to any necessary repairs.

Timber and its selection

Timbers for mass production joinery are chosen mainly because they are inexpensive and easily machined, not because they are particularly resistant to decay.

Baltic redwood (also known as red or yellow deal, red pine or fir) is the softwood most used for exterior joinery; its heartwood is more resistant to decay than its sapwood. The heartwood of Douglas fir is also used.

English oak is the traditional hardwood for exterior joinery, especially cills, in which greater resistance to decay is an asset. The hardwoods teak, utile, gurjun and agba have also proved acceptable. All these should be specified by name; merely to specify 'hardwood' can lead to the use of unsuitable timbers such as abura, beech, obeche and ramin (all with poor resistance to decay). The inclusion of perishable sapwood of an otherwise decay-resistant timber can be avoided by specifying 'Heartwood only'.

Suitable timber species and their properties are set out in Table 2 (on page 7), extracted from CP 153: Part 2: 1970.

As Baltic redwood predominates in window joinery in the United Kingdom, the remarks which follow apply mainly to this timber. However, the principles of prevention and treatment of timber decay do not vary much between any of the different species used.

Preservative treatments

Care in design, construction, handling and maintenance can reduce but not eliminate the risk of decay. The obvious but often too costly remedy is to use naturally durable timber, excluding all sapwood. Alternatively, the risk of decay can be eliminated by adequate preservative treatment.

Recommended preservative treatments include:

Vacuum/pressure impregnation with water-borne preservative
Complete penetration of the sapwood of Baltic redwood can be achieved by this method. Treatment with an aqueous solution and the subsequent redrying that is necessary, however, cause the wood to swell and then to shrink; this can result in some raising of the grain and a risk of distortion.

Double-vacuum treatment with organic-solvent type preservative
The degree of treatment obtained can be controlled by varying the treating cycle used and it is possible to ensure that the net retention of the relatively high-cost preservative is adequate but not excessive. Complete penetration of sapwood is not usually obtained, but the average absorption and penetration achieved is about twice that from immersion treatment below.

Diffusion treatment This is carried out at the sawmill; after processing, seasoned treated timber can be supplied to the joinery manufacturer already penetrated throughout with a water-soluble preservative. This stock can then be converted and assembled in exactly the same way as untreated wood. Because the preservative is water-soluble, there is a risk that some may be leached out if the joinery is exposed to rain for months without paint or other protection.

Immersion treatment with organic-solvent type preservative
Machined components or assembled units are submerged in a tank of preservative for three minutes. This provides satisfactory protection even though sapwood penetration is incomplete. Preservatives used for immersion, and for double-vacuum treatment, often contain water repellents: these improve the dimensional stability of the wood and hence benefit the performance of the joinery.

For further information on preservative treatment see PRL Technical Note 24, *Preservative Treatments for External Softwood Joinery Timbers*; this includes a list of the commercial processes and preservatives suitable for the treatment of external joinery.

Compatibility with glues, paints, mastics, etc, used subsequently should be established with the manufacturers.

Design and fabrication of joinery

Entry of water is most likely to occur at joints. Some modern joints loosen more easily than the old-style mortice-and-tenon joints with wedged tenons, and are therefore more vulnerable to water penetration. Joints are usually made with the grain of one member at right angles to that of another. Quite small fluctuations in moisture content stress these joints severely and once cross-grain movements begin, more water can enter and threaten decay.

The animal and casein glues permitted by some joinery specifications are likely to fail in persistently moist conditions. When this happens the joints in doors and opening sashes are less able to resist sudden stresses; the joints loosen, the paint film is broken, and penetration by moisture follows. The modern, synthetic resin glues are preferred because of their greater resistance to moisture. (See Forest Products Research Bulletin 38, *The efficiency of adhesives for wood.*)

The sectional sizes of timber scantlings accepted for windows have become smaller in recent years. It is bad practice to employ flimsy sections in window joinery, particularly where weather conditions are severe, as in some parts of Scotland. Such sections are prone to distort, permitting ingress of moisture, and they may not provide adequate space for the rebate. In opening lights the strength may be insufficient to prevent racking and consequent water penetration at the joints.

Window designs with horizontal surfaces which do not effectively shed water, still more those that actually entrap it, should be avoided. This applies both to rain-water on the outside of the window and to condensation on the inside.

The present-day omission of condensation channels and adequate means of drainage from them is to be deplored. Often water stands on the sill against the bottom of the frame and seeps into the joint between the two.

Cills present problems because they require timber of larger dimensions, and hence of greater cost, and also because they tend to present a higher decay risk. Whilst decay risk can be met by using more durable timber, increased cost is involved even if such timber is restricted to the cill alone. The current trend is to reduce costs by building up the cill from two smaller dimension timbers; the increased complexity of the two-piece unit calls for greater care in design and manufacture. However, even when Baltic redwood is used, a properly designed jointed cill effectively glued with suitable adhesives and preservative treated as necessary should give adequate service.

Fig 1 Complexity of joint design in a modern frame and cill. Result—joints expose a large surface area to risk of moisture penetration and facilitate decay

Weather protection before installation

Joinery is often to be seen exposed to all weathers while in transit or awaiting installation on building sites. This is thoroughly bad practice. All woodwork should be fully protected from the weather and stacked clear of the ground. Pink primer may look protective but it is rarely effective in preventing penetration of moisture—moisture which may later cause trouble is trapped by relatively impermeable coats of paint.

The window/wall joint

A further contributory cause of moisture penetration, and therefore of decay, may arise from contact between window frames and wet brickwork. There is rarely any damp-proof barrier separating them, nor is it usual to protect the backs of the frames with extra paint before installation. Even when the joinery is set in the inner leaf of brickwork there is risk of dampness continuing in the frames for as long as it takes the brickwork to dry out.

The more usual practice, however, except in Scotland, is to set the frame in the outer leaf of brickwork; not only is this brickwork often permanently damp, the window itself is much more directly exposed to the weather. Clearly this practice carries the greater risk of timber decay. Thorough priming—two full coats of an aluminium based primer—is needed on all timber surfaces that are to be in contact with external walls.

External and internal climates

The direct exposure of windows to driving rain and to rain-water run-off will depend on their regional location and position in the building, ie storey height and orientation (see Digest 127). That decay tends to be most marked in the lower, external parts of ground-floor windows is only to be expected. However, too little thought is given to the effects of internal climate on window joinery; this can be as damaging to the woodwork of single-glazed windows as the weather outside. In bathrooms and kitchens especially, temperature and humidity are often high, and in cold weather condensation on these windows is troublesome. Changed living habits and heating methods have aggravated the problem (see Digest 110). Often there is a pool of water along the lower edge above the back putty. This back putty is rarely as free from defects as that on the face, and water finds an easy entry. (The need for condensation channels at the base of the frame has already been mentioned.)

Fig 2

Outer glazing bead nailed—not glued or sealed. Result—free moisture penetration.

Grooves machined for outer glazing bead run right through mullion/transom joint. Result—void for collection of moisture

Fig 3 External part of mullion/transom joint held by nail. Result—water penetrates freely once the paint film is broken. Failure through decay began after three years' service

Painting and maintenance, primers
(*see also* Digest 106)

As noted, the ability of a single coat of primer, even a good quality lead-based type, to prevent ingress of water is greatly over-estimated. 'Pink' shop primers are of variable quality and many do little more than give the joinery a uniform appearance; after quite a short exposure they become weak or powdery and unfit to take further coats of paint. Many paint failures can be traced back to poor quality primers. Thus it is most important to store joinery under cover; if this is considered impossible much better priming than usual should be specified. A water-repellent preservative plus a good quality primer, or two coats of aluminium primer, would be suitable. (Since aluminium primers will also keep moisture in, they should only be used on correctly seasoned timber, or after the moisture or solvent from preservative treatment has dried out, otherwise blistering may occur.)

Lead-based pink priming paints (BS 2521 :1966) have been regarded as having maximum durability, both as part of a full paint system and if left exposed on site. They are expensive and their toxicity makes their

Fig 4 Gap left beneath tenon in joint between stile and cill or, in this case, between lower rail of main frame and base of mullion. Result—void for collection of moisture and eventual decay

Fig 5 Cupping of paintwork and putty failure associated with decay in lower rail of an opening light

use indoors inadvisable where children could contact them (even under further paint). BS 5358 : 1976 specifies low-lead primers with performance as good as that of lead-based ones.

Acrylic emulsion-based primers, preferably to BS 5082, are often used because they are convenient for joinery manufacturers and are virtually lead free. Although their water resistance is lower than that of the best oil-based primers, they have high durability before and after painting. 'Primer undercoats' may be less durable outdoors.

If a thin, weak or powdery shop coat is present, it should be sanded and a further coat of good quality primer applied. End grain and surfaces in contact with brickwork or masonry should always receive an extra coat of primer. Poor quality putty cracks or loses adhesion easily and allows water to enter at the bottom rail : all putty should be completely painted, with a slight overlap on to the glass. Hardwood cills should have the grain filled with a knifing stopper or filler (not a water-mixed type), preferably between two coats of primer.

Shellac knotting, even if it holds back resin, usually permits adhesion failure of the paint coats; an aluminium pigmented knotting is preferable, but good practice requires large knots to be cut out and the cavities to be stopped.

Selection of species

A guide to the choice of timber species is given in the tables. The classification in Table 1 is based upon general experience of the probable protection requirements needed to ensure satisfactory service. Information on individual timbers is given in Table 2. The terminology used is explained in 'A Handbook of Hardwoods' and 'A Handbook of Softwoods' prepared by Princes Risborough Laboratory and published by Her Majesty's Stationery Office.

Table 1 Protective treatment required

Class	Durability	Sapwood	Protection Needed	
			Preservative Treatment	Finishes[2]
1	Very durable	Must be excluded[1]	Not necessary	For decorative purposes and to protect surface from weathering
2	Durable	Must be excluded[1]	Optional	
3	Moderately durable	Must be excluded[1]	Optional	Protective surface finish essential; should be well maintained
4	Perishable or non-durable	Assumed to be present	Essential	

1. If this is not done the timber, irrespective of species, must be regarded as class 4. Preservative treatment is then essential.
2. These include paint, natural or synthetic varnishes, pigmented water-repellent preservative stains.

Table 2 Timber species and properties

Class and heartwood durability†	Standard name	Sapwood distinct	Resistance to impregnation with preservatives	Woodworking properties		Amount of movement on re-wetting	Paint performance in service	Remarks
				Resistance in cutting	Blunting effect			
Class 1 Very durable	Afrormosia	Yes	Extremely resistant	Medium	Moderate	Small	Good, provided paint is not affected by oily exudations	Non-ferrous fitments necessary
	Afzelia			High	Moderate	Small	*	May discolour other building materials
	Iroko			Medium	Fairly severe	Small	*	
	Kapur			Medium (variable)	Moderate (occasionally severe)	Medium	*	Non-ferrous fitments necessary
	Makoré			Medium	Severe	Small	*	Non-ferrous fitments necessary
	Teak				Fairly severe (variable)	Small	Good, provided paint is not affected by oily exudations	Has been known to cause discoloration of granite
Class 2 Durable	Western red cedar	Yes	Resistant	Low	Mild	Small	Good	Strenght relatively low. Non-ferrous fitments necessary to avoid marked discoloration of the wood under clear finishes
	Agba	Moderate		Medium	Moderate	Small	Moderate, but experience is limited	Log core may contain brittleheart. Resin exudation may occur with some parcels, especially if the timber has been air-dried
	European oak, American white oak, Japanese oak	Yes	Extremely resistant	Medium (variable)	Moderate (variable)	Medium	Poor	Non-ferrous fitments necessary. Occasionally disfigures other building materials
	Idigbo	Moderate			Mild	Small	*	Log core may contain brittleheart. May cause staining of other building materials
	Sweet chestnut	Yes		Medium	Mild	Small	*	Non-ferrous fitments necessary
	Utile				Moderate	Medium	Good	
Class 3 Moderately durable	Douglas fir	Yes	Resistant	Medium	Medium	Small	Moderate	Non-ferrous fitments advisable
	African mahogany		Very resistant	Medium (variable)	Moderate (variable)	Small or medium	*	Log core may contain brittleheart
	Gurjun Yang		Resistant	Medium (variable)	Moderate (occasionally severe)	Large	Moderate	Resin exudation occurs with some parcels of these timbers (especially keruing); select material free from resin for painted work
	Keruing					Medium	Moderate	
	Red meranti Red seraya	Moderate				Small	*	Log core may contain brittleheart
	Sapele	Yes	Extremely resistant	Medium	Moderate	Medium	Good	
Class 4 Perishable or non-durable	Redwood	Yes	Sapwood permeable Heartwood moderately resistant	Low	Mild	Medium	Good	
	Western hemlock	No	Sapwood and heartwood resistant	Low	Mild	Small	Good	
	Whitewood							
	American red oak	Yes	Sapwood permeable Heartwood resistant	Medium	Moderate	Medium	Poor	Non-ferrous fitments advisable
	Beech	No	Permeable	Medium (variable)	Moderate (variable)	Large	Good	
	Ramin			Medium	Moderate	Large	Moderate, but experience is limited	

† When sapwood is present, the timber should be preservative-treated regardless of the durability of the heartwood.

* Seldom painted; there is therefore little painting experience.

Treatment of decay

It is important that all decayed wood should be cut out and paint stripped from adjacent areas so that damp, but not rotten, timber can be given a chance to dry out. If decay is extensive the entire window unit may have to be replaced. Wood exposed by cutting should be treated liberally with a paintable preservative, again allowed to dry, then given a coat of primer. Depending on their size, holes should be made good with stopper or primed timber, suitably shaped. Another coat of primer should be applied to the new surface, followed by undercoat and finishing coats. If paint has been stripped from cills and lower rails of windows, a wise precaution is to apply a liberal treatment of preservative and allow to dry for a few days before priming.

New methods of *in-situ* treatment such as injection of preservative are becoming available. Their ultimate value has not yet been determined but they show sufficient promise to warrant consideration.

Recommendations

1 When making use of Specifications and Codes of Practice bear in mind that their requirements may not be adequate in every circumstance to ensure satisfactory durability of the timber.

2 To ensure adequate service from Baltic redwood and other timbers of low decay resistance, insist on preservative treatment, if necessary with a paintable preservative.

3 If durable hardwood is to be used specify the timber by name and insist on the exclusion of sapwood.

4 Protect joinery from the weather during delivery to the site, and on the site before installation.

5 Refuse to accept low quality shop primers. Specify British Standard primers. Ensure an adequate painting system and sound putty.

Other BRE Digests

 72 Home-grown softwoods for building
106 Painting woodwork
110 Condensation
127 An index of exposure to driving rain
182 Natural finishes for exterior timber
201 Wood preservatives : application methods

Timber fire doors

A well-designed door assembly (leaves, frame, hinges and other door furniture) will fulfil its normal functions of isolation, insulation and security without causing too much hindrance to the movement of people and goods. Delaying the spread of fire and smoke is one important aspect of security.

The precise role to be played by doors in various locations in buildings, the methods of assessing performance and the criteria to be applied are topics under active discussion in this country and abroad. This digest, which can give guidance only of a general nature, reviews the current situation and will be further revised when these activities have resulted in changes in specifications and requirements.
This digest replaces Digest 155 which is now withdrawn.

Fig 1

Different parts of a building may be separated from each other into compartments by a fire-resisting construction; any openings leading to and from them will be closed by doors which will have a precise function to fulfil in case of a fire. First, the door should prevent excessive transmission of products of combustion which can interfere with the safe use of escape routes; second, it should maintain the effectiveness as a fire-barrier of the wall in which it is located. Every fire door is therefore required to act as a barrier to the passage of fire and smoke to varying degrees dependent upon its location in a building and the fire hazard associated with the building or room, bearing in mind its contents, occupants and use.

Functions

The majority of fires start from small sources and develop quantities of smoke in the early stages. There will generally be pressure differences across a door caused either by the wind or by the fire itself. These pressures can act either to force smoke through gaps or cracks in and around the door, or sometimes to oppose its flow. In the absence of effects due to wind or changes in temperature in the fire compartment, the flow into the fire compartment takes the form shown in Fig 2.

A door in the enclosing walls bounding the fire compartment will be subjected to these pressures and smoke will be forced through any gaps. As the fire progresses, there may be some damage to the door which may become deformed and consequently allow greater quantities of smoke to pass through. If the fire becomes large the door is required to withstand exposure to the high temperature conditions without losing its integrity.

The functions of fire doors may therefore be summarised as :

1 To provide adequate resistance to the passage of smoke and other combustion products during the early stages of a fire.

2 To provide a barrier to a well-developed fire without permitting excessive quantities of smoke and hot gases to pass.

Some doors may be required to fulfil only the first function as they may not be subjected to the full severity of a fire because of their location; others may have the main aim of resisting fire penetration as indicated by the second function. Some may have to meet both requirements. At present, fire doors are used as smoke control doors when required to fulfil the first function and fire resisting doors to fulfil the second.

The ability of fire doors to perform their designed function will depend upon their being fully closed at the time of fire; they are, therefore, normally required to be fitted with positive closing devices. Electro-magnetic or similar hold-open devices may sometimes be used which can be released by an automatic detector or alarm signal but any attempt to prevent a door closing by wedges or hooks will have disastrous effects in the event of fire.

Fig 2   Typical movement of air and combustion gases around the edges of a closed door to a room involved in fire (wind and expansion effects ignored)

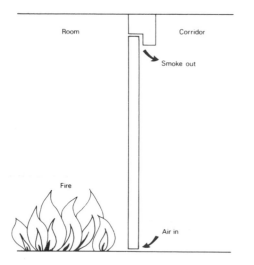

Assessment of performance

The performance of door assemblies as barriers against the passage of fire, ie fire resistance, is judged by subjecting them to standard heating conditions in a furnace (Fig 3). The current test procedure is specified in BS 476:Part 8:1972 and although this replaced the fire resistance section in BS 476:Part 1:1953, tests carried out under the earlier standard may still be acceptable to many authorities. As Part 8 made a few fundamental changes in the procedure for testing, reference will be made to both parts.

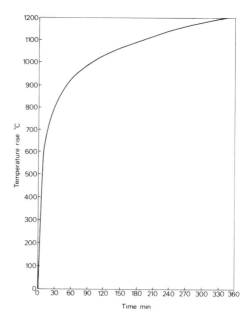

Fig 3   Standard time-temperature curve BS 476:Part 8:1972

Neither Part 8 nor Part 1 specifies how doors should be constructed but both require the specimen door assembly to be representative of the one to be used in practice, including all essential hardware. One of the requirements is that the gap between the door and frame of the assembly to be tested shall not be less than 3 mm unless the gap is controlled in practice (as with a door set). Tests are carried out on a complete door assembly mounted in a wall representing its use in practice (Fig 4). By testing a door in one design of frame and using it in another, no guarantee can be given of its behaviour under fire conditions. The test procedure is fully described in the Standard and consists of exposing one face to the standard heating condition whilst observing the door for the maintenance of stability, integrity and insulation.* Part 8 requires the tests to be carried out with the upper

*Stability: resistance to collapse of the specimen.
 Integrity: resistance to penetration of flame or hot gases which can ignite a combustible fibrous pad. Integrity is also lost when spontaneous flaming occurs on the unexposed face (ie the side of the specimen which is not being subjected to the heating conditions of the furnace).
 Insulation: resistance to excessive temperature rise on the unexposed face.

part of the door under a small positive pressure, to simulate the conditions likely to occur in a fire. It also provides a more objective method of establishing the loss of integrity of a door by using a combustible fibrous pad; this was previously established by visual observation. Part 1 did not require any measurements to be made of the insulation provided by a door against the transfer of heat.

BS 476:Part 8 states that a door which may be required to resist fire from either side shall be tested in the direction which will produce the lower fire resistance. When this direction cannot be identified, duplicate tests shall be made so that the minimum fire resistance of the assembly can be determined.

An International Organisation for Standardisation (ISO) method of test for the fire resistance of doors is specified in ISO 3008. This standard is similar to ISO 834 for elements of building construction but is designed specifically for doors.

Fire behaviour

On exposure to high temperatures, charring of the exposed face occurs leading to surface ignition. Burning of the timber from the exposed face and the consequent movement of moisture inside the section causes deformation of the door panel (Fig 5).

Timber doors are usually provided with two or three hinges along one vertical edge and a latch at about mid-height along the other. The triangular sections at the top and the bottom of the door are free to deform and the maximum movement is likely to occur at the two corners on the closing edge. If the closing face of the door is exposed to the fire conditions, the stops on the frame will restrain this movement but this will stress the hinges and latch. When the opening face is exposed there is no restraint at the corners which are then free to deform. The gaps between the door edges and the frame provide an area which the flames can exploit and

Fig 5   Deformation of door

the extent of charring is greater than through the solid section. The amount of damage is influenced significantly by the initial size of the gaps, by any increase in gap that may occur by shrinkage and warping of the door and by the flow of hot gases through the gaps.

Gradual deterioration of the door assembly along the edges between the door and frame leads to the transmission of hot gases, widening of gaps, appearance of glowing on the unexposed face (Fig 6) and finally flaming. Initial failure is frequently in the upper half of the door, either along the top edge or the vertical sides close to the hinges. Failure in these areas usually occurs before penetration of fire through the door.

Fig 6   Fire penetration along edges

Fig 4   Fire resistance of a door

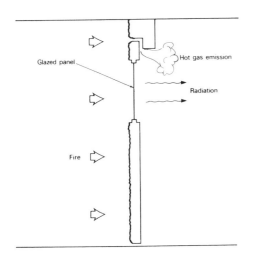

One technique for minimising the susceptibility of door edges to early penetration by fire consists of applying to the edges special materials having intumescing characteristics so that a rise in temperature will cause the material to swell and close the gaps. Intumescent paints have been used but the most successful and reliable technique is to insert an intumescent device, or to inject paste into a groove cut in the door or the frame edge. As soon as the temperature in the vicinity of the protection exceeds 200°C, usually about 10–15 minutes after the start of the standard test, the intumescent product swells and seals the gap (Fig 7).

For the increased protection needed with one-hour doors, a few of these strips, both in the door and the frame edge, may be necessary. The protection must be continuous and not interrupted at hinges and latch plates. In some methods, certain specific types of intumescent material can be located behind a protective timber veneer.

Specifications

Doors are specified by fire regulations in a number of ways, for example:

Constructional specification	– The London Building (Constructional) By-Laws 1972
Performance specification	– The Building Regulations 1976
Type specification	– British Standard Code of Practice, CP3 Chapter IV

Although BS 476:Part 8 allows door assemblies to be judged by three criteria, stability, integrity and insulation, regulations and codes do not usually require compliance with the insulation requirement. *The performance of a given door assembly can be established categorically only by test, but an assessment may be possible from a close study of the design features.* The data given in this section are intended to highlight the important features and measures that are necessary.

Smoke-control doors

At present there is no standard definition or test method for assessing the performance of doors which are required to restrict the passage of smoke but work is in progress under ISO to define criteria and test procedures which may be used for classification.

Doors which are installed solely to limit the spread of relatively cool smoke within escape routes may need little or no fire resistance and therefore the thickness of the door and type and extent of any glazing may not be critical.

Single swing doors must be close fitting in a rebated frame with 25 mm deep stops so that despite a

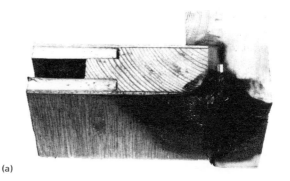
(a)

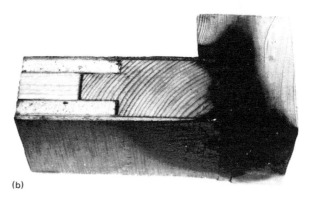
(b)

Fig 7 Exposure to fire on door (a) with intumescent strip and (b) without

pressure difference across the two sides only small quantities of smoke will pass. Additional seals must be provided around the edges if stops are smaller. Normal draught excluders can be satisfactory for a time but will not remain effective under fire conditions.

Doors which are required to swing in both directions, such as in corridors and lobbies, and therefore cannot be rebated, are likely to offer less resistance to the passage of smoke. Smoke-resistance can be improved by fitting smoke seals such as felt brush or flexible polyurethane foam; intumescent strips will not become effective until the later stages of a fire.

Fire-resisting doors

The periods of fire resistance which regulations specify, and for which timber fire doors are generally suitable, are listed in Table 1. Those doors which provide a lower integrity than stability are sometimes referred to as fire-check doors but it is preferable to refer to the door's performance for clarity.

Half-hour (30/20) fire-resisting doors The specification which is given in BS 459:Part 3 is widely used and even with doors of a different design it is customary to use the frame specified in the Standard. The doors are 45 mm thick but some 40 mm doors have been proved successful by test; in all cases the frame has 25 mm deep stops which may be glued and pinned or screwed to the frame. The gap between the door edge and the frame should not exceed 3 mm; two or three hinges and a

Table 1 Fire-resisting doors

Door type	Stability Minutes	Integrity Minutes
Half-hour	30	20
	30	30
One-hour	60	45
	60	60

latch are required to hold the door in the closed position (Fig 8).*

Alternative door constructions which have been shown to provide similar performances are solid timber, compressed straw, extruded chipboard, cork, flaxboard and compressed fibre-board strips.

One-hour (60/45) fire-resisting doors A specification is given in BS 459:Part 3 for 54 mm thick doors of composite construction with asbestos board mounted in an impregnated timber frame with 25 mm stops cut from the solid or in a steel frame with 20 mm stops. The gaps between the door edge and the frame should not exceed 3 mm. At least three hinges and a substantial latch and latch plate are needed.*

Other door constructions which have been shown to provide similar performances include blockboard, compressed straw and cork cores with asbestos facings and veneer.

Half-hour (30/30) and one-hour (60/60) fire-resisting doors These doors are based on similar designs to those found satisfactory for the 30/20 and 60/45 situations, but with additional protection to prevent fire penetration at the edges. It should be emphasised that the only practical constraints on the design of door assemblies tested under BS 476:Part 8

*The performances indicated above for the two types of door construction in BS 459:Part 3 are in relation to the BS 476:Part 1 test procedure. The use of some form of intumescent protection is normally standard practice for all doors now submitted for test and such protection would allow the BS 459: Part 3 doors to satisfy the corresponding criteria under Part 8.

Fig 8 Recommended hinge and latch positions

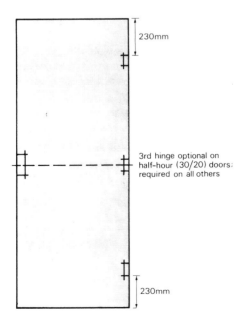

230mm

3rd hinge optional on half-hour (30/20) doors; required on all others

230mm

are to achieve satisfactory performance in terms of stability and integrity. Therefore, different forms of leaf construction, weight and thickness, as well as frame, are available from the industry. Timber door assemblies have also been successfully tested for performance in excess of 60/60.

Glazing

Glazing may range from a small vision panel in a door to a hinged, glazed screen for maximum light transmission. Ordinary glass cracks when exposed to heat and is liable to fall out fairly early in a fire. Wired glass 6 mm thick can withstand exposure to the heating condition in a fire test for at least 60 minutes before it reaches a temperature high enough to soften it. The main reason for this is that nearly 50 per cent of the incident heat is transmitted through the glass by radiation.

The size of the glass and the method of its retention are important factors which influence its performance. As the temperature approaches the softening point a large sheet will tend to collapse earlier than a smaller one. On the unexposed face, beading retaining the glass is subjected to radiant and conducted heat through the glass and to convection currents at the top of the pane. This can raise the temperature sufficiently to ignite timber beading after about 20 minutes (Fig 9). To delay the ignition of beading to 30 minutes it is necessary to provide protection by impregnation, surface coating or a surface covering of non-combustible material. For longer periods of fire protection, an improved retention system for the glazing is needed; so far only non-combustible glazing sub-frames have been shown to be satisfactory. The glass panel should be small and the method of fixing it should ensure that no direct path can be created for the transference of hot gases.

The maximum pane sizes given in CP 153:Part 4: 1972 for wired glazing are 1.2 m² for timber or metal frames and 0.5 m² if the glazing is required to satisfy the integrity requirement of Part 8 for 60 minutes for timber.

Fig 9 Testing fire doors (ignition of glazing beads and door edges)

Fittings and furniture

Hinges and latches have an important role in ensuring the stability of the door. The hinges must remain adequately screwed, in spite of the charring of wood in the vicinity, to provide the necessary fixing to the edge of the door. It is common to use three hinges although tests have shown that with some doors two hinges may be adequate for the half-hour period. Steel and brass hinges are effective for a half-hour door, but only steel hinges are recommended for a one-hour door. For the latter, it may be necessary to use hinges with extended flaps (broad butts) so that fixing is maintained even when severe charring has taken place.

The latch is the only holding device on the closing edge, and so it is important that it should be strong and that the nib of the latch should engage into the latch plate at least 10 mm to ensure that the closing edge will not spring open when the door deforms. Cranked-flap latch plates are advisable for one-hour doors. Where mortice locks are provided, the cut-out in the door should be the minimum necessary to prevent any voids which fire can penetrate. After the edges, the mortice lock and latch areas represent the next zone of weakness. Filling the voids in the cut-out with intumescent paste will markedly lessen the weakness in this area.

Plastics and aluminium handles and knobs will be destroyed on the fire side but this may not have a serious effect on the integrity of the door if steel spindles are provided. Letter plates introduce a weakness in a door and should ideally be positioned in the lower part of the door. Letter plates made of aluminium are likely to melt within the half-hour period of the test and a steel flap may be necessary on the inside of the door to maintain integrity.

Self-closing devices can suffer damage and consequently become inoperative if they are surface mounted on the exposed face. If their sole function is to close the door with a latch, when they have done so any damage suffered need not be critical for the integrity of the door. Recessed self-closing devices will suffer less damage, but can produce a local weakness if fitted in the top of the door leaf. The ideal place is within the sill where it will cause the least interference with the performance of the door. The Building Regulations set out the circumstances in which rising butts may be used: where they are fitted, compensation must be provided for the cut-out from the top edge of the door by increasing the depth of the stop (Fig 10).

A self-closing device used with double swing doors, or any door not fitted with a latch, should not only close the door leaf but also hold it firmly in the closed

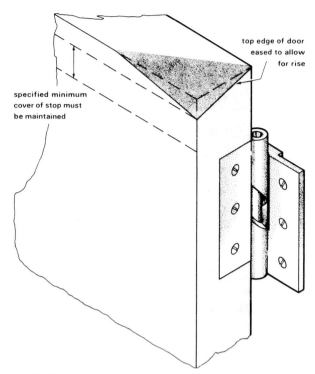

specified minimum cover of stop must be maintained

top edge of door eased to allow for rise

Fig 10 Rising butts need a deeper head stop

position. It needs to be strong enough to keep the door leaf closed against any pressure to which it may be subjected in a fire, and be so designed and fixed that it continues to function even though subjected to high temperatures.

Existing doors

Occasionally it is necessary to improve the performance of an existing door to a half-hour 30/20 or 30/30 standard, although in practice it may be more economic to replace the door rather than alter it.

Panelled doors having stiles and rails not less than 37 mm in thickness are generally suitable for upgrading; flush doors need to have a substantial sub-frame and unless the precise specification of a flush door is known, it is difficult to be sure about its suitability for upgrading.

Various methods of upgrading are available, but for any system involving the use of board materials the importance of fixing cannot be over-emphasised if the additional protection is to be of value. Additional materials must be so fixed to the existing door that under conditions of fire, where thermal movement is likely to take place between the door and protective material, the screws or nails are not stressed so that they are pulled out.

Existing door assemblies can seldom be upgraded to a higher standard than 30/20 or 30/30.

British Standards

BS 459 :Part 3 :1951 Fire-check flush doors and wood and metal frames (half-hour and one-hour types)

BS 476 Fire tests on building materials and structures
        Part 1 :1953 Fire tests on building materials and structures
        Part 8 :1972 Test methods and criteria for the fire resistance of elements of building construction

CP 153 Windows and rooflights : Part 4 :1972 Fire hazards associated with glazing in buildings.

CP 3   Code of basic data for the design of buildings : Chapter IV : Precautions against fire
        Part 1 :1971 Flats and maisonettes (in blocks over two storeys)
        Part 2 :1968 Shops and department stores
        Part 3 :1968 Office buildings

Damp-proof courses

Damp-proof courses are barriers so placed in a building that the passage of moisture between the parts they separate is negligible. Such barriers are needed in floors (see Digests 18 and 54) but this Digest is limited to the other parts of the structure where damp-proof courses are necessary. Components which shed rain directly, such as roof coverings and flashings, are mentioned only when used as, or in conjunction with, damp-proof courses.

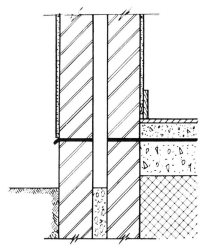

Fig. 1

Movements of moisture

Upward movement of moisture is normally prevented just above ground level; prevention of downward movement is needed at many levels, eg in parapets, chimneys and above lintels in cavity walls. Horizontal movement of moisture must occasionally be prevented, eg where the outer leaf of a cavity wall is returned at an opening to close the cavity, and where wall dpc's are at different levels from those of damp-proof membranes in abutting floors. Examples follow of the main position for dpc's.

Dpc's near the ground

Dpc's are required at the foot of a wall (solid and cavity construction) and should be at least 150 mm above ground level. Cavities must be kept clear. Stopping the dpc short of the external wall face and pointing the joint with mortar is not recommended. External render coats are frequently and incorrectly taken to ground level or below for the sake of appearance. The rendering should be stopped at dpc level (Fig. 1); the weaker the rendering the more necessary this precaution. Materials heaped against an outside wall can bridge the dpc, making it ineffective (see Digest 27).

Where an internal division wall has a solid floor on one side and suspended timber floor on the other (Fig. 2), the intermediate cavity must be kept clear.

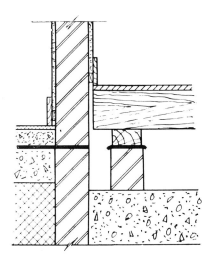

Fig. 2

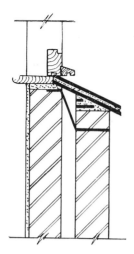

Fig. 3

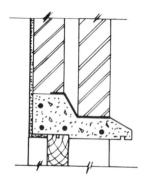

Fig. 5

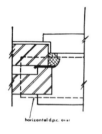

horizontal d.p.c. over

Fig. 6

Fig. 4

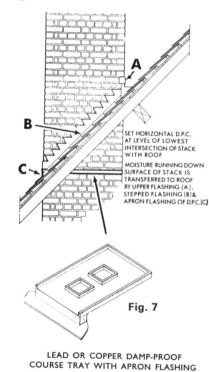

SET HORIZONTAL D.P.C.
AT LEVEL OF LOWEST
INTERSECTION OF STACK
WITH ROOF

MOISTURE RUNNING DOWN
SURFACE OF STACK IS
TRANSFERRED TO ROOF
BY UPPER FLASHING (A),
STEPPED FLASHING (B) &
APRON FLASHING OF D.P.C. (C)

Fig. 7

LEAD OR COPPER DAMP-PROOF
COURSE TRAY WITH APRON FLASHING

Sills

A sill of porous material or of jointed lengths of impervious material should be bedded on a flexible or semi-rigid dpc if it is part of a solid wall or bridges a cavity. In Fig. 3 the flexible dpc extends to the back of the sill. If the sill or its covering is impervious, no dpc is normally needed unless there is a danger of cracking, as in Fig. 4.

Lintels

Similar considerations apply to lintels. Fig. 5 shows a flexible dpc over a boot lintel. Sometimes a precast concrete lintel supports the inner leaf only and the outer is carried on a flat arch. However, the principle of protection against moisture is the same in all cases. A flexible dpc is sloped across the cavity to drain any moisture away from the inner leaf. It is tucked into a joint above the lintel or into a groove in the lintel. It is then brought down to the top of the opening to lie between the outer leaf and the window or door frame. The dpc should extend at least 100 mm beyond the ends of the lintel.

Openings in cavity walls

Where the outer leaf is returned to close the cavity a vertical dpc should be provided (Fig. 6). The dpc may be of two courses of slate in mortar but more usually a flexible sheet material is used.

Chimney stacks

For a chimney at or near the ridge and extending only slightly above it, good weather protection at the top is sufficient in all but very exposed positions. When the exposed part of the stack is more than about 1 m high, a dpc is advisable where the stack emerges from the roof. The simplest and most effective form is a combined dpc and flashing of lead or copper as shown in Fig. 7. Good protection at the top of the stack is also needed.

Table 1 Materials for damp-proof courses

Material	Minimum weight kg/m²	Minimum thickness mm	Joint treatment to prevent water moving: upward	downward	Liability to extrusion	Durability	Other considerations
Group A: Flexible							
Lead to BS 1178	Code No 4		Lapped at least 100 mm	Welted	Not under pressures met in normal construction	Corrodes in contact with fresh lime or Portland cement mortar	To prevent corrosion apply bitumen or bitumen paint of heavy consistency to the corrosion-producing surface and both lead surfaces
Copper to BS 2870, Grade A, annealed condition	Approx. 2.28*	0.25	Lapped at least 100 mm†	Welted†	Not under pressures met in normal construction	Highly resistant to corrosion	Where soluble salts are known to be present (eg sea salt in sand) similar treatment to lead is recommended. Copper may stain external surfaces, especially stone
Bitumen to BS 743: A—hessian base B—fibre base C—asbestos base D—hessian base and lead E—fibre base and lead F—asbestos base and lead G—sheeting with hessian base	3.8 3.3 3.8 4.4 4.4 4.9 5.4	— — — — — — —	Lapped at least 100 mm	Lapped and sealed	Likely to extrude under heavy pressure but this is unlikely to affect water resistance	The hessian or felt may decay but this does not affect efficiency if the bitumen remains undisturbed. Types D, E and F are most suitable for buildings that are intended to have a very long life or where there is risk of movement	Materials should be unrolled with care. In cold weather the rolls should be warmed before use
Polythene, black, low density (0.915–0.925 g/ml)	Approx 0.5	0.46	Lapped for distance at least equal to width of dpc	Welted	Not under pressures met in normal construction	No evidence of deterioration in contact with other building materials	Welted joints must be held in compression. When used as cavity trays exposed on elevation these materials may need bedding in mastic for the full thickness of the outer leaf of walling, to prevent penetration by driving rain
Pitch/polymer	Approx 1.5	1.27	Lapped at least 100 mm	Lapped and sealed			
Group B: Semi-rigid							
Mastic asphalt to BS 1097 or BS 1418	—	—	No joint problems		Liable to extrude under pressures above 65 kN/m². Material of hardness appropriate to conditions should be used	No deterioration	To provide key for mortar below next course of brickwork, grit should be beaten into asphalt immediately after application and left proud of surface. Alternatively the surface should be scored whilst still warm
Group C: Rigid							
Epoxy resin/sand	—	6.0	No joint problems		Not extruded	No evidence of deterioration in contact with other building materials	Resin content should be about 15%. The appropriate hardener should be used
Brick to BS 3921; max water absorption 4.5%	—	—	—	Not suitable	Not extruded	No deterioration	Use two courses, laid to break joint, bedded in 1:3 Portland cement:sand
Slates at least 230 mm long; should pass wetting and drying test and acid-immersion test of BS 3798	—	5.0	—	Not suitable although they may sometimes be used to resist lateral movement of water	Not extruded	No deterioration	

* Where copper is to form in one piece a dpc and a projecting drip or flashing it should weigh at least 4.12 kg/m²

† Copper may be welded, in which case phosphorus-deoxidised copper to BS 1172 should be used

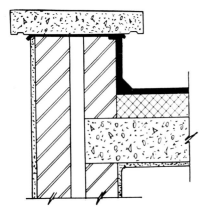

Fig. 8

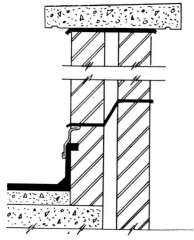

Fig. 9

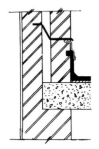

Fig. 10

Parapets

With a very low solid parapet wall there is nothing to be gained by adding a dpc at or near roof level but one under the coping is recommended. The roof covering is extended up the face of the wall and tucked in under the dpc (Fig. 8).

High parapets should contain a dpc at or near roof level which is lapped with the roof covering, as well as a dpc below the coping (Fig. 9).

Roofs at different levels

Where the roofs of adjacent parts of a building are at different levels, the wall exposed between them must have a dpc joined to the lower roof covering to give complete protection against downward penetration of moisture (Fig. 10).

Properties of damp-proof courses

As yet, no Standard lays down performance requirements for dpc materials. BS 743 specifies the quality of some of them and their properties are summarised in Table 1. The table also includes notes on pitch/polymer and epoxy resin/sand not included in the Standard. Group A materials are suitable for most situations and they alone should be used over openings and for bridging cavities. Flexible dpc's over openings in hollow walls should as far as possible be in one piece so as to avoid the sagging that can occur at lapped joints. Flexible materials are suitable for situations where a stepped dpc is necessary; some are also capable of being dressed to complex shapes without fracture.

Group B material is particularly suitable for very thick walls and where there is high water pressure.

Group C materials can withstand heavy loads but are more likely to be fractured by building movement than materials in the other groups. In addition to the materials listed, new types of dpc are likely to come from developments in plastics sheet materials, synthetic resin mortars and synthetic rubbers.

Semi-rigid asbestos bitumen sheet is already used for cavity gutters and flashings and has advantages in rigidity and ease of jointing.

High quality concrete will resist the passage of *liquid* water. As some transmission of water *vapour* through damp-proof courses is normally permissible, dense, quality-controlled concrete might, therefore, come to be accepted without the further protection of a damp-proof course. It is, however, difficult to specify a mix and its compaction to achieve the quality needed.

Methods of damp-proofing existing walls are discussed in Digest 27.

Wall cladding: designing to minimise defects due to inaccuracies and movements

This digest deals with non-loadbearing cladding and facings. It is concerned mainly with the factors that influence rain penetration and dislodgement, commenting on the critical points to be considered in design, execution and supervision, so that defects of these kinds can be minimised. Readers are recommended to read also Digest 217, which deals with the diagnosis of causes of these defects and is relevant, therefore, to 'design' also. Cladding may be required to contribute to building performance in other respects, eg thermal insulation and fire; these, and considerations affecting the building as a whole, such as foundation movements, are not dealt with. The guidance provided is unavoidably in general terms and must be interpreted according to the specific circumstances of exposure, building height and construction materials.

Key issues

Inaccuracies and movements in both cladding and supporting structures affect all claddings and need to be considered in combination. Both can affect fixings, bearings and joints so as to influence weathertightness or safety. For example, when joints are small as a result of inaccuracies, movements may be large in relation to joint width so that sealants are over-strained; rain penetration may then ensue. Further movement after the joint has closed can damage fixings and dislodge cladding. Fixings, because they are between cladding and structure, are therefore between two parts of construction that will almost always move by different amounts and, commonly, in different directions.

Movements caused by changes in temperature or moisture content and by shrinkage are directly related to size. Differential movements between cladding and structure can always be expected to occur and it is particularly important to consider the sizes of those areas of cladding that will behave as an entity (if, for example, joints within an area are incompressible). Listed below are the principal factors determining the effects of movements and inaccuracies. Calculations of these effects provides basic data for use in design:

Size of any part of the cladding which will behave as an entity, and expected change in size with change of temperature and moisture content. Corresponding size of supporting structure or background*, and expected change in size with change in temperature and moisture content, and shrinkage, deflection and creep. Relative direction of movements between cladding and structure or background*: whether movements act together or in opposing directions.

Extent and direction of the movements considered above at joints, fixings, above and below bearings and at other locations such as those where is a change of background materials or construction.
Predicted inaccuracies of cladding and structure (see BS5606).

Predicted effects of inaccuracies on joints, fixings and bearings (see Digest 199).

These considerations are an important part of the basis on which to select, or design, jointing details and materials (including those for special joints such as "compression" joints), fixing details (and the separate provisions for adjustability and for movement that they will need) and bearing sizes and limits.

*The term 'background' is intended to cover the case in which cladding is attached directly, without an intervening gap, for example, tiled rendered brickwork.

Movements

It is critically important to examine potential designs for those dimensional changes in service which will produce *relative* movements between cladding and structure or background. The principle illustrated in Fig. 1 may be a self-evident one, but the design problem is, of course, to translate it into its practical effect at particular locations and in particular circumstances. The dotted "links" in Fig. 1 illustrate how the problem becomes increasingly important with increase in the dimension over which relative movement occurs. Fig. 1, though shown as if it applied in the vertical plane, may equally apply on plan. Also, while it shows the commonest condition, of cladding moving "positively" with respect to the structure, the reverse may also occur, though generally with less damage. The implications of Fig. 1 in practice are made apparent by visualising, imposed upon it, design arrangements for fixings, for eaves overhang, for projecting floors or columns, for compressible or incompressible cladding joints, for adhesion between cladding and background and so on.

The relative movements illustrated by Fig. 1 may be reversible (for example, seasonally, daily, or even over periods of a few minutes) or irreversible (for example, shrinkage of cement-based materials, creep under sustained load, moisture expansion of brickwork). Movements with different causes (also reversible and irreversible) may operate simultaneously and may be characteristic of either cladding or structure or both. And, as noted earlier, the problem cannot be considered in isolation from the effects of inaccuracies. However, if each contributory factor is examined in turn and allocated a value, or discounted if appropriate, their combined effect at critical points can be assessed.

Table 1 lists the kinds of movements that occur. It thus first provides assistance in the choice of materials. Subsequently, more detailed consideration can be given, quantifying the expected movements and thus the amounts and directions of relative movements. The effects of constraints provided by fixings, bearings or containment by other parts, in concentrating relative movements at particular locations, can be evaluated and the implications for the design of joints and fixings can then be examined.

Inaccuracies and movements at joints

So far as movements alone are concerned, joints fall into two main categories: rigid joints that permit no movement (for example, welded, glued or bolted joints) and flexible joints which permit both expansion and contraction (for example, open joints, sealant-filled or gasketted joints). The mortar joint is something of a hybrid of both categories but in this context its predominant feature is its incompressibility.

The importance of rigid joints here is that they produce an assembly, larger than its jointed parts, that will behave as an entity, and so accentuate the problem illustrated in principle in Fig. 1. The importance of joints in the second category is that the limitations imposed by the capabilities of jointing materials (sealants, gaskets, baffles etc.) need to be carefully compared with the effects, at the joint, of movements and inaccuracies. Also in this category are those joints at which substantial relative movement must be accommodated and which, although called "expansion joints", "compression joints", always need in practice to be able to accommodate movement of both kinds. Flexible joints cannot safely be designed on the assumption of a particular single value of intended width. A single width value, such as is commonly specified, cannot be achieved consistently (because of unavoidable inaccuracies) and a joint that chances initially to have the specified width will not remain at that width (because of movements in service). The important characteristic of such a joint, whatever its detail design, is that it has in-built limits of width within which it can perform satisfactorily. The working limits of size can be identified by inspection of the design details—for example, comparing the width of a baffle with the depths of the grooves, or determining the least and greatest compression appropriate to a gasket. The limits so identified may be modified by other factors such as the need for installation clearance. There is little point in determining the limits very precisely provided that one errs in the safe direction. These limits then provide criteria for comparison with the predicted effects of movements and inaccuracies on joint widths, so that the designer can select or design an appropriate joint. Subsequently, the limits can be specified to the builder so that he can know whether or not constructed joints are satisfactory in this critically important respect. He has no means of judging satisfactoriness if, for example, "12 mm joints" are specified. Exactly similar considerations

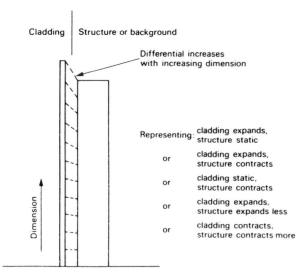

Fig 1 "... the problem becomes increasingly important with increase in dimension over which the relative movement occurs"

Table 1—Movements that may affect cladding

	Cause	Effect	Duration, frequency	Examples of materials or components affected	Significance for design
1	Temperature changes	Expansion and contraction	Intermittent, diurnal, seasonal	All. Where restrained, distortion or damage may occur. Distortion may also result from temperature gradients or from from non-homogeneity	Extent of movement is influenced by thermal coefficient, exposure, colour, thermal capacity, insulation provided by backing
2 a)	Moisture content changes: Initial moisture absorption	Irreversible expansion	Relatively short term, due to absorbtion of moisture after manufacture	Brick and other ceramic products	Depends on age of product most movement occurs within first 3 months of product's life
b)	Initial moisture release	Irreversible contraction	Relatively short term	Mortar, concrete, sand-lime bricks	May require measures to control or distribute cracking
c)	Alternate absorption release of moisture in service	Expansion and contraction	Periodic—e.g. seasonal	Most porous building materials, including cement based and wood or wood based products. Restraints, humidity gradients or non-homogeneity may produce distortion. Laminates of dissimilar materials may bow particularly if their construction is asymmetrical	Generally less significant for cladding than are thermal movements but wood experiences large moisture induced movements across the grain.
3 a)	Loading on structure: Elastic deformation under service loads	Normally insignificant in vertical members but horizontal members may deflect	Continuous or intermittent under live loads; long term under dead loads	Suspended floor and roof slabs, beams, edge beams or spandrels, of all materials (whether they support or "contain" the cladding)	Needs consideration in relation to fixings and bearings for cladding and to possible compression of "contained" cladding: deflections in pre-stressed concrete members may be relatively large
	Creep	Contraction of vertical and deflection of horizontal members	Long term	Reinforced and pre-stressed concrete components as above	Needs consideration as above. May also be significant where load bearing concrete walls or columns have cladding such as mosaic or other tiling directly bonded
4	Wind loading on cladding	Deflection	Intermittent	Lightweight cladding, including fixed and opening glazing; sheet siding	Extent of deflection depends on exposure for a given stiffness. Deflection is commonly designed not to exceed 1/240 of the span in order to avoid damage to sealants or glazing
5 a)	Chemical changes: Corrosion	Expansion	Continuous	Iron and other ferrous metals	Depends on protection or on corrosion resistance of material; electrolytic corrosion may require consideration. Corroding fixings can seriously disrupt cladding
b)	Sulphate attack	Expansion	Continuous	Portland cement based products in construction where soluble sulphate salts (e.g. from high-sulphate bricks) and persistent dampness present	Significant for cladding where the construction affected has cladding such as mosaic or other tiling or rendering, bonded directly to it
c)	Carbonation	Contraction	Continuous	Porous Portland cement products, such as concrete, lightweight concrete, asbestos-cement	Not very significant unless distortion might result—for example, asbestos cement sheets painted on one face only
6	Vibration (from traffic, machinery, wind forces)	Generation of noise, possible loosening of fixings, disturbance of glazing seals	—	Lightweight cladding, sheet siding	Noise discomfort to occupants; possible rain penetration past seals by "pumping" action of glazing or spandrel panels. Natural frequency of cladding or panels may influence response
7 a)	Physical changes: Loss of volatiles	Contraction, loss of plasticity	Short or long term depending on materials, exposure	Some sealants, some plastics	Contributes to age-hardening of some sealants. May lead to embrittlement and distortion of some plastics
b)	Ice or crystalline salt formation	Expansion and possibly disruption in some building materials	Dependent on weather conditions	Porous natural stones, very exposed brickwork	Damage usually confined to spalling and erosion of surfaces

apply to sealant-filled joints. Here, however, an additional step is necessary to take account of the sealant's "movement accommodation factor" (MAF). MAF is expressed as a percentage, which should not be exceeded for that material, thus:

$$MAF = \frac{Movement}{min. \; joint \; width} \times 100$$

For design the expression can be rearranged thus:

$$min. \; joint \; width = \frac{movement \times 100}{MAF}$$

If the total range of expected movement at a joint is 2 mm, say, and a potentially suitable sealant has a MAF of 25%, then:

$$min. \; joint \; width = \frac{2 \times 100}{25}$$

and minimum permissible joint width is therefore 8 mm. Note that this would then be the smallest joint width permissible at *any time in service*. Clearly, if a joint, at the time of erection on, say, a cold day had a width of 8 mm, then the width on a subsequent hot day would be less than the permitted minimum of 8 mm. To safeguard against this possibility, since the conditions that will prevail at the time of construction are not known in advance, the total range of expected movement can be added to the calculated minimum (in the example $8+2=10$ mm) as an adjusted minimum width permissible at the time of assembly. (A different MAF value is provided depending whether the material is used in compression/tension or in shear, but the calculation required is the same in each case). If the minimum width required for installation is larger than the minimum calculated, then that larger width must be adopted as the limit value. The upper permissible working limit of joint width may then be established, for sealant filled joints, by the width beyond which there is a risk that the material will slump or by the cost of the repetitive applications of sealant that may be necessary in very wide joints.

Digest 199 and the BRE Graphical Aids handbook [1] indicate how the working limits of width established for a joint can be compared with inaccuracies and movements in service so as to determine the optimum sizes for components and construction and obtain the best probability of satisfactory assembly and performance in service.

Inaccuracies and movements influence both the performance of joints and the durability of jointing materials and many joint failures would have been avoided if more careful consideration had been given to these influences. However, failures due to degradation of jointing materials cannot be wholly avoided if their durability is less than that of the cladding, as is usually the case. Building owners know that paintwork will need to be renewed, and the probable frequency with which the need will arise. In the case of jointing materials, though, the building owner is often not aware of the need to renew and cannot know the jointing materials on which design, in respect of inaccuracies and movements, was based, unless he receives guidance from the designer.

Inaccuracies and movements at fixings

The design of fixings to resist loads is not dealt with here; the aim of this digest is to draw attention to factors that may negate an otherwise satisfactory design. These factors include movements and inaccuracies in terms of their effects both on the fixings themselves and on the cladding.

Fixings between cladding and structure are of two main types, supporting or restraining, though both types also position the cladding units in relation to each other and to the structure. For present purposes the important feature of the "supporting type" is that, where it provides a rigid connection between cladding and structure, it provides a datum from which relative movements in both will operate (as at the base of Fig. 1). It is essential therefore to assess the amount of relative movement that will accrue as a result elsewhere (for example, at restraining fixings, at joints, at the underside of the next bearing above) and make corresponding provision. Provision for movement at fixings introduces a potential conflict of design requirements for accommodation of relative movement and for mechanical soundness and rigidity. The design problem is further complicated by the need to make separate provision for inaccuracies.

Solutions to the problem depend on the form of the cladding. Some solutions may be primarily intended to provide adjustability though permitting some movement (as in Fig. 2a); others may take more deliberate account of relative movement (as in Fig. 2b) but place appreciable demands on accuracy. Codes of Practice such as CP 297 and CP 298 provide useful guidance on differential movements, but both Codes consider that "accuracy in the construction of of the background structure is essential, otherwise the fixings . . . will not fit". Unfortunately, the parts of the structure most concerned are usually those least amenable to the achievement of accuracy, and adjustabilities in fixings commonly prove inadequate. As explained in Digest 199, inaccuracies follow probability distributions. There is never certainty that inaccuracies will lie within required limits without correction, only an increasing probability that they will do so as the required limits are increasingly widely spaced. Conversely, if the limits are close, for example because the adjustability range of a fixing is small, there is increased probability that inaccuracies will exceed the limits.

Some commonly used cladding fixings have adjustability ranges that set very close limits. The practical significance is not merely the increased probability that inaccuracies will exceed the adjustability but that, very often, it is practicable neither to rectify the inaccuracies nor to devise on site an entirely satisfactory way to accommodate them. For these reasons also, even the best supervision on site does not necessarily solve the problem. A BRS survey of curtain walling [2] in the 1960s suggested that adjustment horizontally at right angles to the cladding needed to cover a range of 75 mm. This large value reflects the difficulty of controlling the plan shape of the structure at any one floor level, coupled with the need to take account of relative misalignment between all successive floors. For the latter reason the survey report also suggested a design separation distance of 50 mm between curtain wall cladding and structure. Experience and the measured data in BS 5606 suggest that in most circumstances, whatever the form of the cladding, adjustabilities smaller than ± 25 mm, in any of the three major axes, are likely to carry appreciable risk of unsatisfactory fit. Some pitfalls in the design and construction of adjustable fixings are illustrated in BRE Current Paper CP 28/77 [3].

Inaccuracies have an indirect but important influence on the durability of fixings. Inadequate design consideration of inaccuracies often leads to the adoption of poor site practices intended to overcome the resultant problems of fit at fixing positions and bearings. When it is unnecessary to devise ad hoc solutions as construction proceeds it is much more likely that mechanically secure and durable fixings can be achieved, There remains the potential problem that fixings, upon which the security of the cladding depends, may be permanently concealed from view in environments that may encourage corrosion, and subjected to loads and movements that may disturb them. Designers should consider the need to provide access for periodic inspection during the life of the building; such access also makes possible the future replacement of cladding components.

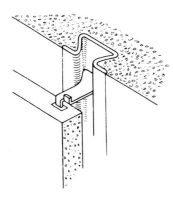

Fig 2(a) "Some . . . provide adjustability though permitting some movement"

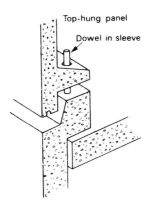

Fig 2(b) ". . . others may take more deliberate account of relative movement"

Distribution of movements by fixings

The character of fixings is illustrated in principle in Fig. 3, and the corresponding design implications can be summarised as:

Supporting type A: if the fixing provides a rigid connection between cladding and structure then its effects in distributing relative movements elsewhere need to be assessed.

Supporting type B: need to provide for relative movements in the direction "X".

Restraining type C: need to provide for relative movements in the direction "Y".

Restraining type D: need to provide for relative movements in directions "X" and "Y".

All types: need to provide for inaccuracies in each of the three major axes, noting that inaccuracies in the axis horizontally at right angles to the cladding plane may be large and require both large adjustability and a separation distance.

Practice commonly departs from these principles and often no problems arise because, for example, sizes are small or stresses are not damaging or rigid fixings "give" a little. However, the diagram indicates the factors that need to be assessed so that there is no departure from principles without prior consideration of the consequences in a specific application. Where cladding is supported directly by the structure, rather than indirectly via supporting fixings, there is a similar need to consider the effects of the supporting bearing on the distribution of relative movements. As

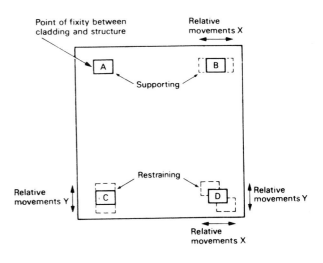

Fig 3 A top-hung cladding unit (in elevation) illustrates in principle how the distribution of relative movements can be determined from examination of the arrangement of fixings. In this example, fixing A is a type that permits no relative movement.

with designs in which more than one fixing provides a rigid connection between a cladding unit and the structure, the distribution will be influenced by the frictional restraints offered by fixings and bearings. In Fig. 4, for example, each cladding unit is supported by two fixings, either of which might offer the greater restraint to relative movements in service. In this case it is safer to assume that the movements in any two adjoining units will be concentrated at the joint between them, rather than that they will be shared equally by all joints. Alternatively, fixings may be so designed that, as in Fig. 3, the distribution of relative movements conforms to a predictable pattern.

Finally, in this section, consideration is given to fixing by adhesion, such as the bond between rendering and background, rather than by mechanical means. Relative movements are then important in that they can be accommodated only by stress in the materials and at interfaces.

In traditional uses of renderings the need to provide "soft" joints at intervals did not arise. However, in more recent uses of rendering, often as a base for mosaic or other tiling, new factors are present. These are the use of renderings on structural in-situ concrete, the greater heights of buildings, and the use of uninterrupted renderings across the changing backgrounds provided by composite construction. As a result of the first of these factors, relative movements arise from initial and long-term shrinkage in the in-situ concrete and from compression and creep under load.

The problems are accentuated by the second factor, the greater sizes producing greater total relative movement between structure and rendering. The third factor, changing backgrounds, introduces the possibility that different parts of the background are differently loaded or behave differently under similar loadings. At the same time, the differing backgrounds may respond differently to changes in ambient conditions and provide differing bond strengths at their interface with the rendering. All of these circumstances introduce the need for "soft" joints at intervals in tiled or rendered and tiled finishes. It is normally sufficient to provide horizontal soft joints in these finishes at storey height intervals and vertical or horizontal soft joints to coincide with joints, or changes in materials or form, in the background.

Desirable features of cladding fixings

There is, of course, no optimum design of fixing with universal application. However, in the following list each feature might be considered in turn for its relevance to a particular design context:

provide, where appropriate, a "designed clearance" between cladding and structure;

separate "provision for adjustment" from "provision for movement";

provide for movement, where necessary, following explicit consideration of amounts and directions, and of the effects of inaccuracies or provisions made for movement;

ensure that adjustability is not constrained by other parts;

avoid methods for providing adjustability that cannot be dissociated from strength (eg varying depth of engagement of a bolt in a socket);

provide largest practicable adjustability in each of the three major axes;

avoid a multiplicity of parts, particularly if they might be wrongly interchanged;

provide adjustments that can be readily made on site (a good solution, where practicable, is to design so that fixing devices can be plumbed and aligned as a separate operation before attachment of cladding);

provide adjustments that can be readily locked in their final positions to produce a secure fixing;

avoid different bolt sizes that require different torques;

design so that it will be apparent on visual inspection whether or not a fixing has been made as intended;

design for periodic inspection during building life.

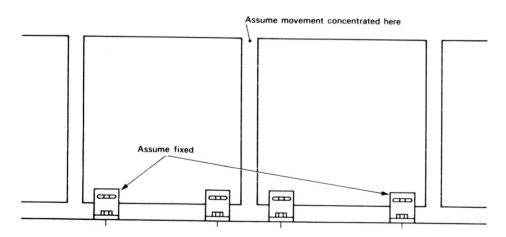

Assume movement concentrated here

Assume fixed

Fig 4 "...safer to assume that the movements in any two adjoining units will be concentrated at the joint between them..."

References and further reading

1   Graphical aids for tolerances and fits; HMSO, London;
    £15·50.
2   Adjustable fixings for curtain walling; BRE Current Paper
    Design Series 29.
3   Jointing specifications and achievement: a BRE survey;
    R B Bonshor; BRE Current Paper CP 28/77.

BRE Digests

199   Getting good fit
217   Wall cladding defects and their diagnosis

British Standards

CP 297 :1972 Precast concrete cladding (non-loadbearing)
CP 298 :1972 Natural stone cladding (non-loadbearing)
BS 5606 :1978 Accuracy in building

Wall cladding defects and their diagnosis

Two kinds of defects in cladding cause particular concern: rain penetration and dislodgement. Both are important in themselves. Unless rectified when warning signs appear, further deterioration is likely. Diagnosis of potential dislodgement of cladding over public ways is particularly important. This digest gives guidance on how to spot latent defects likely to lead to rain penetration or dislodgement and how to interpret warning signs. Unless warning signs are correctly interpreted, remedial work can be unsuitable and may even make matters worse. This digest deals with non-loadbearing cladding. Defects arising from external causes affecting the building as a whole (foundation movements, fire etc.) are not discussed.

Key issues; fixing, bearings, joints

The potential defects considered, rain penetration and dislodgement, can have a variety of origins as indicated in the following tables. However, inadequacies in fixings, bearings and joints have one potential origin in common: movements and inaccuracies which exceed the provision made in design. Faults of this kind may be local or general in the cladding: probably few claddings are totally free of them.

Inspection and diagnosis should, therefore, particularly try to assess whether the construction of fixings, tie-backs and supports has overcome inaccuracies without loss of security and durability, and whether joints are within their working limits of size and likely to remain so. Inspection and diagnosis should take into account that the life of many sealants, even under ideal conditions of use, is usually considerably less than that of the cladding and in some cases may be only about five years.

Differential movements are a common source of defects. While inspection and diagnosis should be made with all the potential causes of such movements in mind, particular consideration should be given to long term shrinkage and creep in in-situ concrete structures. Because of the effects of vertical loads, the amount of movement per unit length is greater in the vertical than the horizontal direction. Where the structural frame can creep independently of the cladding, the differential between cladding and structure will be progressively greater towards the top. This differential movement is potentially damaging unless compressible horizontal joints are used in the cladding. As a guide to the adequacy of horizontal compression joints, the total reduction in the height of a reinforced concrete-framed structure can be of the order of 30 mm in 30 m. During inspections, a particular watch should be kept for joints that are closed or nearly closed and for excessive areas of cladding in which joints are filled with mortar.

Detection of latent defects

Some defects may not be apparent from visual inspection and may be revealed only by dismantling or discovered by studying project documentation (drawings, specifications, etc) or records of previous repairs. No building owner wants to have work opened up unnecessarily. But where a serious defect is reported in similar buildings, or inspection shows that design or construction is substandard so that there is a risk of serious defects, opening up may be necessary. The construction drawings for the building are useful in diagnosis and wherever possible should be obtained and kept with maintenance records. However, they must be interpreted with care: they represent an idealised condition and may not show construction modifications even where these provided acceptable and satisfactory solutions to unforeseen problems arising during construction.

Many cladding defects are traceable to faults present from the start, pointing to the value of thorough inspection before the building is handed over. To be effective, initial inspection should go beyond items such as paintwork, aiming to spot items that, though minor at the time, may be early indications of significant defects.

Inspections at appropriate intervals can provide the opportunity to spot latent defects before they become serious. The frequency of inspection should take account of the age and previous performance of a building, its importance and its proximity to areas open to the public: Table 1 suggests a programme.

Table 1 Building facades: illustrative frequency of inspection

New buildings; older buildings after major alterations and repairs	Initially and then annually for first five years
Parts of all buildings where risk of damage by vandals or vehicle impact	Annually
Parts of buildings subject to severe exposure conditions, including all work above ninth floor of high structures	Every third year
Parts of all buildings over public areas	Every third year and after severe gales, heavy snowfall or other extremes of weather
Other buildings, and other parts of buildings in the categories above	Every five years, or when repainting is being scheduled if more frequent*
Parts of buildings known to contain latent defects	As appropriate to the nature and seriousness of the defect

*There are advantages in inspecting for defects during an inspection of the exterior of a building preparatory to repainting: warning signs of latent defects will not have been obscured by recent paintwork; making good of work opened up for inspection can be included in the repainting contract; any special provision needed for access can serve both purposes.

Places where defects are likely will be where exposure is greater (eg parapets) and where movement may show first (eg salient angles) because of a change in built form or at joints between different materials.

Design or construction faults might generate defects and the aim is to think what provisions ought to have been made and to see, or assess indirectly, if they have been.

What to look for

In all cases it is important to see whether a defect is repeated in a consistent pattern which may indicate how serious it is and provide clues to its diagnosis.

Defects which in themselves may be minor but, if not remedied, will lead to more serious defects. An example is a defective rainwater gutter or downpipe which, if not replaced will cause damp penetration followed by corrosion of metals, rotting of wood, frost damage and so on.

On cladding units or materials, look for cracks, spalling, staining, looseness and misalignment. For example, on concrete panels, iron stains may indicate iron-bearing aggregate (unsightly but not serious) or, if accompanied by cracking, may be an early indication that reinforcement or fixings are corroding: a more serious defect; check whether other units are stained and whether the pattern of reinforcement or fixing locations is apparent (see Table 2).

On jointing materials, signs that are common to both vertical and horizontal joints (eg hardening and splitting of a sealant) indicating ageing of the materials; signs that are different in horizontal and vertical joints (eg diagonal creases in the sealant in one but not the other) indicating the presence, the amount and the direction of relative movement (see Table 2). Where open-drained vertical joints are used, check that baffles are tucked under the flashing at the head and extend to the foot of the joint. Examine flashings at joint intersections to see if rainwater can gain access beneath them. Note that vertical open-drained joints will not function as such when used on sloping surfaces. (They will function as single-stage joints sealed at the back, their effectiveness depending wholly on the seal).

On cladding generally, signs of defects that seem related to particular locations, for example at changes in cladding materials, between cladding and in-situ work, and at salient or re-entrant angles; also at locations most exposed to weather, such as parapets (see Table 3). Look also for incorrectly detailed or badly executed work, for example, absence of throating under sills and copings (see Table 4).

On fixings, where accessible, look for indications that parts of them are absent or that there are gaps between parts intended to be tightly bolted. Check for signs of distortion or displacement that might indicate overloading, and particularly for corrosion, even if it appears only superficial. Where the particular combination of dissimilar metals has required the use of isolating sleeves and washers, check that these have been correctly and consistently used. Corrosion of fixings not accessible for inspection may be indicated by staining or disruptive expansion at points where fixings might be expected. Look also for indications of localised damage near fixing points, for example in GRP cladding. These may be due to forces exerted by the over-tightening of fixings, or to the restraint offered to intended cladding movement by over-tight fixings.

Design provision in fixings for construction in-accuracies is often inadequate to accommodate the worst inaccuracies that occur on site, and ill-considered modifications to surmount the problem may have produced insecure fixings. Look for excessive overhangs and for improvised packing pieces particularly of degradable materials. Examples are the use of excessive packings on bolts, reducing the depth of engagement of the threaded portions. The packings used may have been the first to come to hand, such as plain mild steel washers. Look also at restraining dowels to see whether the protruding lengths are large or differing, indicating that they do not all engage fully in their pockets. Packing pieces intended as temporary supports or spacers may not have been removed after final fixing. If of unprotected mild steel, the expansion accompanying their corrosion may displace cladding. Their presence may also concentrate cladding movement at unfore-seen positions.

The conditions in the cavity should be noted, looking particularly for signs of persistent damp due to rain penetration or condensation. If the conditions seem likely to encourage corrosion of fixings, inspect a 'sample' of fixings in similar locations. If a signi-ficantly corroded or otherwise unsatisfactory fixing is found, a general inspection of such fixings may be necessary. Except in these circumstances it will not usually be practicable to examine more than one or two major fixings in any one routine inspection. The inspection notes should record the location of the fixings examined so that, if they were found to be satisfactory, future inspections can include fixings at other locations.

When cladding is of bricks, stone or pre-cast concrete, the major fixings are not readily accessible for a routine inspection. It may be possible however to inspect at a particular location in the cladding (eg by removal of a parapet coping) to identify the type of fixing and make an assessment of the restraint that fixings might offer to dislodgement of cladding by thermal or other movements. Such inspection would certainly be justified if there are indications (such as closure of joints, cracking, spalling) that the cladding is subject to either vertical or horizontal compression.

If direct inspection of fixings is not practicable at any point, some evidence of their effectiveness (or of their possible omission during construction) can be adduced from the construction or the condition of the cladding. In brick cladding, for example, it is more probable that ties will be absent if the inner leaf is of in-situ concrete than if it were also of brick. If misalignment of adjacent cladding units in stone or pre-cast concrete facing appears greater than 2 or 3 mm it is possible that a fixing is defective or absent. In some cases, inspection of concealed parts can be made using fibre optics equipment.

Correct diagnosis is not unlike the detection of crime, in that it is a matter of gathering evidence and testing it critically for compliance with known facts. Some of the questions that should be asked about apparent evidence are listed in Table 5.

How to record the findings

It is important to record the findings of an inspection, including even apparently trivial pieces of evidence, so that:

future routine inspections can include items thought suspect;

the development of early signs of latent defects can be related to passage of time (as important evidence about their nature and origin);

current and immediate past environmental condi-tions at different inspections can be compared as part of the evidence;

the location of early signs of potential defects can be found for future inspections.

Sketches (identified as to location and date, including the year) should be made of actual or potential defects and annotated with relevant dimensional information (for example, joint width and taper in elevation, misalignment of faces on either side of joint). Photographs are often useful and those of the 'instant' kind can be annotated at once with location, orientation and date, and particular features ringed or arrowed. Careful subsequent examination of a photograph can sometimes draw attention to features overlooked in the inspection proper. An inspection record should be drawn up to reflect the features of the building concerned, but a basis that may be useful for development in this way is provided in Table 6.

Tables 2, 3 and 4 list some of the indications of potential or extant defects. The lists cannot be exhaustive because of the almost infinite variety of construction forms, materials and conditions. They do, however, represent a typical set of faults and defects and, perhaps more important, indicate how a systematic approach may be applied.

Table 2 Latent defects indicated by pattern of occurrence

Indication	Significance
Walls constructed of clay brickwork	
Fair-faced brickwork, rendered brickwork and brickwork finished with mosaic or tile*	
(1) Cracks, predominantly horizontal and at bed-joint intervals.	May be sulphate attack of mortar. Requires presence of sulphates, cement and persistent dampness – the cause of which should be sought.
(2) Cracks at bed-joints at regular intervals of coursing.	May be corrosion of wall ties.
(3) 'Hollowness' or detachment of rendering or render coat for tiles.	May be sulphate attack as above.
(4) General fine cracking in rendered finishes.	May be due to initial drying shrinkage in rendering; may lead to rain penetration and promote sulphate attack as above.
Fair-faced brickwork (wall appears faced with bricks but brick slips used to face floor slabs)	
(5) Cracks, later spalling and possibly outward displacement, all at or near floor levels.	Suspect that brick slips used at floor levels; shrinkage in height of structural frame permits dead load of brickwork to be transferred eccentrically to brick slips. If 'soft' joints appear to have been provided they may be inoperative (seek reason). Dislodgement of slips may occur; security of remainder dependent upon bearings and ties. Moisture expansion of bricks may contribute.

*Mosaic and tile finishes are commonly bedded on a cement-based rendering applied to brickwork, blockwork, in-situ or precast concrete or combinations of these, for example a brick panel in a concrete frame. Most failures are of the rendering rather than the tile finish. Failure may be due to sulphate attack, movement of the background, differential movement between different backgrounds, or to movements in the rendering, for example, rain penetration via the joints in the tiling may produce moisture movement in the rendering. All of these may cause loss of adhesion between rendering and background.
Detachment of tiles at the adhesive layer is often due to delay between application of adhesive and positioning of tiles. Where adhesive was applied with a notched trowel the presence of an undisturbed notched pattern where tiles have become detached may be a supporting indication of the cause.

Indication	Significance
Stone or pre-cast concrete cladding	
Non-loadbearing cladding formed by stone or pre-cast concrete facing units	
(6) Cracks, uniform in width or closed; at a later stage, spalling especially at edges or corners of cladding units, possibly accompanied by misalignment of faces.	Cladding units under compression due to inadequate allowance for differential movement between cladding and supporting structure; more likely to occur where structure is in-situ concrete. Check provision and effectiveness of horizontal 'soft' compression joints. Check for corrosion of reinforcement.
(7) Cracking or spalling of cladding units in a regular pattern which seems to indicate position of fixings; no evidence of compression (see 6).	Possible corrosion of ferrous fixings: check from drawings or specification. If serious, remove unit, otherwise keep under observation.
(8) Misalignment between faces of adjoining units.	If excessive, suspect either potential compression failure (see 6) or fixings absent or defective.
(9) Iron stains on surface of pre-cast concrete units, random occurrence.	If units unreinforced, likely to be iron-bearing aggregate. If reinforced, (see 10).
(10) Iron stains on surface of pre-cast concrete units, occurrence suggests a pattern.	If units reinforced, likely to be corrosion of reinforcement. If adequate cover, suspect also possible use of excessive calcium chloride in manufacture, especially if cracking or spalling evident; check whether defect occurs with particular units which may have been replacements for units damaged during construction and calcium chloride used to speed up casting of replacements.
Sealant-filled joints	
Horizontal 'soft' joints, often at storey-height intervals, provided to avoid compression of cladding	
(11) Sealant considerably extruded from joint or wholly extruded and edges of cladding units in contact.	Insufficient allowance for movements; risk of future cracking, spalling or displacement of cladding. If apparent within first 5 years, keep under annual observation.
(12) Sealant not deformed, suggesting no compression occurring at joint.	Beware – compression joint may be inoperative due for example to the concealed presence in it of mortar or other solid incompressible material. Examine cladding for indications of compressive stress (see 5 and 6).
Compression joints and all other sealant-filled joints in cladding	
(13) Sealant wrinkled at an angle to the line of the joint.	Sign of differential movement between cladding units in the direction of the line of the joint; seek cause and assess consequences.
(14) Sealant split or adhesion lost.	Greater movement at joint than can be accommodated, especially by aged sealants; more likely to lead to rain penetration into impermeable cladding than into brick cladding.
Light cladding, curtain walling	
Aluminium alloy framed light cladding and curtain walling	
(15) Cracks, loss of adhesion, of sealant at joints between frame members.	Frame may be assembled from separate mullions, transoms, etc, so that thermal movements are concentrated at butt joints, for example, between transom and mullion, leading to failure of sealant. May often lead to rain penetration either directly into building (especially at bottom corners of fixed glazing or spandrel panels) or via hollow extruded frame members to other points, including cavities between cladding and structure.
Aluminium alloy or steel-framed cladding	
(16) Glazing (or spandrel) retaining beads distorted.	May have been distorted by cleaning cradle or ladders or during replacement of broken glazing. If beads are 'sprung on' (as opposed to screwed) check their security and that sealant makes good contact.
(17) Glazing (or spandrel) sealant not in contact with glass or panel.	Spacers omitted or of insufficient thickness, so that movement of glass or panel under wind load displaces sealant. In this condition rainwater may be 'pumped' past the joint by repeated movement.

Table 3 Latent defects indicated by location of occurrence

Indication	Significance
Observed at salient or re-entrant angles, at other changes in built form or at junctions between different materials	
(1) Cracks, predominantly horizontal, in cladding below eaves overhang, possibly later accompanied by spalling.	Thermal movement of the roof slab may be transmitted to upper part of cladding. May lead to displacement or dislodgement by a 'ratchet' effect.
(2) Tearing or loss of adhesion of sealant in vertical joints between cladding and other construction.	Thermal movements may be concentrated at these joints, especially if cladding is lightweight and thus responds quickly to temperature changes. *See also Table 2 (13).*
(3) Cracks at end of projecting stone or pre-cast concrete window sills in stone or pre-cast concrete cladding.	Sill may be firmly held within opening in structure, but projects through cladding facing. Differential movement between cladding and structure may apply bending load to sill.
Observed on parapets of brickwork, including rendered brickwork with or without mosaic or tile finish	
(4) Horizontal cracks at bed-joint intervals.	Probably sulphate attack of mortar (requires presence of cement, sulphates and persistent dampness (seek cause). *See also Table 2 (2).*
(5) Heavy efflorescence on either face of parapet.	May be forerunner of (4).
Observed at or near salient corners or parapets	
(6) Looseness, vibration or detachment of cladding units.	Wind loads are usually more severe at these locations and fixing weaknesses may show here first.

Table 4 Design or construction faults or omissions: for use in interpretation of existing indications, or the future possibility, of latent defects

Affecting security against dislodgement

(1) **Compression joints** Differential movement occurs in all cases where there is a load bearing structure and non-load bearing cladding: long-term shrinkage and creep in the structure reduce its height and apply compressive loads to cladding unless there are compressible horizontal joints of sufficient width in the cladding. If the horizontal joints between units of cladding are not compressible, compression joints, usually at storey-height spacing, are needed. These must also accommodate vertical thermal movements.

(2) **Joints to accommodate horizontal movement** Even where the materials used in the cladding and the structure are the same (eg steel-framed cladding to a steel-framed building), differential thermal movement will occur because of differences in mass and in exposure to solar radiation. As in (1) if joints between units of cladding are not compressible, then vertical joints to accommodate cumulative differential movement will be needed.

(3) **Fixings** Fixings may be designed with insufficient range of adjustability to accommodate inaccuracies, especially in the direction horizontally at right angles to the plane of the cladding and at external corners (erectors may have devised unsatisfactory expedients to overcome this problem). Fixings may restrain differential movements between cladding and structure in such a way that local stresses damage the fixings or the cladding. Isolating sleeves and washers, needed for some combinations of dissimilar metals in fixings, may have been omitted in design or construction, with risk of bimetallic corrosion.

Affecting dampness (and its consequences for rot, corrosion, chemical attack and frost resistance)

(4) **Throating and 'drips'** If projecting horizontal members are not profiled so as to drain water away from horizontal joints immediately above, and to shed water clear of horizontal joints immediately below, there is increased risk of rain penetration and greater reliance on initial and long-term effectiveness of the joints concerned.

(5) **Flashings** Flashings are used where there is an expectation that rain would otherwise penetrate; it is therefore particularly important that they are correctly installed and arranged to drain freely outward. Rain penetration may take a path underneath the flashing or through inadequately lapped and sealed joints in the length of a flashing. Drainage from the upper surface of the flashing may be obstructed. Flashings are more likely to be defective at corners, steps or other changes in geometry where they have been cut and shaped. Satisfactory performance depends on there also being a barrier or seal behind the flashing to prevent the passage of wind-blown rain; the upstand at the back of a flashing will not be sufficient protection if wind can blow through the joint.

(6) **Cavity trays** The latent defects are similar to those for flashings. Additionally, upstands may be of insufficient height or, especially at the ends, omitted, leading to rain penetration. Weep holes may be omitted or blocked.

(7) **Cappings** (eg to parapets) Metal cappings to jointed sections are prone to leakage at fixing points and at joints, where thermal movements can be large; top surfaces may not be formed with sufficient slope to provide rapid drainage.

Table 5 Testing apparent evidence

Evidence	Tests
Thermal movement	Does it appear greater on S-facing than N-facing walls ?
	Does its timing match temperature changes (diurnal, seasonal) ?
	Is it greater in dark-coloured components than in similar light-coloured ?
	Does its magnitude match expected values for thermal movements ? (Caution : restraints may modify movements in practice).
Moisture movement	Are the materials concerned susceptible ?
	Does movement appear greater where construction is exposed to wetting and drying than where protected ?
	Is the timing right ?
Moisture expansion of clay brickwork	Is the timing right ? (Most of the expansion occurs in the first three months of the bricks' life).
Sulphate attack of brickwork	Are all three ingredients present ? (Cement, sulphate salts, persistent dampness).
	Is expansion greater in the height than the length of brickwork ? (Caution : strictly, expansion is greater in the direction containing the greater number of joints ; thus a 'soldier course' at the top of a wall expands more in the horizontal direction).
Compression of cladding	Are there compression joints in the cladding ?
	Have they closed completely ?
	Are they genuinely compressible or merely sealant applied over a rigid material ? Or sealant concealing the edge of a supporting shelf angle ?
	Can sources of compressive movements be identified ? (eg shrinkage of reinforced concrete framed structure, moisture expansion of clay brickwork, thermal expansion of cladding).
Corrosion of reinforcement	Is there likely to be reinforcement present ?
	Could the concrete contain chlorides ? *See also Table 2 (10).*
	Does cracking follow a linear pattern ?
Rain penetration	Could it be partly or wholly condensation ?
	Do the conditions and construction make condensation likely ? *(see below)*.
	Could it be rising damp ?
Condensation	Can the cladding 'breathe' or is it impermeable ?
	If impermeable, especially sheet metals and glass, are cavities between structure and cladding ventilated and drained ? If not, condensation on inside face of cladding is likely and accumulation of condensate is possible.
Cracking due to any supposed cause	Testing the diagnosis of the cause of a crack is often helped if the following questions are posed : Does a straightedge, applied across the crack, reveal misalignment of the faces ? (may indicate lateral displacement of one part and thus the source and direction of movement). Is the crack of approximately constant width throughout its length or is it tapered, and if so, in which direction ? (taper may indicate hogging or sagging). Is the crack close to short returns ? (may indicate rotation of the returns and thus the direction of movement). Is the crack accompanied by spalling ? (may indicate compression). Is the line of the crack at an angle to the line of the affected construction ? (may indicate shear forces). Is there evidence of the age of the crack ? (eg paint or organic growth on the crack faces indicate that the crack is not recent). Is there evidence of time of occurrence ? (eg a crack, interrupted by uncracked mortar where scaffolding putlog holes have been made good, must have occurred before scaffolding was removed). In all cases, look for corroborative evidence provided by repetition in other similar locations.

Table 6 Basis for development of an inspection record

1   Name of inspector
2   Date of inspection
3   Weather at inspection (include temperature, rainfall)
4   Weather prior to inspection (include temperature, rainfall and any unusual climatic conditions)
5   Sketch plan and elevations as necessary, with orientation
6   Detailed sketches/photographs as necessary
7   Indications (not necessarily defects) :
    in construction : cladding (or cladding components)
                        framing
                        fixings
                        glazing (fixed, opening)
                        spandrels, opaque panels
                        joints : vertical
                            horizontal
                            intersections
                            at specific locations : perimeter joints, expansion joints, joints at change of construction, compression
                                                    joints
                        other construction
    in performance : indication of rain penetration
                        indication of inadequate rainwater disposal (defective rainwater goods, blocked gutters etc)
                        indication of movement : thermal
                                                    moisture
                                                    loading, including wind
                        indication of relative movement
                        indication of cracking, displacement
                        indication of mechanical damage (ladders, cradles, vandalism)
                        indication of other performance faults
8   Assessment : indications (not necessarily defects) thought to be significant
9   Recommendations : eg inspect at next routine inspection, bring forward, further examination now, remedial action now
10 Action taken :

Fixings for non-loadbearing precast concrete cladding panels

In the last 30 years it has become common to cover the frames of buildings with large precast concrete cladding panels secured at only a few fixing positions, making consideration of the fixing critical. Yet ambivalent attitudes seem to exist in the cost of the fixing items; they may be regarded as only a small fraction of the cost of the building or as much as 20 percent of the supply price of the panels. Certainly remedial measures at a later date can prove very expensive.

This digest gives guidance on the factors to be considered in the design and use of the fixings; detailed solutions cannot be given as they will vary to suit particular circumstances and will often be designed in detail by the supplier or consulting engineer.

The digest is intended as an aid during the design and specification of a building and if account is taken also of the guidance given for control during construction, many of the problems that have arisen recently with fixings should be avoided in the future.

Experience and a recent BRE survey have highlighted some causes of fixing problems. Where fixings were galvanised, the specification for the protective treatments was not always adequate and mild steel items had sometimes been used when non-ferrous had been specified. In a few buildings, the dimensional deviations and constructional variations of the structural framework resulted in some fixings being omitted because of difficulties of fit; indeed, a particular fixing was sometimes repeatedly missing along a run of panels in the same elevation. In some cases, adequate provision for movement was not made, fixings were found not properly tightened and unrecorded fixing solutions have been used.

Fixing function

A fixing arrangement is considered here as comprising the items at each attachment point used to secure the panels to the building frame, each fixing usually consisting of a number of anchorages with a connecting link. It can have one or more of the following functions:

Transferring dead weight Designed to support the dead weight of one or more claddding units, and to transfer this load to the structure. Such a fixing can usually be designed to accommodate inaccuracies but not movement. More commonly, a panel is supported by a structural member of a building frame with a restraining or locating fixing used to maintain it in position. CP 110 gives recommendations for bearing width for precast units.

Restraining Designed to tie cladding units to their structural frame, or to one another. Allowance for movement is usually necessary.

Locating May also be required to restrain; assists in the alignment of the cladding units. The fixing arrangement may need to allow for movement between panels and between the panel and the structure.

Accommodation of dimensional changes

The design of some fixings will need to allow for overall relative movements between panels and structure. Alternatively, the forces resulting from restraint of movement should be allowed for in the design. Allowances must be made for dimensional changes in buildings and can be considered under the following headings (CP297 and Digests 227, 228 and 229 give data for determining the likely extent of these movements):

Drying shrinkage and moisture movement The effects of drying shrinkage diminish with time but provision should be made unless it is certain that cladding will not be assembled until at least six months has elapsed from the time of casting of the components and the structure.

Elastic deformation under load The elastic deformation of a structure should be taken into account when deflections are significantly large. Allowance for movements at some fixings will need to be made to accommodate deformations arising from structure and cladding dead loads, especially if the structure is not completed before assembly of the cladding commences.

Creep of concrete under sustained load Creep in concrete structures may be long-term and, due to gravity, will be greater in the vertical than the horizontal direction. When panels are supported by the structure, the maximum differential movement at fixings will occur towards the bottom of the building but the reverse will be true if the structure creeps independently of the cladding.

Thermal movement of the structure For the United Kingdom, a temperature range of 40°C should be used for calculating the movement of both shielded concrete and light-coloured concrete structures. A range of 45°C is necessary for structures with dark-coloured surfaces exposed to the sun. These ranges allow for extreme temperatures that could occur in unoccupied buildings.

Thermal movement of the cladding The temperatures that determine the average effect on a panel will be of the same order as those for the exposed structure. Panels incorporating materials of high thermal resistance can have large temperature gradients and require special consideration. Panels with dark surfaces exposed to the sun will tend to reach higher temperatures, and expand proportionately more, than light-coloured ones.

Foundation settlement Consideration should be given to whether angular distortion, due to the differential settlement of a building, will induce movements in the elements of the structure that will have to be allowed for at the fixings.

Accuracy in building

A fixing must be adjustable to accommodate the inevitable dimensional deviations arising from the building and manufacturing processes. Provision for adjustability should be treated separately from provision for movement.

BS 5606 outlines features of the building process which affect accuracy and which need consideration at the design stage, and BRE Digests 199 and 223 give guidance on determining the amount and possible locations for providing adjustability. Although adjustment can be made on site even if there was no designed provision, the result may be an improperly secured fixing, unacceptable cutting of panels or structure, and almost certainly an inefficient construction process.

The consequences of some inaccuracies are often overlooked because assembly drawings are not provided and considered. Figure 1 is a simple example where the design provided what was thought to be an adequate allowance at a panel fixing, but which proved insufficient due to a slightly misaligned socket. A misalignment of 3 mm over its 75 mm length reduced the allowance for adjustment from ±9 mm to ±2 mm.

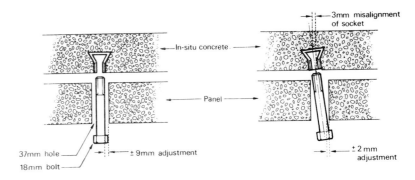

Fig 1 Effect of misalignment of socket

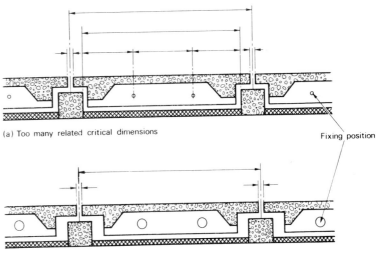

(a) Too many related critical dimensions

Fixing position

(b) Few critical dimensions by using large erection clearances where possible

Fig 2 Avoiding critical dimensions – horizontal sections

The positioning of cast in-situ fixings or pockets for fixings in the structural frame requires close site control. It is easier to obtain accuracy by positioning the fixings after the structure has been built, but the designer must ensure that the reinforcement will be sufficiently clear of the fixing position. Provision for adjustment is easier if the location of the cladding is not closely dependent on the position of the frame or fixings. This can be achieved by ensuring that the number of related critical dimensions is kept to a minimum, and that large erection clearances are provided (Fig 2).

As a general principle, it is better to provide a few substantial fixings rather than rely on the correct relative positioning of many small ones. In setting out, site templates could be used to locate those fixings that must relate accurately with each other. It is helpful, before assembling the cladding, to determine the location for the panels from site measurements of the building frame and the panels. It must not be forgotten that the standard of workmanship required to place and assemble the fixings must be within the limits that can be effectively achieved on site.

Assembly adjustment in three dimensions can be provided with an angle cleat restraint fixing which has a vertical slotted hole for fixing to the panel, a horizontal slotted hole for fixing to the building frame, and provision for packing pieces for adjustment perpendicular to the wall (Fig 3). When the cleats are fixed at the sides of a panel, the slots must be aligned to accommodate the same planes of adjustment as above. The

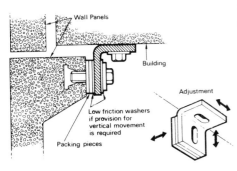

Fig 3 Angle cleat

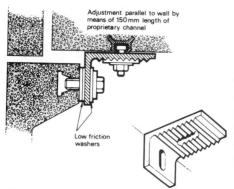

Adjustment parallel to wall by
means of 150mm length of
proprietary channel

Low friction
washers

Fig 4 Angle cleat with serrated surface

maximum number of packing pieces that may be used while ensuring sufficient engagement of the bolt in the socket should be specified. Alternatively, the use of packing pieces can be minimised by the use of a serrated cleat which, after positioning, is locked by a matching serrated washer (Fig 4). Inaccuracy in the other direction can be accommodated by means of a proprietary channel cast into the structural frame. A locating stud that projects out of the channel should then be used. (An inwardly directed bolt can screw only as far as the back of the channel, when the reaction may split open the front of the channel - at the same time the assembly may not be tight).

Recommendations: dimensional deviations arising from the manufacturing and building processes must be allowed for; the designer should clearly distinguish the critical dimensions, and their permissible deviations, from other dimensions.

Structural requirements

Fixings must be designed to resist the worst combinations of shear, axial force and bending caused by vertical and horizontal loads. The various types of load are as follows (recommendations on the loads to be assumed are given in CP3: Chapter V):

Dead loads
Eccentric loads caused by the panel centre of gravity being offset from the support.

Wind loads

Impact loads During erection, the risk of placed panels being subjected to impact should be assessed. Accidental impact at low levels has been found to be surprisingly frequent by vehicles and should be considered if traffic has access to the area adjacent to the wall. Maintenance equipment should also be considered. Potential internal or external forces due to explosion should be either dissipated, or confined, to cause negligible damage to the essential structure or injury to occupants and passers-by.

The design for strength of a fixing must take account of a number of factors:

The strength of the fixing itself when at its proposed limit of adjustability.
The strength of the components to which the fixing is attached. If the fixing is in tension, it may break through the component or, if loaded laterally, it may fail by shearing through the fixed component. Many fixings rely on a degree of friction between themselves and the material into which they are fixed. Friction depends on tightness of fixing and the strength of the material in which the fixing is embedded, both being widely variable. BS5080 assists designers to request test data in a consistent form.

Vibration and cyclic loading

Care should be taken to ensure that all fixings are effective and properly installed. However, for safety reasons and because of the critical role played by fixings, they should be designed to ensure that the cladding panel would be adequately supported if any one of the fixings became ineffective. In addition, fixings for handling and temporary positioning should be provided separately so that the permanent fixings are not inadvertently strained. If hoisting points are provided each point should be capable of supporting the total load of the panel, including, for example, wind load.

In no case should the permissible load for a fixing be established by calculation unless supported by test data. It has been shown [1] that the maximum load resisted in normal short-term tests is often larger that the load at which creep will take place with sustained loading and it is recommended that the tensile load at which first slip (ie movements additional to that caused by elastic extension) occurs should be used as a basis for quantifying the safe load.

Recommendations: that the structural engineer sets down the functional requirements of the fixings, the movement of the cladding for which allowance is to be made, together with the anticipated movement characteristics of the building frame; the formal calculations made during the design of a fixing should always be available.

Fire

Fire resistance tests relate either to the performance of materials or to the overall performance of elements of building construction. The behaviour of fixings in a composite structure must relate to the performance of that construction. However, satisfactory results in a fire resistance test does not necessarily imply that all components remained in position for the whole period of the test. The fixings on a building should be of the same type and be fitted at the same locations as those used in fire test specimens if regulation approval has been granted for that building on the basis of results from those fire test specimens.

Limited investigations [2] on the behaviour of fixing assemblies in short-term fire conditions have shown that failure generally occurs in the metal parts projecting into the fire, i.e. bolts, nuts and studs. However, the anchorage of fixings secured using resin, plastics or rubber mechanisms failed more quickly in pull-out tests. Consideration should be given to the implications of possible displacement or collapse of cladding as a result of deterioration of the fixings.

Recommendation: where resistance to fire is required fixings must be adequately protected; fixings incorporating resin, plastics or rubber parts as the main anchorage components are not likely to meet fire resistance requirements, whether protected or not.

Methods of attachment

Each fixing arrangement can involve one or more of the following common methods of attachment:

Cast-in anchorage A threaded socket, with an external taper or projection that is cast within the concrete, sometimes with linkage to the reinforcement. Sockets are often used in the back of panels to receive the bolt securing an angle cleat; if possible, these should be cast just proud of, or at least level with, the concrete surface. This ensures that any excess loading of the bolt during tightening will remain as an axial load on the socket and not be transferred to the interface between the socket and concrete, which may pull the socket out.

Expanding anchorage A threaded socket with expanding shields (metal, plastics or rubber) or anchors which exert a radial force against the sides of the hole into which they are inserted. They may be secured before assembly, e.g. by forcing a tapered plug into the lower end (Fig 5) or at the time of assembly, e.g. tapered fixing stud expanding a loose metal shell (Fig 6). Careful selection is necessary from the many fixings available.

Recommendations: check the accuracy required of the hole depth and diameter; when selecting, check whether a reaction against the fixture to the tightening force is required so that the expansion procedure can start; ensure that the fixing has adequate cover to prevent bursting of the concrete.

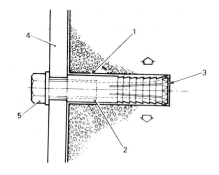

Fig 5 Expanding anchorage

1 Pre-drilled hole
2 Self-drill anchor
3 Plug
4 Fixture
5 Bolt

The self-drill anchor incorporates a core drill that is used to cut a hole. The hole is then cleaned out and a conical expander plug inserted in the toothed end. Anchorage is obtained by driving the drill over the plug at the lower end so as to expand the cylindrical walls of the drill against the sides of the hole. The fixture is placed over the anchor and a bolt inserted and tightened.

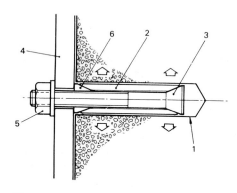

Fig 6 Expanding anchorage

1 Pre-drilled hole
2 Shell
3 Tapered stud
4 Fixture
5 Nut
6 Wedge

Expansion of a loose metal shell parallel to the sides of the stud when the nut is tightened is achieved by the closing action of the wedge and the tapered end of the stud.

Link between attachments

Corrosion of metal parts

Resin bonded anchorage A threaded stud or socket bonded into a hole. The adhesive may be synthetic resin-based, usually either epoxy or polyester resin with perhaps a quartz granule or other filler and marketed in glass or plastics packs which are inserted into the hole. The adhesive should have suitable flow setting characteristics when used in horizontal or overhead holes. The recommended drill must be used to produce the correct size hole and an appropriately keyed surface. The wrong size can hinder the proper shredding of the pack and thus prevent full mixing of the two-part components. Debris must be flushed out of the hole; some drills have an action which does this.

A show of synthetic resin at the mouth of the hole after installation generally indicates that the fixing is fully bedded, although care should be taken to ensure that any voids in the base material exposed by the drilling have not allowed the adhesive to escape. Setting time may be affected by temperature; for example, a resin might require a curing period 10 times greater at 5°C than at 20°C, and for many a minimum ambient temperature for application is recommended.

The interfacial bond along the length of the hole relies mainly on physical resistance to movement of the adhesive fill. The adhesive must possess physical, chemical and mechanical properties compatible with the base materials throughout its intended service life.

Recommendations: note manufacturers' instructions and in particular check that the shelf life of the adhesive has not been exceeded; check that the adhesive is appropriate, particularly where damp conditions are likely; check that the installed resin is curing properly by testing some fixings out of each batch with a torque wrench to the structural engineer's recommendation.

Grouted-in anchorage Dowel bars are often grouted in on site and used for location or for restraint at panel nibs. The use of an oversized hole is an effective means of providing for dimensional inaccuracies in the structure.

Recommendations: a minimum of 48 hours should be allowed for mortar grout to mature before it is subject to stress; proprietary grouts must be carefully selected and used strictly in accordance with the supplier's instructions; dowel bar holes should be located in relation to the concrete reinforcement to ensure that adequate strength is provided.

Angle cleats These are often used in restraint fixings to form the link between anchorage points. They can provide for adjustment during assembly and for panel movement (Fig 3). Provision for movement can be made using large (say 60 mm dia) washers of neoprene, nylon or ptfe positioned each side of the angle; small washers are not suitable as they tend to deform or abrade. The use of locking washers or nuts is recommended and care should be taken not to over-tighten the connection.

It is essential that no part of a fixing assembly is subjected to corrosion so that its performance in service is impaired. Although fixings will usually be protected from the direct effects of wet weathering, they are liable to be exposed at times to condensation and humidities above the critical level for steel corrosion. It should also be noted that failure due to rusting can be accelerated by the expansive forces of the large volume of rust produced; the hydrated oxide formed may be many times thicker than the reduction in thickness due to corrosion. Though it is possible to apply a protective coating for a life of 20 years or more, it is necessary to inspect the coatings earlier. Blast-cleaning may be necessary as part of a remedial treatment but is not easy. Inspection is also unlikely unless the inner wall leaf is easily demountable.

Care must be taken to ensure that dissimilar metals within the fixing assembly, or against any structural steel framing members or reinforcement, do not come into direct contact in potentially damp conditions to form a bimetallic electro-chemical corrosion cell whereby the metal forming the anode is attacked. Mild steel with virtually any other metal is particularly vulnerable. Insulating washers and sleeves may be used between different metals to prevent a cell from forming. BS PD 6484 gives guidance.

Exposure in industrial or marine atmospheres may be relatively severe and requires special consideration.

Recommendations: an inherently corrosion-resistant fixing is preferable and should always be used on high-rise buildings (suitable non-ferrous metals are given in CP 297); mild steel items, with insufficient concrete cover, should be protected against corrosion and be accessible for inspection; a standard for protection should be specified.

Access to fixings

Ideally, fixings should be accessible for inspection; this is not always possible but can be achieved by the use of demountable inner wall linings. It is also possible with masonry linings if the process can make use of aids for viewing in wall cavities. For example, a fibre optic probe requires a hole diameter of 15 mm or less through the lining to allow the condition of a fixing to be observed (Fig 7).

The cost of this equipment, which provides an instrument of considerable general use to a building surveyor, could be very small in relation to the cost of producing special access hatches. The prerequisites for the successful future use of this type of equipment are that documentation exists to locate all fixings from within the building, and that a hole can conveniently be made, or left, through a suitable location in the lining. Inspection of this type will identify fixings that appear to be at risk. If some risk is apparent, further inspection could involve some dismantling.

Specification

A technical specification dealing with all aspects of the supply and /or fixing of the cladding should be prepared by the structural engineer and/or architect and this should include definitions of the nature of any special tests required to be carried out on the fixings in advance of the work. The fixings should be specified fully giving the materials, and dimensions of the various parts. This applies to all items including the nuts and washers. Mistakes are less likely if items of the fixing arrangement are supplied by the same manufacturer, and the number of different types of fixing on any one job is kept to a practical minimum.

The designer, having determined the requirements for adjustability and assembly, must ensure that his intentions are clear to the builder. Exploded assembly drawings showing the critical dimensions should be available on site. A set of drawings showing the cladding fixings in detail should be retained along with the other essential drawings following the end of the defects liability period. A set may prudently be lodged with the building deeds.

Where an architect relies upon the cladding sub-contractor to decide fixing arrangements and does not consult a structural engineer, the division of responsibility must be clearly defined.

Recommendation: the structural engineer should be consulted about any changes to the specification, either at the tendering stage or on site.

Fig 7 Fibre optic probe in use

Site work   Fixings should be checked on delivery for number, type and conformity to specification.

Bolts should ideally be tightened to a specific torque. This becomes more critical when they form part of an expanding bolt mechanism, for the grip against the sides of the fixing hole depends on the force applied through the bolt. However, large variations in the effective tightening can occur, due to the variable energy absorbed overcoming friction between the bolt head/washer and bolt threads/socket. To obtain a better consistency of effective torque loading, lubricant and a torque wrench may be used but only as directed by the supplier of a proprietary fixing or the structural engineer. The use of a hardened washer can give a worthwhile improvement in achieving a constant torque. The design and position of fixings should allow for visual inspection on completion to check that they have been correctly assembled before concealment.

Recommendations: delivered fixing items should be checked for compliance; assembled fixings should be checked before they are concealed; all 'as-built' alterations to the designed fixing detail should be marked on a master set of the client's retained drawings.

References

1   Selection and use of fixings in concrete and masonry; CIRIA Guide No 4; 1977. (See also note in CIRIA News, Feb 1978).
2   Indicative fire tests on fixings; CIRIA Technical Note 92; 1978.

Further reading

BRE Digests

199   Getting good fit
217   Wall cladding defects and their diagnosis
223   Wall cladding: designing to minimise defects due to inaccuracies and movements
227   Estimation of thermal and moisture movements and stresses: Part 1
228   Estimation of thermal and moisture movements and stresses: Part 2
229   Estimation of thermal and moisture movements and stresses: Part 3

Graphical aids for tolerance and fits; BRE Report; HMSO; 1974
Criteria for structural adequacy of buildings; Institution of Structural Engineers; 1976.
Guide to precast concrete cladding; Concrete Society Technical Report No 14; 1977.
Technical Guidance; Precast concrete; Non-loadbearing cladding; PSA DOE; 1978.
Second Report of the Standing Committee on Structural Safety for the year ending 31 March 1978.
Precast concrete cladding; Cement and Concrete Association; 1978.

British Standards

CP 3: Code of basic data for the design of buildings;
        Chapter V Loading; Part 1: 1967 Dead and imposed loads; Part 2: 1972 Wind loads
CP 110: The structural use of concrete;
        Part 1: 1972; Design, materials and workmanship
BS 729: 1971 Hot-dip galvanised coatings on iron and steel articles
BS 5080; Methods of test for structural fixings in concrete and masonry:
        Part 1: 1974; Tensile loading
BS 5493: 1977; Code of Practice for protective coating of iron and steel structures against corrosion
BS 5606: 1978; Code of Practice for accuracy in building
PD 6484: 1979; Corrosion at bimetallic contacts and its alleviation

Reinforced plastics cladding panels

This digest outlines briefly the materials and moulding techniques used in the manufacture of glass-fibre reinforced plastics cladding panels and compares some properties of the finished panels with those of other materials. The importance of involvement of the manufacturer in design, from the sketch-plan stage onwards, is emphasised and some guidance is offered on various aspects of specification and quality control.

Description and uses

Glass-fibre reinforced plastics (GRP) consists of glass-fibre reinforcement impregnated with resin, incorporating fillers, pigments, etc, and suitably catalysed to harden during the curing process.

For building use, GRP first appeared as corrugated roofing sheets but its use is now extended to other external claddings. It can be formed to a wide variety of shapes, in various colours and textures; components made from it are light in weight and its mouldability allows the incorporation of features and details that would be impossible with other materials.

To meet the total performance requirements of a panel, GRP can be combined successfully with other materials. A core of cellular plastics or other lightweight material can provide structural stiffness in sandwich construction; steel has been used to provide means of fixing to the building framework; aerated concrete has been used to improve thermal insulation and fire characteristics; plasterboard and glass-fibre reinforced gypsum plaster panels may improve fire resistance. Much design detail can be moulded into the material but it will often be advantageous to introduce additional detailing at joints, window openings, etc, by the incorporation of components fabricated from other materials or from a different form of GRP.

Limitations Lack of rigidity and some decline in mechanical properties at high temperatures restrict some structural uses and allowance must be made for the time-dependence of these properties for components to be used under stress.

GRP is combustible and building and other regulations impose some restrictions on its use. Flame-retardants reduce its ignitability and improve the surface spread-of-flame characteristics but have very little effect on the burning of materials that are fully involved in a sizeable fire.

From the point of view of fire hazard, the suitability of plastics cladding must be determined by a full and systematic evaluation of all the relevant features (size, usage, access, etc) of the particular situation. This should be done at a very early stage of design, in consultation with local fire authorities and other local and, where appropriate, national bodies.

Feasibility The facing of a building with GRP panels is still a relatively new technique and there is no simple method of ensuring that panels will meet all the requirements of the designer. A comprehensive statement of performance requirements should be prepared before an irrevocable decision to use GRP is taken.

Materials

Resin systems Polyester resins of various types are the most commonly used. General purpose resins combine good water and weather resistance with average mechanical properties. A stabiliser is sometimes included to improve resistance to yellowing by exposure to ultra-violet light.

Resins incorporating flame-retardant additives can achieve surface spread-of-flame characteristics[1] as low as Class 1 (but see 'Limitations', above) and further improvement is possible with appropriate fillers. The additives adversely affect curing, mechanical properties and weathering, but the smaller the proportion used the less will it affect these properties.

Opaque panels can be coloured with filled resins and a small proportion of pigment. Pigments should be chosen for their long-term colour stability. Usually a fully-pigmented resin system is used only in the surface layer but a translucent surface layer, with better weathering characteristics than pigmented resin, is sometimes used over pigmented laminates.

Reinforcement The stiffness, tensile strength and impact resistance of polyester resins can be improved by reinforcement with glass fibres. 'E'-glass reinforcement is normally used; this is a borosilicate glass which has good resistance to moisture and to chemical attack.

Chopped strand mat is most widely used. It consists of 20–50 mm long chopped strands of glass fibre held randomly together with a resinous binder to form a mat. It is low in cost, with equivalent physical properties in all directions, good inter-laminar bond due to the interlocking action of the fibres, and it can be formed into fairly complex shapes.

Glass rovings, which consist of a number of continuous glass-fibre strands held loosely together, are sometimes used to give directional reinforcement, or in continuous manufacturing processes where they are cut and sprayed with resin on to the mould. Woven rovings and cloths of various types are used to achieve particular moulding effects and to increase strength, particularly with orientation in highly-stressed areas.

A surfacing mat is a tissue of single glass-fibre filaments held together as an open-textured membrane sometimes used to reinforce a resin-rich gel-coat.

Moulding processes

Contact moulding The choice of material for the mould depends on the length of run and the edge and surface details of the panel. A simple open mould of wood, plaster, metal, glass or reinforced plastics is often satisfactory.

A 'gel-coat' of resin, which will form the surface layer, is first brushed or sprayed on to the mould and partially cured before building up the rest of the laminate; the gel-coat sometimes contains an additive to improve its flexibility and a surfacing mat may be incorporated. Alternate layers of glass-fibre mat and resin are placed over this by hand and consolidated with rollers before the laminate is cured.

The hand lay-up process is slow but effective for short runs. In skilled hands good control is possible; unfortunately, the converse is also true and a careless operative can cause undesirable variations in the product.

It is sometimes possible to use a technique of 'spray-up' which is faster and cheaper for long runs; this permits reinforcement to be built up at salient points but gives less control in the overall distribution of glass fibre.

Contact moulding allows for variations of structure, thickness and strength where required, and the incorporation of stiffening inserts at any convenient point, even at later stages of production if testing shows the initial design to have been inadequate. Design details can be incorporated but this adds to the cost, though not disproportionately unless many undercuts are required.

Matched-die moulding 'Hot' and 'cold' matched-die moulding techniques are also used. The former, in particular, requires expensive metal moulds and is likely to be used only for very large production runs though closer tolerances and savings in material are obtainable because of the more uniform thickness. It is sometimes difficult to obtain a resin-rich and consequently better weathering finish.

Shape and size

GRP panels can be moulded to virtually any shape but some limitations are imposed by performance. If the panels are to be of economic thickness, they might not be sufficiently rigid and may need to be used either in sandwich form or with a more rigid backing sheet. Stiffness can be achieved by double curvature, folded-plate or pyramidal shapes. It is important to make provision for thermal movement, if excessive distortion is to be avoided and the joints are to perform satisfactorily.

The size of panel is restricted by production, transport and handling facilities, but thermal movement will usually be the limiting factor. If panels have to fit within a framework and are to be butt-jointed, their dimensions should be restricted to 3–4 m to avoid the need for very wide joints to provide for thermal movement, but larger sizes may be used if the joints are to be lapped. If the cladding is to extend the full height of the building, with thermal movement accommodated at the top or bottom, longer panels are permissible.

Table 1 of BS 4549 [2] lists the normal tolerances for the thickness of a moulding but this is not necessarily important for cladding panels provided that the specified strength is attained throughout. Width and height can be expected to be controlled within 3–8 mm depending on the size of the panel. The designer should inform the manufacturer of the accuracy likely to be achieved at fixing points but he should avoid a design for the cladding that relies on exceptional accuracy in the supporting structure. The shape should be accurate and there should be no surface distortion noticeable after installation.

Weight

A GRP cladding panel is likely to be about 3–6 mm thick, the equivalent weight being 5–10 kg/m²; increased thickness at edges and fixing points may double this weight. The addition of lightweight thermal insulation and plasterboard, asbestos-cement, glass-fibre reinforced gypsum or other boarding, to improve fire and/or sound insulation may increase the weight to about 40–60 kg/m².

Appearance

Surface texture   Even slight distortion of a nominally flat surface is noticeable but a textured surface will help to mask this. Patterned glass and stiffened embossed wallpaper have been used satisfactorily as mould surfaces. The texture might, however, increase the retention of dirt so that patterns due to differential washing by rainwater become more obvious.

Aggregates of varying degrees of coarseness may be used as surface fillers. Fine fillers must be chosen with care for their effects on moulding; sand or coarser aggregates need relatively thick gel-coats and might even encourage surface cracking or chalking. Aggregates coarser than sand must be embedded deeply enough to ensure that particles cannot fall from the surface. An exposed coarse aggregate finish may protect the resin binder against degradation but there is only limited experience of the long-term durability of this type of finish.

Colour   In general, the brighter colours are the less stable. Some white pigments have a tendency to chalk and although this may pass unnoticed on white panels it might not be acceptable if other colour is involved. Although the darker colours, greys, browns, near-blacks, are less likely to fade, they may result in higher surface temperatures (see *Thermal effects*).

Properties

Table 1 shows the orders of magnitude of some properties of GRP compared with other materials. The values for the strength properties of the GRP materials were determined in short-term laboratory tests; in designing for use under stress, particularly in moist conditions, values between one-fifth and one-tenth of those quoted may have to be assumed.

Table 1   Comparative properties

Material	Density kg/m³	Ultimate tensile strength N/mm²	Flexural strength N/mm²	Compressive strength N/mm²	Youngs modulus (tension) N/mm² ×10³	Maximum working temperature °C	Coefficient of linear expansion ×10⁻⁶ per °C
Glass-fibre chopped strand mat/polyester resin	1300–1800	70–170	140–280	100–200	5·5–10	175	30
Glass-cloth/polyester resin	1500–2100	200–450	280–620	170–300	18–24	175	12
Mild steel	7700–7800	360–410	150 yield stress	230–260	200	400	12
Aluminium alloy	2700–2800	280–590		280–590	68–72	200	23
Redwood (*pinus sylvestris*)	510 at 15% mc		84	45	10	—	—

Panels must be able to support their own weight and the weight of any inserts, such as windows, with a minimum of deformation. It is not easy to design so as to ensure adequate rigidity and there is a tendency to over-design for this in terms of basic strength. A fortunate consequence is that, although the material may suffer from continuing distortion (creep) in use, there is normally so little demand on the strength properties that the effect of creep can be ignored.

Resistance to external loading

None of the Codes of Practice helps to determine the permissible deflection under wind load and the designer may have to set arbitrary limits. For most building panels, engineering design is not sufficiently sophisticated to permit a rigorous mathematical approach to the limitation of deflection. The most reliable way to determine this, and the effects on joints and fixings, is by simulated wind loading tests, but these are costly and the use of additional layers of reinforced plastics to increase strength and stiffness may be more economical. CP 3: Chapter V [3] provides data on which wind loading tests should be designed.

In the event of a prototype panel proving too weak or flexible under test, it is relatively easy, particularly for contact moulded panels, to increase the strength and stiffness by locally increasing the thickness of the material and the amount of reinforcement, or by building into the panel stiffening ribs, etc. This 'design-as-you-go' approach is not, however, recommended and will certainly complicate costing.

Fire

The Building Regulations for England and Wales require the use of materials of Class O spread-of-flame characteristics in some situations. It is common practice to produce GRP of Class II grading, as defined in BS 476: Pt 7 [1], but where Class O is required it may be wiser to consider the use of some other material rather than to accept the lower performance associated with a high concentration of flame-retardant additive. As stated earlier, the use of flame-retardants have very little effect on the burning of materials once they are fully involved in a sizeable fire.

A gel-coat of general-purpose resin will improve the weathering qualities of a fire-retardant laminate; panels with factory-applied films of polyurethane paint have also been used. Class O requirements are unlikely to be met by the former finish but have been met by the latter type when properly designed.

Moisture effects

Although not completely impervious to moisture, for normal building purposes GRP may be regarded as impermeable. Water absorption is low and moisture movement negligible; water reduces the strength of the material but condensation on the reverse side of panels is not likely to have any significant effect.

Thermal effects

Working temperature The performance at high temperature depends on the frequency and duration of exposure and the state of stress in use; cycling between hot and cold conditions also has an effect and, in the long term, moist heat is likely to be more severe than hot dry conditions. Most GRP can withstand occasional exposure to temperatures as high as 175°C, isophthalic-based polyesters rather higher, but for the climatic conditions likely to be encountered in the UK an upper continuous working temperature of 100°C is more than adequate. Even with a thick layer of thermal insulating material behind a dark panel, the effect of temperature on mechanical properties is not likely to be significant.

Thermal movement The coefficient of linear expansion varies approximately with the resin/glass ratio within the range $10-40 \times 10^{-6}$ per °C. Table 1 compares this with the thermal expansion co-efficients of some other materials. The differences are significant in a composite panel in which GRP constitutes only the surface skin and has relatively low thermal conductivity; on exposure to solar radiation it will become much warmer than the other components and will expand differentially. This causes problems in the design of panels to avoid distortion as a result of solar heating. Shaped panel surfaces, particularly if they incorporate a degree of curvature, may be able to accommodate some of the movement but it is very difficult to allow for movement in more than one direction.

It is important to know the surface temperatures likely to be attained in service. Lighter and more reflective surfaces will get less hot than dark ones. Predictions of performance are possible from a knowledge of the materials involved but full-scale trials or experience from actual use might be necessary, particularly with smooth-faced panels in which any surface defect will be obvious, to avoid unsightly distortion.

Joint design

Estimates of the extent of thermal movements are required for the correct design of joints (*see* Digest 137). The joints must also allow for inaccuracies in manufacture and in the supporting structure and for deflection; they must resist fire penetration and perform the obvious functions of excluding wind and rain and might sometimes have to contribute a degree of mechanical support and restraint.

Fixing

Fixing is normally by mechanical means, such as bolting through moulded flanges or metal inserts. Thermal movement should be allowed for in the design of the fastenings, so as to avoid stressing and deforming the GRP.

For crane handling, specially designed fixings may have to be incorporated or a lifting cradle used.

Durability

UV radiation is responsible for initiating degradation in GRP and it varies with location and orientation; surface wetness and temperatures also play a part in determining the rate and form of degradation.

The appearance of some building materials is enhanced by weathering but in general this is not true of GRP. Some unevenness in weathering might result from slight differences in orientation of parts of a panel and this can be anticipated in design. For example, one surface of a pyramidal panel may retain more dirt than the others because it catches less rain but this will serve to accentuate the pattern.

The effect of flame-retardant additives on weathering behaviour is most significant in the resin base of the gel-coat. Excessive flame-retardant in a very lightly pigmented and filled surface is likely to lead to yellowing within a very few years of exposure in sunlight; the lighter the original colour, the more will this discoloration show. The use of a high content of filler may permit a reduction in the amount of additive but the surface might then be prone to erosion. A glass-fibre tissue (surfacing mat) in the gel-coat can improve the resistance to surface cracking. The weathering qualities of laminates made with flame-retardant resins are improved by a general-purpose resin gel-coat.

Joints must be able to accommodate irregular thermal movements over long periods and any jointing material should be of proven durability or capable of easy replacement.

Maintenance

Mechanical damage, during erection or in service, can be patched and an attempt made to match the original but site conditions are not usually favourable for proper curing of the resin and a patch is likely to show after a period of weathering. It is better to replace a complete panel, if this is practicable, although it might still be difficult to achieve a match that will weather in precisely the same way as the original.

Restoration of a degraded surface can also be difficult. In the extreme case of the glass fibres becoming badly exposed, they must be scrubbed off completely before any new surface treatment is applied. Acrylic or polyurethane paints may be applied to surfaces that have deteriorated but, again because site conditions can seldom equal controlled factory standards, the performance may be little better than that of ordinary paint films and repeated maintenance may become necessary.

Design and specification

It is most important to involve the manufacturer as early as possible, to work closely with the designer from the sketch-plan stage onward. Problems of feasibility, mould ownership, quality control, etc, can then be solved, and estimates of probable costs obtained. The designer must either be familiar with the materials and manufacturing processes or enlist the aid of a specialist consultant.

A satisfactory specification of materials, manufacture, quality control and approval procedure is essential. Even then, different manufacturers' tenders may differ widely with tenderers wishing perhaps to adjust some aspect to suit their operating arrangements.

Raw materials BS 3532[4] specifies resin systems for use in fibre-reinforced plastics; BS 3496[5] specifies glass-fibre chopped strand mat for the reinforcement of polyester resin systems. Other types of glass-fibre reinforcement are covered by BS 3396[6], 3691[7] and 3749[8]. The requirements of these standards will achieve some measure of control of the material used.

Finished laminates The quality of the finished laminates can be controlled by stating tolerances on agreed values for the following, to be determined by the tests described in BS 4549:[2] glass and inert filler content; resin content; cure of resin as determined by hardness measurement or extraction; weight of resin per unit area; water absorption and change of strength in boiling tests; mechanical properties such as tensile strength, modulus of elasticity in flexure and shear strength.

Although the properties of reinforced plastics are liable to some variation, a manufacturer should be able to define limits above and below the specified values for his product.

Completed panels The colour may be specified by reference to BS colours, but because of the nature of the material and possible requirements for surface texture, it might be more realistic to specify panels to match an agreed sample; this should be large enough to give a fair representation of the surface and not to suffer change by excessive handling

Other properties that may have to be determined before or during full-scale manufacture are: resistance to wind loads; the effects of thermal cycling and thermal shock; the effects of impact by hard and soft bodies; the tensile and shear strength of fixings and the effects on them of cyclic loading. The effects of these on associated components, fixing points, jointing materials, etc, should also be considered. Appropriate test methods are outlined in the Agrément Board's *Common directive on lightweight cladding*.

Quality control Poor control in manufacture can have a harmful effect on most aspects of performance, particularly on weathering and durability. Destructive full-scale testing of large and expensive panels is difficult and costly. Samples can be prepared simultaneously with the panels but control in the manufacture of a small sample may be different from that of a large panel and, if obtainable, off-cuts are likely to give more representative results. Although the value of testing samples and offcuts during production is somewhat limited, it is worth while to make this a normal control requirement.

Continuous external supervision is normally impracticable and the purchaser will not necessarily have the required expertise. It is, however, essential to ensure that the panel manufacturer exercises control over the care and skill with which the moulding is produced, particularly when laid up by hand. On very large contracts, a quality control supervisor may be placed at the manufacturer's plant to ensure the maintenance of standards. Agreement should be reached beforehand on the quality control technique.

For a large project, a prototype panel should be tested, if necessary by a specialist consultant, before the design is finalised.

BS 4549[2] indicates some of the methods that might be used to implement an inspection procedure. Thickness, weight, appearance, evenness of colour, uniformity of aggregate distribution, dimensions and strength requirements might also be included. Dimensional requirements should include control of tolerances, squareness, flatness and the positions of fixing points and inserts.

Requirements such as these may increase the tender price, but they are well justified in terms of satisfactory performance.

References

1 BS 476 *Fire tests on building materials and structures;* Part 7: 1971 *Surface spread of flame tests for materials.*

2 BS 4549 *Guide to quality control requirements for reinforced plastics mouldings;* Part 1: 1970 *Polyester resin mouldings reinforced with chopped strand mat or randomly deposited glass fibres.*

3 BS CP 3 *Code of basic data for the design of buildings;* Chapter V, *Loading:* Part 2: 1972 *Wind loads.*

4 BS 3532: 1962 *Unsaturated polyester resin systems for low pressure fibre reinforced plastics.*

5 BS 3496: 1973 *E glass fibre chopped strand mat for the reinforcement of polyester resin systems.*

6 BS 3396: Part 3: 1970 *Finished (woven glass fibre) fabrics for use with polyester resin systems.*

7 BS 3691: 1969 *Glass fibre rovings for the reinforcement of polyester and of epoxide resin systems.*

8 BS 3749: 1974 *Woven roving fabrics of E glass fibre for the reinforcement of polyester resin.*

Sanitary pipework: Part 1
Design basis

This digest discusses the design of simplified (ie unvented) above ground drainage systems for high and low-rise domestic, public and office buildings. Design data are based on the same basic performance criteria as those given in BS 5572 Code of practice for Sanitary pipework. This digest, which is published in two parts, combines and up-dates the information contained in Digests 80 and 115, both of which are now withdrawn.

This digest gives recommendations for simplified above ground drainage systems serving the sanitary appliances in low and high-rise dwellings, office buildings and public buildings. It does not cover systems for the more specialised type of appliance for such buildings as hospitals, laboratories and factories. Simplified systems do not require ventilation pipework; for more complex or larger systems needing such relief venting reference should be made to the *British Standard Code of practice for Sanitary pipework*, BS 5572. Guidance on such topics as materials, pipe fixing and jointing is also given in the Code.

Many different terms are used to describe the parts of above ground drainage systems and so, to avoid confusion, the same terms given in the Code of practice are used in the digest, eg discharge stack for the main vertical pipe conveying the discharges from all types of sanitary appliances.

Design basis

The basic requirements for any discharge system are that waste materials should be carried away quickly, quietly, without blockage and without the escape of foul air into the building. Trap water seals help to prevent the latter from occurring but to be sure that an adequate water seal depth is retained at each appliance, the air pressure fluctuations within the discharge branch and stack pipes must be limited. The pressure effects that may change the depth of water in the appliance traps are:

Self-siphonage The suction due to full bore flow in the branch pipe which may reduce the depth of water seal in the appliance which is discharging (Fig 1).

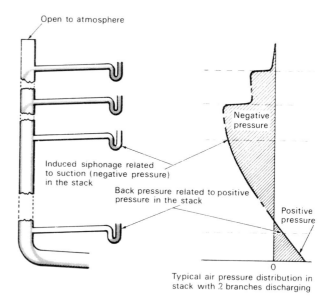

Fig 1 Self-siphonage in branch discharge pipe

Induced siphonage The suction normally associated with air and water flow down the discharge stack which may reduce the depth of water seal in the appliances connected to the stack in the vicinity of the fluctuations (Fig 2). It can also occur due to full bore flow in branch pipes, affecting appliances which are connected to the branch pipe downstream of the discharging appliance(s) (Fig 3).

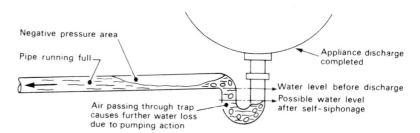

Fig 2 Air pressure in discharge stack - induced siphonage and back pressure

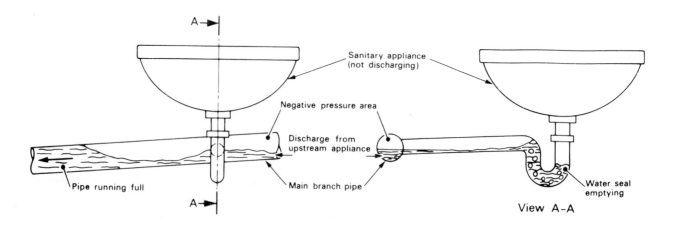

Fig 3 Induced siphonage in branch discharge pipe

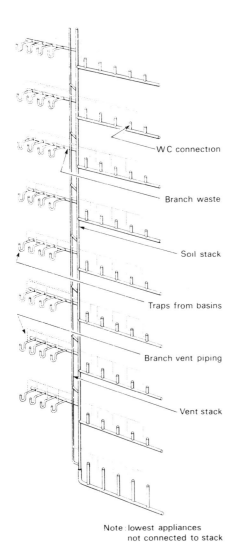

WC connection

Branch waste

Soil stack

Traps from basins

Branch vent piping

Vent stack

Note: lowest appliances
not connected to stack

Fig 4 Traditional fully vented system

Back pressure The positive pressure associated with air and water flow down the discharge stack and restrictions to this flow due to offsets and the bend at the base of the stack (Fig 2). This may cause foul air to be bubbled through the trap water seal or, in extreme circumstances, complete ejection of the water seal.

The traditional way to limit these pressure fluctuations is to use ventilating piping which, if correctly sized, ensures that design limits are not exceeded. It does, however, significantly increase the cost of the discharge system and in the housing field the use of the so-called single stack system, which requires no venting, has become widely used. More recently, these simplified systems have been used in offices and similar buildings where ranges of appliances, each individually vented to a separate ventilating stack, are typical features in a traditional system as illustrated in Fig 4. This particular situation would normally have been designed using a 100mm discharge stack, with a 50mm diameter ventilating stack and 50mm ventilating piping to each WC, and 30mm diameter venting to the wash basin ranges. But it has been found that if the design is correct, much of this pipework is unnecessary or can be reduced in size, saving up to 40 per cent of the cost.

Designs in this digest require trap water seal depths of 75mm for all appliances except the WC, and are based on the experience that some loss of water seal is acceptable provided the residual depth is not less than 25mm after discharges have taken place. A WC, though, has an initial seal depth of only 50mm and it has been found that the negative pressure, or suction, in the stack must be limited to $-375N/m^2$ or the seal depth will be reduced unacceptably. Positive pressures are limited, somewhat arbitrarily for convenience, to $375 N/m^2$.

The frequency of use of sanitary appliances is also taken into account since it is unreasonable to design any discharge system on the assumption that all or most of the appliances discharge at the same time. Table 1 shows the basic assumptions on this aspect as well as typical discharge rates for appliances in the UK.

Provided pipework and fittings are to the appropriate British Standards, use of the following design data will ensure that the discharge system operates within the pressure limits described without the need for additional ventilating pipework. However there are other external factors which can affect performance and which restrict the use of simplified systems:

Surcharging of the underground drainage pipework Some areas of large cities have old sewers which are overloaded often causing connecting drainage pipework to run full bore. In such situations, the simplified designs given in this digest should not be used as the air which normally flows down the stack and into the underground drainage system during a discharge is trapped and high back pressures can result. Relief venting is necessary to reduce this positive pressure ; this is described in BS 5572.

Intercepting traps Although not now generally recommended, these fittings are still sometimes used; their effect on the stack air flow can be similar to that of drain surcharging and relief venting is often necessary.

Wind effects Wind blowing over roofs and around buildings can give rise to pressure fluctuations causing excessive trap water seal loss. Venting cannot easily control this effect and so both simplified and vented systems are similarly affected; care must be taken to position stack terminations away from areas of high pressure variation, for example near parapets and corners of buildings.

Table 1 Flow and frequency of use of appliances

Appliance	Capacity litres	Discharge data		Frequency of use (T) s	Individual probability (p) of discharge $p = \dfrac{t}{T}$
		Maximum flow rate, l/s	Duration (t), s		
Washdown WC	9	2.3	5	1200 600 300	0.0041 0.0083 0.0167
Urinal (per person unit)	4.5	0.15	30	1200 900	0.025 0.0333
Wash basin (32 mm branch)	6	0.6	10	1200 600 300	0.0083 0.0167 0.0333
Sink (40 mm branch)	23	0.9	25	1200 600 300	0.0208 0.0417 0.0834
Bath (40 mm branch)	80	1.1	75	4500 1800	0.0167 0.0417
Automatic washing machine	180	0.7	300	15000	0.0200
Shower	-	0.1	-	-	-
Spray tap basin	-	0.06	-	-	-

Some design solutions given later include the use of resealing traps with wash basins to avoid excess water seal loss from self or induced siphonage in the unventilated discharge branch pipe. These traps have been proved in practice but they may be noisy at the end of the discharge and less efficient in resealing if they fill with deposits. The noise should not be a problem, though, if their use is restricted to a single wash basin or a range of basins in a single toilet room. They should not be used to relieve the effects of excessive air pressure fluctuations in the discharge stack, through undersizing for example, nor should they be used on appliances likely to produce heavy deposition, such as sinks.

Sanitary pipework: Part 2
Design of pipework

The main features of a simplified discharge system are shown in Fig 5. A discharge stack, without offsets, and with a large radius bend at its base, is connected to the underground drainage system and collects the discharges from the appliance branch discharge pipes. Self and induced siphonage in the branch pipe are controlled by the correct choice of pipe size, gradient and bends and by the appropriate number of appliances. The need for ventilating pipes is therefore avoided. Stack venting is avoided by restricting the number of appliances connected to a particular size discharge stack, by the correct design of branch/stack fittings (thereby controlling induced siphonage) and by avoiding offsets and using a large radius bend at the base of the stack (minimising back pressure effects).

The following data can be conveniently dealt with by considering branch discharge pipes and discharge stacks as separate components.

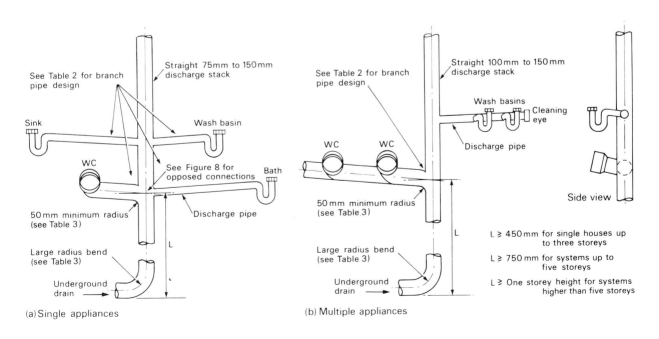

(a) Single appliances

(b) Multiple appliances

Fig 5 Simplified system – main features

Branch discharge pipes

A summary of the requirements for branch discharge pipes is given in Table 2. In general, the pipework should be kept as short as possible, with uniform gradients and without unnecessary bends but where bends are unavoidable they should be of large radius. Access for clearing deposits and blockages is important, especially for sinks and urinals. The following notes explain this design data.

Wash basins The risk of self-siphonage is much more dependent on the design of the branch than it is for other appliances. For single basins fitted with P-traps the usual 32mm pipes normally run full and so cause self-siphonage at the end of the discharge. One remedy is to limit the length and slope of the pipe as shown in Fig 6 for a P-trap arrangement. When the basin is more than 1.7m from the stack a 32mm diameter trap with a short 32mm tail pipe can be connected to a 40 or 50mm branch pipe. This should prevent the branch from running full (which is sometimes noisy) and thus reduce the self-siphonage effects. An alternative solution is to use a resealing trap, with the 32mm branch. S-trap arrangements produce particularly severe self-siphoning conditions which can be relieved only by a suitable resealing trap or by the venting systems detailed in the Code of practice.

Ranges of wash basins generally require ventilating pipes or resealing traps, especially when S-trap arrangements are used. However, one solution avoiding these precautions, for up to four wash basins, is shown in Fig 7, using a 50mm main branch pipe. Spray tap branch pipes do not normally run full even when the branch is only 30mm diameter and trials have shown that up to eight basins can be connected to this size of pipe. However, pipes serving spray tap basins are prone to become blocked by sedimentation and regular cleaning is usually necessary.

Sinks, baths and showers These appliances are generally fitted with 40mm branch pipes and so self-siphonage effects are not significant. Also, trap refill occurs at the end of a discharge from water draining from the flat bottom of the appliance, which tops up any seal loss.

Urinals Self-siphonage does not usually occur and trap refill from the trail off of the flushing water will top up any losses. Depostion can occur very rapidly and regular cleaning may be necessary, especially in hard water areas where scaling can be severe.

Washing machines The most usual arrangement with washing machines is a vertical 40mm standpipe connected to the stack or external gully via a special P or running trap and 40mm branch. The important feature is the provision of an air gap where the washing machine hose enters the top of its standpipe to avoid siphonage during operation of the machine.

Discharge stacks

A summary of the requirements for discharge stacks is given in Table 3. In vertical pipework serving appliances on different floors means must be found to limit the effects of induced siphonage and back-pressure. These effects depend on such factors as the number and distribution of appliances, pattern of use, height of the building, dimensions of the branch and stack pipes and the design of the branch/stack connections. Diameters of 75mm, 100mm and 150mm are commonly used for drainage stacks and these sizes have therefore been taken as the starting point for the sizing data given in Table 4.

Branch to stack connections The shape of the WC branch connection to the stack is most important as it influences induced siphonage in the stack. The recommendations in Table 4 assume that WC branch connections are swept in the direction of flow. Smaller diameter branch connections are not so critical and a swept entry is unnecessary.

Table 2   Design of branch discharge pipes

Appliance	Number of appliances	Trap size mm and type	Branch pipe Max. length m	Branch pipe Size mm	Bends in branch pipe	Design precautions Principle action to be guarded against	Trap design	Branch gradients	Other requirements
Wash basin	Single	32 P	1.7	32	Not more than 2 (min radius 75 mm to centre line)	Self-siphonage	Tubular	See Fig 6	Recommendations for BS 1188 wash basins with overflow. Some bottle traps will be suitable.
	Single	32 P	3.0	40	Not more than 2 (min radius 75 mm to centre line)	Self-siphonage and excessive deposition	Tubular or bottle	1° to 2½° (18 to 45 mm/m)	Connect 40 mm branch to trap with 32 mm tail pipe, 50 mm long.
	Single	32 P or S	3.0	32	Any bends to have min radius of 75 mm to centre line	Self-siphonage and excessive deposition	Resealing	1° to 2½° (18 to 45 mm/m)	See Code of Practice for vented arrangements
	Range of up to 4	32 P	3 Main 0.74 Branch	50 Main 32 Branch	None	Self and induced siphonage and excessive deposition	Tubular or bottle	1° to 2½° (18 to 45 mm/m)	Swept entry fittings at connections between 32 mm and 50 mm branches
	More than 4	32 P	10 Main 1 Branch	50 Main 32 Branch	Any bends to have min radius of 75 mm to centre line	Self and induced siphonage and excessive deposition	Resealing	1° to 2½° (18 to 45 mm/m)	Swept entry fittings at connections between 32 mm and 50 mm branches. See also Code of Practice for vented arrangements.
	More than 2	32 S	10 Main 1 Branch	50 Main 32 Branch	Any bends to have min radius of 75 mm to centre line	Self and induced siphonage and excessive deposition	Resealing	1° to 2½° (18 to 45 mm/m)	Swept entry fittings at connections between 32 mm and 50 mm branches. See also Code of Practice for vented arrangements.
Bath, Sink	Single	40 P or S	3	40	Any bends to have min radius of 75 mm to centre line	Self-siphonage and excessive deposition	Tubular or bottle	1° to 5° (18 to 90 mm/m)	Longer branches possible but noisier discharge and/or blockage may result. S-trap arrangement will also give noisier discharge.
Shower	Single	40 P or S	3	40	Any bends to have min radius of 75 mm to centre line	Self-siphonage and excessive deposition	Tubular or bottle	1° to 5° (18 to 90 mm/m)	
Washing Machine	Single	40 P or running trap	3	40	Any bends to have min radius of 75 mm to centre line	Siphonage from machine during refill	Tubular or bottle	1° to 2½° (18 to 45 mm/m)	40 mm standpipe, 600-900 mm high (depending on machine) with air gap at hose opening.
WC	Single	75 to 100 P or S	6	100	Avoid knuckle bends	Excessive deposition	–	1° min (18 mm/m)	Branch pipe size of 75 mm can be used with syphonic WCs.
	Range of up to 8	75 to 100 P or S	15	100	Avoid knuckle bends	Excessive deposition and induced siphonage	–	½° to 5° (9 to 90 mm/m)	Swept entry fittings needed between WC branches and main branch.
Urinal	Single Bowl	40 P or S	3	40	Any bends to have min radius of 75 mm to centre line	Excessive deposition	Tubular or bottle	1° to 5° (18 to 90 mm/m)	Access for cleaning important.
	Range of up to 5 bowls	40 P or S	As short as possible	50 Main 40 Branch	Any bends to have min radius of 75 mm to centre line	Excessive deposition and induced siphonage	Tubular or bottle	1° to 5° (18 to 90 mm/m)	Access for cleaning important.
	Range of stalls	65 or 75 P or S	As short as possible	65 or 75	Large radius bends	Excessive deposition	Tubular	1° to 5° (18 to 90 mm/m)	Access for cleaning important.

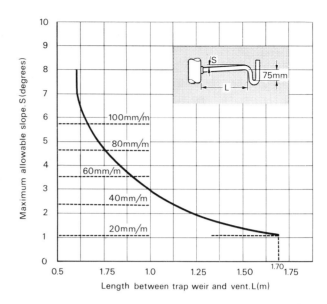

Fig 6 Design of branch pipe for single wash basin
Design curve for nominal 32mm branch pipe and 75mm seal P-traps connected to single BS wash basins. The minimum desirable slope is 20mm/m (approx 1¼°). The slopes recommended are allowable maxima but the pipes need not be fixed at exactly the gradients read off the graph.

Bend at base of stack A sharp bend at the base of the discharge stack can cause back pressure to affect the seals of the lowest branch connections. It can also cause a build-up of detergent foam especially in systems serving multi-storey dwellings. The bend should therefore be of large radius; a further precaution for buildings over five storeys high is to connect the ground floor appliances directly to the drain or manhole or to use a bend which is one size larger than the stack itself, provided this does not oversize the drain.

Opposed branch-to-stack connections In any discharge system, fully vented or simplified, the discharge from one branch connection to the stack must not be able to back up an opposed branch connection. This becomes especially critical when one of the opposed branches serves one or more WC's. Figure 8 illustrates the positions on a stack which should be avoided when a small diameter branch pipe, for example serving baths, has to be connected opposite a WC branch connection. A connection may be made level with the point where the centre lines of the WC and opposed branch coincide, but not within 200mm below it. Connections on the same side of the stack within this distance are permissible but generally are difficult to carry out in practice.

Offsets An offset in the discharge stack above the topmost connection has little effect on the performance of the system. Offsets below the topmost connection should be avoided or ventilating pipes may be required to prevent large pressure fluctuations in the stack.

Termination of discharge stack To minimise the effects in discharge stacks due to wind blowing across the roofs of tall buildings, the stack terminations should be sited away from known areas of high suction. These are usually at corners of the roofs and edges of parapets. Normal venting arrangements will not provide a remedy but a protective cowl may be of benefit.

Rainwater connections Where it is permissible for the discharge pipe system to carry rainwater, the discharge stack in a simplified system can be used provided certain precautions are taken. The roof area served by a stack should not be greater than 40m^2 and the building should not be more than ten storeys in height. Where easy access to the roof exists, the roof gulley linking the roof to the stack should be trapped.

Table 4 gives data for discharge stack sizing for the more common arrangements; for other systems, reference should be made to the Code of practice. Table 5 gives additional information for office and public buildings to enable discharge stacks serving WC's, basins and urinals to be sized from Table 4. The four combinations of appliances given are based on the provision of two Statutory Instruments made under the Offices, Shops and Railway Premises Act 1963 and these are equated to the hydraulic equivalents of WC/basin combinations.

Neither this digest nor the Code of practice can cover every possible arrangement of pipework. For other designs, especially where a long branch pipe or venting a long range of appliances is considered, a test or mock-up is recommended. Test procedures are given in the Code of practice.

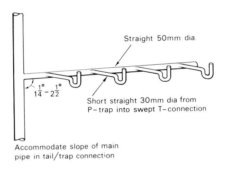

Fig 7 Design of branch pipes for up to four wash basins

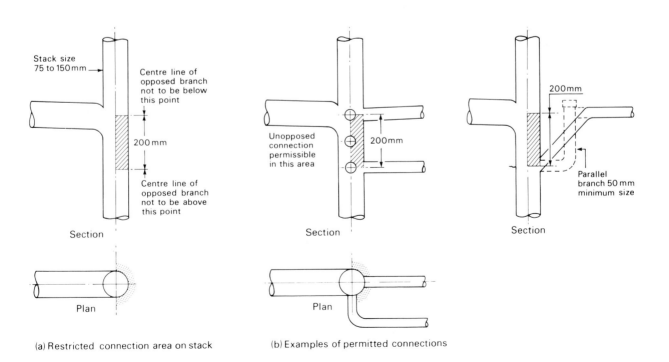

Fig 8 Opposed branch pipe connections to discharge stacks

Table 3 Design of discharge stack

Component	Action to be guarded against	Recommendations
WC (100 mm) branch connections	Induced siphonage	To be swept in direction of flow with minimum sweep radius of 50 mm (but see Note in Table 4)
Bend at base of stack	Back pressure and build up of detergent foam	Bend to be of large radius, at least 200 mm radius to centre line but preferably two 45° large radius bends. Bend can also be enlarged by one size but this may oversize the drain.
Lowest stack connection	Back pressure effects	Distance between lowest branch connection and invert of drain to be: 450 mm for single houses up to three storeys; 750 mm for multi-storey systems up to five storeys; One storey height for systems over five storeys.
Offsets	Pressure effects	Avoid offsets in wet part of stack.
Opposed branch connections	Backing up of WC branch discharge into opposed branch	Position of opposed connection to be as shown in Figure 8

Table 4 Discharge stack sizing — *stack and branch design to Tables 2 and 3*

Stack size mm	Use		Number of floors of appliances	Max number of appliances/floors
	Description	Interval between use mins		
75	Domestic	20	Up to 2	1 Domestic Group*
100	Domestic	20	Up to 10	2 Domestic Groups*
	Commercial	10	Up to 8 Up to 4	2 WCs + 2 wash basins 5 WCs + 5 wash basins
	Congested	5	Up to 8 Up to 4	1 WC + 1 wash basin 3 WCs + 3 wash basins
150	Domestic	20	Up to 30	2 Domestic Groups*
	Commercial	10	Up to 24 Up to 8	3 WCs + 3 wash basins 5 WCs + 5 wash basins
	Congested	5	Up to 24 Up to 16 Up to 8	2 WCs + 2 wash basins 3 WCs + 3 wash basins 5 WCs + 5 wash basins

*1 domestic appliance group is 1 WC, 1 sink, 1 wash basin, 1 bath (and/or shower) and 1 washing machine.
Note: For non-swept WC branch connections, with 2 groups of domestic appliances per floor:
   A 100 mm stack can be used for systems up to 4 floors in height
   A 150 mm stack can be used for systems up to 15 floors in height.

Table 5

WC		Urinal		Wash basin			WC		Wash basin
2	+	1	+	2	Equivalent	2	+	2
2	+	2	+	3	to:	3	+	3
3	+	3	+	4		4	+	4
4	+	4	+	5		5	+	5

Other simplified systems

Some pipework systems do not need to conform to all the requirements given under *Design basis* or to the general arrangements shown in Figure 5; for example:

Ground floor appliances not connected to the discharge stack Ground floor appliances are sometimes connected to the underground drainage system via an external gulley or, in the case of the WC, directly to the drain without a ventilating stack.

Where branch pipes discharge into a gulley, the appliance traps are not subject to significant pressure fluctuations or to drain air, and so the trap seal depth can be reduced to 40mm. However, it is preferable to fit a 75mm seal trap to a ground floor wash basin as self-siphonage losses may effectively empty the trap and so allow air to be blown through the pipework into the bathroom.

A ground floor WC can be connected directly to the drain without using a discharge stack or ventilating pipework provided that the vertical distance from the crown of the of the trap to the invert of the drain is not more than 1.5 metres. Excessive water seal losses can result if a larger vertical drop is used especially when bulky objects, such as disposable nappies, are flushed from the WC.

Stub Stacks In some areas it has become common practice to connect the domestic sanitary appliances in single-storey buildings to a short straight 100mm discharge stack with the top closed by an access fitting. This arrangement performs satisfactorily provided the distance from the crown of the WC trap to the invert of the drain is not more than 1.5 metres and the distance between the topmost connection to the stack and the invert of the drain is not more than 2 metres. However where a drain serves a number of dwellings equipped in this way, the upstream end of the underground drain should be vented either by a separate ventilating stack or by a conventional discharge stack as already described.

Ventilating valves In recent years, ventilating valves have become available which relieve negative pressures in the discharge system but prevent foul air entering the building if positive pressures occur. The valve can be incorporated into a trap (an anti-vacuum trap) or can be connected to the system as a separate component. Generally valves or anti-vacuum traps fitted to small diameter branches should only be used to relieve siphonage conditions in the branch pipe and not induced siphonage effects from the discharge stack through, say, undersizing of the stack. Larger valves can be used to ventilate the discharge stack provided they are fitted to a WC branch and/or the top of the discharge stack but manufacturers instructions must be closely followed. Design of these valves vary significantly and each must be judged on its merits; only those that have been granted Agrement certificates should be considered. When a number of homes are equipped with the ventilating valves, any common branch drain should be ventilated by an open stack at its upstream end.

Further reading
BS 5572: 1978 Code of practice for Sanitary pipework

Hospital sanitary services: some design and maintenance problems

Some of the lessons to be learned from a preliminary study by the Building Research Station of hospital sanitary services are instructive in showing how critically the design and use of these installations determine subsequent maintenance needs and the ease with which these needs can be met. The main observations contained in this digest are directed principally to those involved in the design and maintenance of hospital services, but they have a wider relevance for the design of complex installations in general.

The advantages of single-stack plumbing for housing, the subject of the previous digest, are best realised when there is a close grouping of sanitary appliances round a vertical service duct. When appliances are more widely spaced apart, as they often are in hospital wards, it may be impracticable or even impossible to use a single-stack method.

In wards it is common practice for a drain to be run at a gradual slope beneath the floor and to receive the discharge from many appliances on its way to a stack. While this more or less horizontal arrangement may be economic and may fit in with architectural requirements, it has disadvantages in that the risk of blockage is likely to be greater than in vertical pipes, particularly if the drain has bends and junctions in addition to a shallow slope. There is a lack of information about the performance of these systems and of their anti-siphonage requirements. For these reasons the Station, with the encouragement of the Ministry of Health, began to study sanitary services in hospitals. The first stage of this work, involving the examination of several existing and proposed schemes, is reported below.

Pipework in existing hospitals

In several important respects the design of drainage systems in modern hospitals shows little advance over that of a hundred years ago. Admittedly, most

piping is now installed internally rather than externally, and there is greater provision for anti-siphonage devices, but there are still many different drainage layouts, including vertical and horizontal main drains within the building, and pipe systems which take tortuous paths through the structure (*see* Fig. 1). The main reason for this seems to be lack of co-ordinated planning of the different services, both with each other and with the main structure. The result is a network of piping which is spread throughout hospital buildings and which reveals how little thought has been given to the need for adequate access to the pipework.

Fig. 1.   ...tortuous path through the structure...

Fig. 2. Three short-radius bends close together

Fig. 3. An unnecessary offset

Layout of pipework in relation to stoppages

The complexity of pipe layout directly affects the number of stoppages which have to be cleared— expensive and often troublesome operations. Not only do they disrupt the work of the hospital, they may be a possible cause of cross-infection. Most stoppages seem to occur where the pipework is complicated by knuckle bends and sharp offsets and $92\frac{1}{2}^{\circ}$ junctions. None was reported where straight lengths of 100 and 150 mm pipes sloped gradually. The kind of problem is well illustrated by Figs. 2 and 3. No excuse is offered for saying again that better design, planning and overall integration are called for.

Misuse of system during construction

Stoppages may result also from misuse of the build-ing while under construction. Builders' rubbish was frequently found in the drainage system above and below ground. The open ends of soil branch con-nections are often to be seen on site stuffed with sacks or cement bags to keep out rubbish (*see* Fig. 4)—an unreliable method if these materials have to be removed as rubbish themselves from the completed system after handover.

While this kind of misuse occurs with all types of buildings, in hospitals it seems to have been particularly prevalent, and is of course particularly unfortunate in its effects. Plastic caps have been recommended for closing the ends of heating pipes during installation and there is much to be said for using this type of protective cover on soil and waste pipes also. In general, improved site supervision of the contract could help a lot in preventing the carelessness which causes trouble later.

Misuse of system during occupation

Special appliances such as sluices, slop hoppers and cleaners' sinks are available to ward staff for the disposal of materials unsuited to removal by con-ventional drainage systems. However, some misuse of these appliances was reported and dressings, sanitary towels, floor cloths, mop heads, syringes, spatulas and rubber gloves are known to have been among articles removed from the systems surveyed; cases were also reported of a blanket, a stainless steel bowl, false teeth and tea cloths contributing to stoppages. In addition, traps are readily blocked by match sticks and cigarette filter tips.

There is a special problem concerning goods such as plastic syringes and spatulas. Sometimes it is not appreciated by hospital staff that these 'disposables' should be incinerated rather than put into the normal drainage system. In other cases it appears that ward incinerators are much less efficient than they need to be and this leads to the misuse of drainage systems as the first alternative to hand.

Kitchen refuse also causes stoppages, and the misuse of kitchen appliances such as grease traps can lead to the accumulation of grease in the

Fig. 4. Floor access point blocked with polythene sheeting

drainage system. Regular cleaning of grease traps is essential, yet only one of the fifteen hospitals visited had arranged for this.

While it is important not to get the incidence of misuse out of perspective, there is no doubt that improved staff training in these matters would help, as would better refuse disposal facilities.

Access to drainage pipework

While much could be done to improve the layout and prevent misuse of drainage systems, some risk of stoppages will always remain. It is important, therefore, and particularly in hospitals, that adequate provision be made for access to the pipework. Many complaints were made of lack of access into ducts—it was either too small, blocked by other services, or in the wrong place. On the pipework itself cleaning eyes often could not be used effectively; some were partly embedded in concrete or turned towards the wall or ceiling, as in Figs. 5 and 6. Access to others was blocked by other services. In many cases it was not possible to use 0.6 m drain rods. Permanent lighting was absent from some ducts; a torch does not give a plumber adequate light to work by.

Some vertical and horizontal pipes with cleaning eyes were encased in brick or hollow pot ducts without access doors. In one example, a stoppage occurred in the enclosed pipe, no drawings were available and holes had to be knocked in the duct to locate the access point; eight hours were needed to clear the blockage which had occurred at a knuckle bend as a result of a build-up of kitchen waste on top of builders' rubbish.

Some horizontal pipes are enclosed within false ceilings, with removable panels providing access. This means that when a stoppage occurs by misuse of an appliance say, on the third floor, it has to be cleared from the second floor since this provides access to the drain above. The routine of two floors is therefore affected, whereas better design might

limit the disruption to one floor. Several medical authorities were concerned at the need to clear blockages within the clinical area. In one check test reported by a hospital pathologist, infectious bacteria were found in sewage that had discharged into a clinical area. As well as this risk there is the possible hazard of carrying dirty tools and wearing infected overalls in clinical areas.

Cases were also reported of electrical services being disrupted as a result of sewage leaking round lighting fittings.

Recommendations

While the internal drainage pipework is not normally among the most costly of hospital service systems, the foregoing notes will have indicated the serious consequences of poor design and misuse. Improvements are needed at every stage, from the preliminary sketch plans to the work of the subcontractor and site supervision, and finally to the use and maintenance of the services. Broad recommendations for each stage can be made as follows:
1. Adequate service space is fundamental to the design of a hospital. The services must be planned within the service area and installed in accordance with the plan. Service inlets and outlets should not be neglected at this stage; the position of sanitary appliances on the sketch plan, and the position and amount of piping needed beneath the floors, must be considered together. The service space should be well lit and capable of being easily cleaned.
2. Bends of large rather than small radius are always to be recommended but are particularly important beneath a ward floor. Similarly, oblique junctions are preferred to T-junctions since they allow loads to flow more readily from branches to main drains.
3. Access doors are advised for all changes of direction except the most gradual. They are also needed at all junctions on horizontal drains. Access doors should of course be easily accessible within

Fig. 5. Access door turned towards wall

Fig. 6. Two access doors turned towards ceiling

the service space. Flexible connectors between soil appliances and piping allow their ready removal if this should be necessary for rodding.

4. Planned maintenance is a necessity and thought must be given to the arrangements for maintenance staff to do their work with minimum interruption of ward routines or threat to hygiene. Drawings must be available to them showing the drainage layout and access points. Washing facilities should be provided for them.

5. The education of staff in the properties of sanitary equipment and services is essential.

Single-stack drainage

There are many cases in hospital buildings of various types where a stack serves several appliances close to it on different floors. This is a situation in which single-stack principles are likely to be applicable, and a study of the literature will show the possibilities in this direction.

Further reading

BRE Digest 80: *Soil and waste pipe systems for housing*.
BRE Digest 115: *Soil and waste pipe systems for office buildings*.
AFE Wise and R Payne. Sanitary services for hospitals: a review of current faults. Architects Journal, 1965, 142 (21st July), pp. 153-6.

Institution of Heating and Ventilating Engineers. Hospital Engineering Services: Present and Future, Symposium held on 12th January, 1966.

Soakaways

A soakaway should have sufficient storage capacity to accommodate a large amount of water from a severe, but comparatively rare, storm and should be able to disperse water at the (lower) average rate of flow into it.

This digest describes a simple test for the permeability of the soil in which a soakaway is to be constructed and how to convert the test results to size of soakaway for a given rate of stormwater flow. Some constructional details are included.

The design rules proposed are applicable to any part of the country, whatever its annual rainfall.

A sewerage system may be 'separate' to accept foul sewage only, all surface water being discharged either to a separate surface-water sewer or direct to watercourses or soakaways; it may be 'partially separate, accepting foul sewage and some surface water with the balance discharged as above; or it may be 'combined' in which a single sewer carries the whole of the foul sewage together with all surface water from roads, footpaths, roofs and yards. Both the partially separate and combined systems will involve spasmodic rushes of storm sewage at the treatment works and this has some practical disadvantages. In general, the present tendency is to favour the adoption of the separate system, with a consequent need for soakaways in some situations.

British Standard Code of Practice CP 301 : 1971 *Building drainage* suggests that a common method of designing soakaways is to provide water storage capacity equal to at least 13 mm of rainfall over the impermeable area but that on some sites tests of the permeability of the soil through trial boreholes may be needed. This digest indicates a simple method of making such a test and how to interpret the results so as to design a soakaway that will accept all the rainwater from a house or similar small building.

Rainfall
The total amount of rain which falls on a house each year varies with its position in the country, but the amount which falls during a storm of given duration is not so very different in different parts of the country and the most difficult task for a soakaway is to deal with the maximum flow during a rainstorm. The peak rate of rainfall, at the height of a storm, does not last very long, so that the longer the storm lasts the lower the average rate of rainfall is likely to be. This means that a soakaway will have to accept a certain quantity of water in a few minutes but that over several hours, or a day, the average rate of flow of water into it will be less. A successful soakaway is one with sufficient storage capacity to accept the sudden inflow of water and a sufficient rate of dissipation to deal with the average rate of flow.

On the basis of summarised rainfall data in the appropriate form, which is more or less applicable to the whole country, Fig 1 has been prepared. It is very likely that some improvement of this figure could be made for a given locality, by fuller consideration of the actual rainfall data available and applicable for that place. But it is considered that this improvement would not greatly affect the practical recommendations that are advanced here for permeability tests and soakaways.

Dispersion

The rate at which water will disperse into the ground depends largely on the permeability of the soil and this can vary tremendously from place to place. Clays such as London Clay, Oxford Clay and Gault are almost impervious (they have been used to line canals and for water cut-offs in dams) and no soakaway formed in them would be able to disperse much water. Sands and gravels, on the other hand, can be very permeable and a soakaway will be able to disperse a great deal of water into this type of soil. The word 'soil' is used here in an engineering rather than an agricultural sense. Between these two extreme types of soil there is a whole range with varying permeabilities.

A soakaway will only be effective when it is wholly above the water table and any available information about the seasonal rise and fall of the water table should be considered in relation to the depth of the soakaway.

Test

An indication of the permeability of a soil is given by the rate at which water will disperse into it from a shallow borehole. By using a trial borehole of the same depth as the proposed soakaway, water from it will soak into the same strata that will have to take water from the soakaway and the measured rate of percolation will be applicable.

The hole should be bored with a 150 mm diameter hand or power auger in the position proposed for the soakaway and initially taken to a depth of 1 m, corresponding to the bottom of the smallest soakaway likely to be required. To perform the test, water should be poured into the hole to a depth of 300 mm and an observation made of the time required for it to soak away. The depth of water can be gauged by marking a stick so that when it is held down the hole its end is 300 mm above the bottom of the hole. If the hole has been cut by the auger to a fairly exact size, $5\frac{1}{2}$ litres of water will give the required depth. The time at which the water is poured into the hole and the time when the water level is seen to reach the bottom of the hole should be noted and the elapsed time expressed in minutes. Where practicable, the test should be repeated once or twice to get an average time.

On completion of this first group of tests, the hole should be bored for a further 1 m, to make it 2 m deep, and a second group of tests made, again using a 300 mm depth of water above the bottom of the hole. If necessary (as discussed below) the hole should be extended in about 1 m steps, and tests made at each depth.

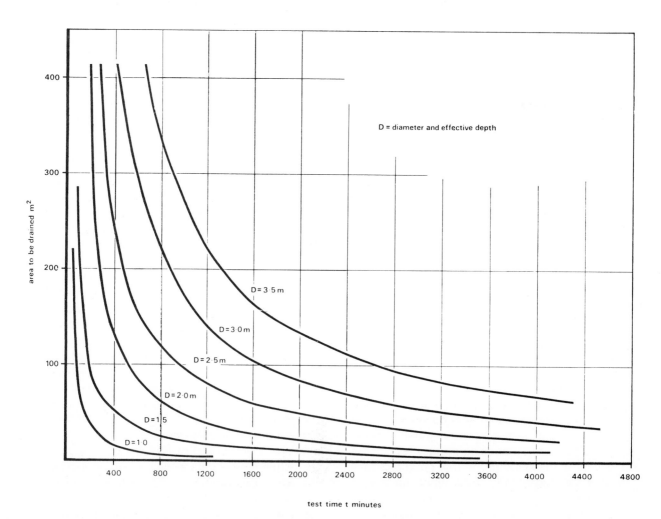

Fig 1 Size of soakaway determined from permeability test time and drained area

Design of soakaway

The rate of rainfall corresponding to a two-hour storm occurring on average not more than once in ten years is 15 mm/hour and this is the basis of the recommendations in this digest. On this basis, overflowing of a soakaway for as long as two hours is unlikely to occur more than once in ten years and this seems a reasonable risk to take. If a soakaway can accommodate the rate of rainfall in a two-hour storm, it will be able to accommodate the rate of rainfall in longer storms. Also, a soakaway designed for this two-hour storm rate will probably accept the higher rainfall from shorter storms if it is not already full of water; at worst, it might overflow for a period of not more than two hours.

It has been assumed that the soakaway will be cylindrical in shape and will have a diameter about the same as its effective depth, the depth below invert level. The relationship between the diameter (or effective depth) required for the soakaway to suit a give area of roof and/or paved area, and the time t given by the tests, is shown by the curves in Fig 1. To use these curves, a vertical line is drawn upwards from the test time, t minutes, and a horizontal line drawn from the area to be drained. To illustrate the method, if the test time t was 880 minutes and the soakaway is required to take the water from a plan area of 103 m², the diameter (and depth) of the soakaway, from Fig 1, should be 2·5 metres.

If the ground is not very permeable, the size of soakaway can be kept down by splitting up the area to be drained into several parts, with a separate soakaway for each part. In the case of a small house, for example, the two sides of the roof and the paved driveway or yard could be drained to three separate soakaways.

Where the permeability of the ground increases with depth, tests in the deepened holes will give lower values of t, so that it may be cheaper to build a smaller soakaway at a greater depth below the surface.

Construction

Soakaways can be constructed in two main forms, filled and unfilled, depending to some extent on their size.

For small soakaways, an excavated hole can be filled with a coarse granular material such as broken bricks, crushed sound rock, or river gravel with a size range of 150 mm to 10 mm, see Fig 2. The end of the inlet pipe should be surrounded by only the large pieces, to ensure that the rainwater can flow freely into the main mass of granular material. Above the pipe, the size of the pieces should be gradually reduced until the surface of the granular material, at about 0·5 m below ground surface, can be blinded to take a layer of topsoil. This topsoil covering can form a part of a garden or support a lawn.

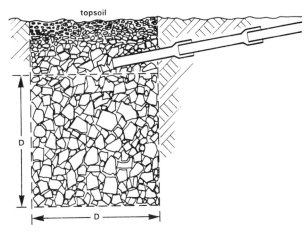

Fig 2   Small filled soakaway

For larger soakaways, the excavated pit may be lined with brickwork laid dry, or with jointed honeycomb brickwork. Alternatively, they can be built with a rigid lining such as perforated precast concrete rings or segments, laid dry, surrounded by granular material to lead the water into the soil, see Fig 3. The top can be covered with a standard reinforced concrete manhole top to suit the rings or segments, fitted with an access cover so that it is possible to clean out accumulated silt and rubbish.

Caution

Soakaways should be built on land lower than, or sloping away from, buildings and they must be kept at a safe distance from buildings. In land overlying chalk there may be a serious risk of swallow holes and these may be activated by the concentrated discharge from a soakaway. There have been cases of collapse of the corner of a building caused by a soakaway built too close to it, and an example of a swimming pool which lost one end into a swallow hole which developed under a soakaway built to take water from the pool itself. Because of the wide variations in soils and site conditions, it is not possible to give any generally applicable guidance as to the 'safe' distance from a building but the local authority can usually offer advice on this, based on their detailed knowledge and experience of the locality.

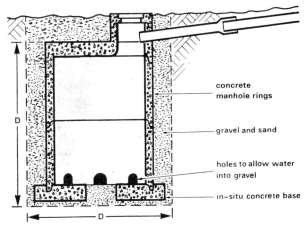

Fig 3   Soakaway pit with rigid lining

Plumbing with stainless steel

Small-bore stainless steel tube for plumbing and for domestic heating systems is claimed to be stronger than copper and as versatile and corrosion resistant; it can also be supplied at competitive prices. This digest discusses the properties of stainless steel and its suitability for plumbing installations.

For any plumbing application the resistance to corrosion is the most important single factor determining durability. There are three main kinds of stainless steel whose corrosion resistance varies according to their composition. Table 1 summarizes this.

The carbon content of steels is an important factor in determining durability; for welded steels under corrosive conditions a low carbon content is required. Three types of corrosion may be distinguished: pitting, stress corrosion cracking and weld decay, although nowadays the problems associated with weld decay are negligible for plumbing tubes.

Table 1 Classification of stainless steels

Type	Typical constituents	Heat treatment
Austenitic	Chromium 18% Nickel 8%	Softening by cooling in air or by quenching from 1000 to 1100°C
		Cannot be hardened by heat treatment
Ferritic	Chromium 16% to 22%	Softened by cooling in air from 750 to 820°C
Martensitic	Chromium 12% to 20% Nickel Nil to 3%	Hardened by oil quenching at 950–1000°C, followed by tempering at temperatures up to 750°C
		Carbon content of up to 1 per cent

Note: Titanium or niobium are added to stainless steels, principally of the austenitic variety, to improve their welding properties; molybdenum is added to improve corrosion resistance.

Pitting

Water containing high chloride concentrations can be highly corrosive. The chlorides interfere with the natural repair of the oxide film on the surface of stainless steel; increasing the chromium and nickel content of the alloy helps to offset the tendency to pitting and is one reason why the austenitic 18/8 steels are the most popular for use in water systems.

Stress corrosion cracking

This occurs with austenitic stainless steels through the combined action of a corrosive environment and stress. It rarely occurs in water services and is unlikely to cause problems at temperatures below 80°C, but highly stressed stainless steel components in chloride environments are at risk. Few failures are known with stressed tubing but cast stainless steel boilers, where misalignment can increase the inherent stresses already present, are liable to attack and BS 3377 carries a warning that such boilers should not be used in hard water areas and that care must be taken to ensure that no air space remains when the boiler is filled with water. Chlorides concentrate behind hard water scale and by water evaporating in the air spaces. This leads to stress corrosion cracking and failure of the boiler. Good practice is to minimize the level of stress in the components and to avoid external contact with all chloride-bearing materials.

Stainless steel tubes for domestic purposes

Steel used for domestic tubes is of the austenitic type (see Table 1) designated 302 S 17 in BS 1449. It contains 17·0–19·0 per cent chromium, 8·0–11·0 per cent nickel, 0·50–2·00 per cent manganese, 0·20–1·00 per cent silicon and with a maximum carbon content of 0·08 per cent.

British Standards

Table 2 compares the dimensions of stainless steel tubes to BS 4127: Part 2 *Light gauge stainless steel tubes,* and copper tubes to BS 2871: Part 1 *Copper tubes for water, gas and sanitation.* It shows that the

Table 2 Dimensions of stainless steel tube to BS 4127: Part 2 and copper tube to BS 2871: Part 1

| | | Nominal thickness (2) | | | |
| | | Copper to BS 2871: Part 1 | | | Stainless steel To BS 4127: Part 2 |
Nominal size mm	Maximum outside dia mm (1)	Table X Half hard light gauge mm	Table Y Half hard and annealed mm	Table Z(3) Half hard thin wall mm	mm
6	6.045	0.6	0.8	0.5	0.6
8	8.045	0.6	0.8	0.5	0.6
10	10.045	0.6	0.8	0.5	0.6
12	12.045	0.6	0.8	0.5	0.6
15	15.045	0.7	1.0	0.5	0.6
18	18.045	0.8	1.0	0.6	0.7
22	22.055	0.9	1.2	0.6	0.7
28	28.055	0.9	1.2	0.6	0.8
35	35.07	1.2	1.5	0.7	1.0
42	42.07	1.2	1.5	0.8	1.1

(1) Minimum outside dia is 0.08 mm less for copper and 0.105 mm less for stainless steel
(2) Thickness shall not vary by more than ± 10 per cent.
(3) Bending this tube is not recommended.

outside diameters are the same for both materials; the tolerances on thickness of stainless steel tube walls are within those specified for light gauge copper tubes. The minimum hydraulic pressures that stainless steel tubes are required to withstand are equal to or higher than those for copper. Stainless steel's tensile strength of 510 N/mm^2, compared with 250 N/mm^2 specified for copper, ensures greater protection from accidental damage and necessitates fewer fixing clips. The ductility of stainless steel tube is less than half hard copper (Table X and Y of BS 2871) but is sufficient for Type B compression fittings to be used. BS 4127 requires that stainless steel can be expanded 25 per cent of its original diameter compared with 30 per cent required by BS 2871.

Working the tube

Capillary and Types A and B compression fittings to BS 864 are suitable for use with stainless steel tube to BS 4127 and have been approved by the British Waterworks Association. For the metric sizes shown in Table 2, Part 2 of each of these standards is applicable. Part 1 of each standard applies to imperial sizes. Tubes so joined must meet the hydraulic test requirements of 20 bar or 300 lb/in^2, respectively. Many of the fittings can be obtained in a nickel-plated or satin chrome finish which blends well with the finish of the tube. With a suitable flux, stainless steel can be joined by capillary fittings but as it has a lower thermal conductivity than copper it is advisable to use a smaller flame and to direct it at the fitting, not at the tube.

Experience has shown that acid chloride fluxes have caused severe pitting corrosion of stainless steel plumbing tube, particularly where liquid fluxes have been used in excessive amount and where a long period—weeks or even months—has elapsed between making the joint and admitting water. To overcome this risk, safer fluxes have been developed and some are available in liquid or paste form based on phosphoric acid. Safe fluxes based on phosphoric acid should always be used for soft-soldering. By their very nature in cleaning material to take solder, all fluxes are corrosive to some degree and should not be left in contact with metal for longer than necessary. Manufacturers of fluxes often give recommendations for their use in soldering and these should be strictly observed.

The tube can be bent by either an internal spring or machine. More force is needed than for copper, and spring bending of tubes above

Fig 1 Applying the flux

Fig 2 Making the joint

12 mm diameter is not recommended. Spring bending of smaller diameter tubes is satisfactory but the springs used should be those suitable for thin-walled copper tube, to BS 2871. Satisfactory bends are produced by machine-bending, irrespective of diameter and position of the weld.

Acceptability

The tube has been accepted by the British Waterworks Association and most local Water Authorities in the United Kingdom for use with compression (Types A and B) and capillary fittings.

Tests have shown that stainless steel can be safely incorporated into existing copper systems without risk of bimetallic corrosion. In areas where dezincification of brass occurs, gunmetal or copper fittings must be used.

Back boilers

Stainless steel back boilers give satisfactory service in soft-water areas. They should be installed in accordance with BS 3377, correctly aligned so that no air space remains when the boiler is filled with water.

British Standards

BS 864 : Part 2 : 1971   Capillary and compression tube fittings of copper and copper alloy
BS 1449 : Part 2 : 1975   Stainless and heat resisting steel plate, sheet and strip
BS 2871 : Part 1 : 1971   Copper tubes for water, gas and sanitation
BS 3377 : 1969   Back boilers for use with domestic solid fuel appliances
BS 4127 : Part 2 : 1972   Light gauge stainless steel tubes

Reliability and performance of solar collector systems

Digest 205 (first published in 1977) deals briefly with the practical aspects of using flat plate solar collectors for heating domestic water in the UK and discusses some of the causes of system failure. There has been a considerable increase in the number of solar systems installed during the last four years and there is now sufficient experience to provide additional advice for design and installation of systems using liquid heat transfer.

Overall, it has become apparent that failure to ensure adequate standards of design and workmanship can result in poor thermal performance, unreliable operation and building-related problems. The cost of the necessary repairs, often comprised largely of labour charges, can far exceed what could be expected to be the marginal extra cost of ensuring satisfactory initial design and installation. Attention to good design is especially important with items such as control systems that are difficult to check on site and whose correct functioning is often taken as a matter of trust.

A principal lesson of the last four years is that it is not sufficient merely to design a solar collector system around proven plumbing components; only a total system approach that considers component interaction and integration with buildings can ensure success.

This digest discusses some of the more common problems and their possible solutions and gives guidance on methods of checking system operation.

Much of this digest has been condensed from a BRE book that contains guidance on many aspects of solar technology and application. Whilst some of the faults described in the book may now occur in only a fraction of new systems, continued awareness on the part of designers, specifiers and installers will be an aid to preventing further occurrence of recognised problems.

Since publication of the book, little change has occurred in the design of simple solar water heating systems. Figure 1 shows two common designs in which the collectors are kept permanently full of heat transfer fluid. In some of the alternative types untreated water can be used provided the collectors can be drained to prevent frost damage. Thermosiphon systems are not yet widely used in the UK but they have potential for lower cost and greater reliability in service. Figure 2 shows an indirect system using a cistern for fluid expansion.

Some of the more common types of problems that have been experienced in the UK are summarised in Table 1, and suggestions for their possible remedy in both present and future systems are discussed. Methods for checking the operation of systems in all

buildings are important and whilst few firm recommendations can be given at the present, guidance of an interim nature is set out. The emphasis is on domestic hot water heating but much of the advice could have wider application.

The following checklist may be helpful in avoiding repetition of some of the problems of solar collector systems that have been highlighted since 1977:

Specify good quality plumbing components, to British Standards specification where possible.

Ensure compatability of all system components, particularly where dissimilar metals are involved.
Specify a good quality control system and ensure that the temperature sensors are installed correctly.
Specify the collectors having regard to factors likely to affect thermal performance and mechanical integrity.
Ensure that the collector mounting system is strong enough to survive severe wind and snow loading conditions, will have good durability and will not impair the building's weathertightness.
Incorporate simple equipment to check system operation.

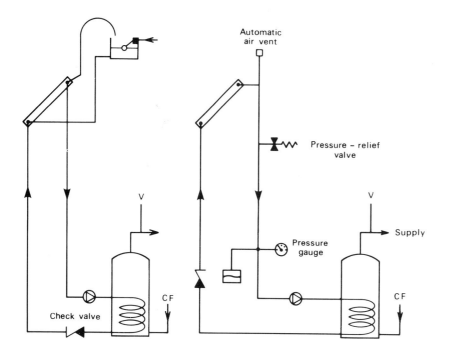

Fig 1 Vented and sealed indirect systems with pumped circulation – the check valve prevents reverse circulation

Table 1   Main problem areas of UK solar water heating equipment

Table 1   Main problem areas of UK solar water heating equipment

Basic design of collectors
Excessive condensation within collector units. Failure of absorber plate surface coating and/or insulation material due to overheating (use of unsuitable types of materials).
Cracking of cover glass especially in double-glazed collectors.
Inadequately secured cover glass.
Poor thermal performance often caused by inadequate thermal contact between absorber plate and fluid passages.

Plumbing and system design faults
Incorrectly specifed components.
Inappropriate layout of pipework.
Air-locking; inadequate venting points.
Excessive flow rate leading to pump hunting.
Frost damage.
Leaking pipework joints.
Poor flow distribution in collectors.

Damage to roofs
Damage caused to roof covering during installation.
Cutting of roof members.
Insufficient support of extra water stores.

Integrity of collector fixings
Unsatisfactory methods of securing collectors to roofs.
Unsatisfactory methods of weathering entries of pipes and fixings through roof surfaces.

Degradation of materials
Reaction between heat transfer fluid and collector plate fluid passages particularly in mixed metal systems. (Internal corrosion). Corrosion of fixing brackets and other components exposed to the weather. (External corrosion.)
Hose failures.

Electronic control systems
Poor circuit design. Use of low quality components. Difficulty of detecting incorrect control system operation. Unsatisfactory installation of sensors.
Failure to match control system characteristics to real control requirements.

Design and fixing
Collector design

The early years of the UK solar industry were characterised by the manufacture of a large range of collector designs, some with faults affecting thermal performance or structural integrity. Experience has helped to ensure that fewer design faults now feature in production models but specifiers should continue to assess collector designs for their likely reliability, durability and ease of repair so as to help minimise failures in service. Condensation within collectors has been a common problem and whilst it is not too serious in itself, some insulating materials become less effective when wet and the condensation may accelerate other processes such as corrosion, growth of spores on glass surfaces and degradation of absorber plate surface coatings. As mentioned under *Degradation of materials*, ventilation of the insulation itself in addition to ventilation of the space between the absorber plate and the glazing may be advisable to minimise the risk of corrosion. However, care should be taken both in design and installation to ensure that vent holes do not allow rain or snow penetration.

The high temperatures (perhaps up to 200°C) that can be experienced inside even a single-glazed flat plate collector preclude successful use of many materials and surface finishes. For example, expanded polystyrene is not suitable for use directly beneath an absorber plate. Of wider significance may be the thermal cycling and exposure of absorber plate surface coatings and any resulting degradation. The simplest advice seems to be to ensure that the

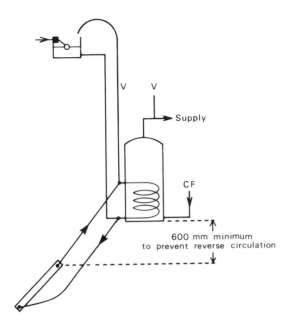

Fig 2 Indirect system with thermosiphon circulation

V V

→ Supply

C F

600 mm minimum
to prevent reverse circulation

specification requires a surface finish suitable for the conditions that may be experienced in service. In the case of a special but unproven surface finish, simple high temperature cycling and stagnation tests should show whether it is likely to survive a few years' use.

The pollution and high humidity of the UK atmosphere are not favourable conditions for many types of surface coatings and so proven durability in other climates does not guarantee good performance. Therefore, this area remains one in which some judgement may have to be exercised.

As an alternative to glass, lightweight translucent glass fibre reinforced materials are often specified for use in solar collectors. Overseas experience has led to some doubt about long-term durability in extreme climates but the next few years should provide a good indication of whether significant degradation may be expected to occur in either optical properties or mechanical stability when used in the UK.

Bad design caused cracking of the cover glass in solar collectors in some early models. Glass manufacturers can advise on the thickness of glass for various applications, provision for thermal expansion and avoidance of severe thermal stress and compliance with their advice should ensure a low failure rate. Earlier problems with cover glass slipping out of position seem to have been overcome although continuing care in design of fixings is essential.

Methods for estimating the thermal performance characteristics of flat plate solar collectors as a function of their principal design parameters have been available for many years. Nevertheless, the performance achieved by a few contemporary designs has proved disappointing and in some cases may be attributed to an insufficient thickness of rear insulation. For water heating it seems likely that a minimum of 50 – 70 mm of rear insulation will continue to be recommended.

System design

Problems can be divided into two groups: those originating in poor basic plumbing practice and those deriving from lack of appreciation of some of the special requirements of solar systems. Foremost amongst the first category are lack of proper protection against frost damage, failure to provide drain cocks, isolating valves and venting points where necessary and the use of cast iron-bodied pumps in direct circuits. The remedies are obvious enough and although the proportion of systems now being installed with basic plumbing faults may be smaller than it was a few years ago, a reminder of the importance of general good practice is appropriate.

An example of a serious design fault is a system installed to work in combination with an instantaneous gas water heater and in which incorrect operation of valves by the householder led to discharge of gas-heated hot water from the warning pipe serving the feed cistern. System design should in all cases comply with the requirements of the local water undertaking and sensible layout of the system should always be considered. Wherever possible storage vessels should be located close to one another and to the points of use to minimise deadleg losses. Long lengths of small-bore pipework in collector primary circuits are less of a problem, since if well insulated they will be responsible for only a small fraction of the heat loss from this part of the system.

A few control and plumbing difficulties have been experienced because oversized pumps have been used in small domestic systems. Prior to the introduction of pumps designed especially for this application few alternatives were available and the only obvious choice was one from the ranges used for central heating purposes. It is recommended that at the design stage the flow resistance of a circuit should be calculated and a pump selected so as to give a flow rate in the range 0.014 – 0.03 $l/m^2.s$ for an aqueous-based heat transfer fluid. Some collector plates may have special requirements and the design flow rate in a system using a non-aqueous liquid may be as high as 0.05 $l/m^2.s$.

Air locking problems have occurred in systems of all sizes and can be divided into two types: those resulting in a complete cessation of flow within the circuit and those affecting only part of an array of collectors. The second type of fault is the more difficult to avoid and detect, but careful realignment of the collectors and provision of one or more open or automatic air vents should produce a cure. Correct sizing and layout of pipework in the neighbourhood of an air vent is important and in the case of recurring trouble use of a centrifugal air separator may be considered worthwhile.

Problems have been experienced with sealed systems using either a glycol-based antifreeze mixture or a mineral oil as the heat transfer fluid. Slight leakage of the fluid, often past compression fittings, may first be detected from a steadily falling system pressure. An oil leak inside the building might mean replacement of plasterboard and redecoration. Where possible, capillary or cone joints should be used with these fluids. A pressure relief valve should always be incorporated in sealed systems, with its outlet taken to a safe place of discharge. Some sealed primary circuits using a flammable oil have been installed without a relief valve and whilst no problem may occur under normal operating conditions the risk of an uncontrolled discharge during a fire is an improbable but nevertheless alarming prospect. In industrial and commercial situations, where the installation can be kept under the eye of a maintenance engineer, such fluids may be used with greater confidence.

There is little experience in the UK with large interconnected arrays of collectors but flow distribution problems have been suggested as one cause of poor performance. (It should not be expected that the flow distribution in any system will be perfect – all that can be hoped for is that no area of any collector is significantly hotter than it would be under ideal conditions). Infra-red thermometers might be useful in site investigations but they detect radiation only within a narrow band of wavelength and misleading results could be obtained owing to local changes in reflectivity.

Damage to roofs

Minor damage caused to slates and tiles during installation of solar collectors should largely be avoided by observing appropriate precautions (see, for example, BS 5534). However, where a collector is to be installed above granule-coated tiles, avoidance of cosmetic damage may be difficult.

Damage caused to slates and tiles by their having to support directly the mass of a solar collector is a debatable issue and one that will probably only be resolved fully in the light of experience. A heavy collector laid directly on slates or tiles with few points of contact produces high local forces. Slight but recurring movement caused by wind pressure or differential thermal expansion could abrade a protective finish such as galvanising and lead to premature failure. Also, a collector laid directly on a pitched roof can experience high wind uplift forces. Fixing clear of the roof surface is, therefore, advised.

Structural damage to domestic pitched roofs seems to have been limited to a few cases in which trussed rafters were either cut or had additional loads imposed upon them causing undue deflection. If an existing roof access has to be enlarged to enable an extra water storage vessel to be installed it is not advisable to cut a tie without first trimming both ends to adjacent members. Any additional damage should also be made good using standard roofing techniques. In no cases should large water storage vessels be installed unless adequate provision is made for load distribution. In all roof types additional water stores should if possible be located near to or over a load bearing wall. In flat roofs, penetration of the

Fig 3 All the load from the collectors is transmitted through the roof by six galvanised support posts secured to timber binders. The sarking felt is raised by the metal collar, thus ensuring that any water penetrating higher up the roof is channelled to each side of the support posts.

Fig 4 It might not be possible to manoeuvre timber binders of the required length into the roof space. Here, each binder is in two equal lengths, each secured to four rafters.

Fig 5 Support posts and rails attached to the roof ready to receive the collectors. The clearance between the roof tiles and the underside of the collectors is sufficient to prevent collection of debris.

membrane by bolts or screws may cause dampness and decay in the underlying structure. Collectors installed on flat roofs could be secured to a framework that itself requires fixing to the roof structure at a few points only but water penetration can produce such serious problems that alternative sites for collectors should be selected wherever possible.

Integrity of collector fixings

Collectors need to be securely fixed to a building or other substantial structure so as to minimise the risk of wind damage. To date no catastrophic failures resulting in severe injury seem to have been reported but there have been cases of whole collectors becoming detached from their mountings and of rain penetration into roof spaces.

Water penetration through pitched roofs as a result of the installation of a solar collector may be due to a lack of appreciation of the characteristics of this type of roof and to inadequate sealing and flashing. In particular, there has been reliance on mastics and silicone sealants which, although used outside their intended applications, seem to have functioned well sometimes for years. In the long-term however, and in view of the damage to building components and decorations that can occur as a result of water penetration, it is considered that methods of fixing should incorporate proven weathering details. This does not preclude the use of new techniques on an experimental basis but if the number of systems installed on domestic premises increases, it is to be hoped that the industry will continue to work towards the adoption of designs that are suitable for the purpose, particularly now that wind loading data are available. The system used in one of the BRE trials offers potential, and is illustrated in Figs 3, 4 and 5. In another method, shown in Fig 6, support posts and pipes were let through specially prepared holes in the tiles; this has the advantage that complete tiles do not need to be moved and smaller areas of flashing are needed.

A solar collector may rarely be inspected after installation and in view of the life of 20 or more years that might be anticipated from a unit of good design, care needs to be taken to ensure that fixings retain both their structural integrity and their weathertightness, if not their appearance, for at least this period.

Degradation of materials

As noted in Digest 205, the use of incompatible materials, particularly metals, can give rise to corrosion or other degradation. However, whilst many systems using aluminium collector plates with copper pipework failed in service within a few months, a test system at BRE has been running at high temperature for over three years. A not unexpected conclusion may be that these systems are sensitive to cleanliness of installation and if this could be guaranteed, a wider

Fig 6 Smaller areas of flashing are required if the support posts can be let through holes cut in the roof tiles.

choice of system design could be offered. However, there is no reason to suppose that standards of workmanship will in general be any higher than in the domestic plumbing sector and systems that are tolerant to flexibility in installation practice may continue to prove the most reliable. One example of corrosion that has been experienced in the last few years is that of aluminium collector plates in contact with wet insulation material. The problem may be due primarily to the creation of differential aeration cells but where alkalinity is produced by the insulant unprotected aluminium can be attacked more severely. A protective finish such as anodising may prevent this depending on the expected life of the unit and on the degree of exposure to moisture. Certain stainless steels may also be susceptible to attack. It is advisable, therefore, to provide sufficient ventilation to prevent sustained condensation within the collector.

Until recently there was little UK experience with the use of silicone rubber hose in solar water heating and similar applications but it was thought that long-term satisfactory service could be assured. However, the failure of several of these hoses after a few months of service at water temperatures and pressures that were well within design ratings suggests that it would be premature to place complete confidence in this material. It is recommended that good access be provided both to flexible hoses and to the isolating valves that should be installed in situations where failure could result in copious leakage within the building.

Electronic control systems

All mains voltage wiring should be in accordance with the IEE Wiring Regulations. The operation of differential temperature control systems has proved to be one of the most troublesome areas and although advances have occurred in the past few years, there is still room for improvement both in the understanding of real requirements and in quality of design.

One of the basic requirements for this type of control system is that the thermal characteristics should remain stable over many years. Other requirements are that the sensors should be adequately isolated from mains supply voltage and that the controller neither generates electrical inteference nor is unduly affected by it. The most intractable problem is how to ascertain whether or not a control system installed on site is operating correctly.

The principal control function in a simple system is to activate the pump whenever there is sufficient heat available for collection. Almost invariably, the information is obtained from two temperature sensors, one in contact with the water store and the other within the collector.

Since it is thought that the operating life of pumps may be shortened by excessive stop-start operation, time-delay circuits are sometimes incorporated, to supplement the hysteresis that is an essential part of the control function. Whilst there is insufficient accurate information available on the performance-in-use of various designs to draw many firm conclusions, it is clear from experiences in field trials that some systems do not inhibit the number of pump starts to the degree that might be desirable and further development seems likely. Certainly there is a need for installers to be aware that the correct location and fixing of temperature sensors is most important.

More general problems are the long-term performance of temperature sensors when used within solar collectors, and the lack of a standard specification that could ensure interchangeability for repair purposes. Any change in the electrical characteristics of a sensor can be difficult to detect on site but stability is essential for successful operation over many years. Sensors should be suitable for exposure to high humidity and temperature levels and no cable joins or termination boxes should be located outside the building. Satisfactory designs incorporate either joins within the roof space or a continuous length of cable connecting the sensor to the controller. The former has the advantage that a long and perhaps inaccessible length of cable would not have to be replaced if the collector sensor had to be renewed.

There has recently been an increased interest in 'forced stratification' of water stores. Designs may incorporate complicated electronic controls and one of the aims is to maximise the solar contribution by transferring energy to different storage vessels or to different zones within the same vessel depending upon the state of the system and the expected future demand pattern. In this way it is hoped to trade off the decreased collection efficiency that may occur if small volumes of water are heated to a high temperature against a decrease in auxiliary energy requirement if the system ensures availability of hot solar heated water at times of demand.

Essentially, the philosophy is one of modulating the effective preheat storage volume per unit area of collector and it seems likely that the greatest benefits could occur in systems in which the total preheat volume is larger than might be considered necessary; it is in these situations that low average temperatures may be attained for much of the time. In systems in which a single preheat vessel is used and for which the demand pattern is unknown there may be little point in sacrificing collection efficiency by producing small volumes of hot water because of the de-stratification that may subsequently occur. Whilst it is acknowledged that complicated control and heat management systems may be useful in buildings in which large amounts of heat can be diverted or otherwise controlled the potential in single-family housing may be limited if only by the probable maintenance requirements of mechanical hardware. Certainly the widespread use of multi-function control systems could become restricted to those situations in which there is a demonstrable need for complexity.

Operational problems
Checking system operation

Because of the failure rate in solar water heating systems in the UK considerable interest has developed in methods that could be used both by installers and owners to check the operation of systems. Table 2 shows what are thought to be the most appropriate types of simple instrumentation that could be installed in domestic or similar premises. The cost of solar systems may preclude widespread use of expensive instrumentation but the high cost of labour suggests that simple instrumentation that could speed diagnosis or repair of faults may be considered a worthwhile investment. The notes given below on the use of some of the types of equipment specified in Table 2 are derived principally from experience in field trials but it is recognised that there is room both for further types of instrumentation to be developed or included and for greater understanding of how to interpret the readings given by the types discussed here.

Air-locking and measurement of flow rate

Partial air locking of a collector array is one of the most difficult faults to detect. If a significant part of the total collector area is affected there will obviously be a commensurate decrease in system performance and storage temperature. Ground-based infra-red thermography or a hand-held infra-red thermometer may be helpful but since it is the cover temperature that will probably be measured small faults may not be detected. Depending upon the system characteristics partial air locking can produce a slight fall in flow rate;

Table 2 Simple instrumentation for fault checking

Check \ Fault	Partial air locking *May be undetectable except by panel inspection*	Low flow *Caused almost exclusively by poor design and/or installation*	No flow	Fuse	Control system fault *Difficult to check – 'Fit & forget' systems required*	Low system pressure *Easy to check*	
Lights or buzzers			✓	✓	?	✓	Could be part of automatic fault detection system
Flow rate indicator			✓				Flow rate meter is worth extra cost
Flow rate meter	?	✓	✓				Equipment not available for thermosiphon systems
Flow switch		?	✓				Could be part of automatic fault detection system
Storage temperature	?				?		Requires interpretation
Pump run-hours			?		?		Requires interpretation
Pump starts		?	?		✓		Can warn of incorrect control system settings. Has proved useful in practice
Pressure gauge						✓	Appropriate only for some system types
Silicon cell			?		?		Could be part of automatic fault detection system

a sensitive flow rate meter may be able to detect this provided a reliable reading for the flow under correct conditions is available. The most suitable types appear to be variable-area meters constructed from tough shatter-resistant, high-temperature plastics. Incorporation of one of these devices into a solar system would render diagnosis and repair far easier and with correct installation it should last as long as the other system components. The transparent tube may in some cases also serve to indicate whether corrosion products are building up in the heat transfer fluid and if suitable chemical indicators are added can be used for a visual check of the pH of glycol antifreeze mixtures.

Control systems

The on-site detection of faults in electronic differential temperature control systems is an intractable problem. The principal difficulty is that whilst complete failure of the collector sensor may be detected from within the building there is no easy method of checking whether its electrical characteristics have drifted outside the original specification. Without this information all that can usually be achieved from within the building is to check the operation of the controller itself by using either standard resistances or millivolt sources to simulate the sensor's response to various temperatures. This can be time-consuming and if the full specification of the controller is not available cannot in any case lead to confirmation of correct operation. Replacement of the controller with an exchange unit is, however, no substitute for the more expensive option of checking or perhaps replacing the complete control system. In all cases, one of the first checks should be to ensure that temperature sensors are correctly installed.

Changes in the electrical characteristics of one or more of the temperature sensors (or of the controller itself) can manifest itself either as an excessive number of pump starts per day or as an excessive (or low) number of hours of pump operation.

Whilst repeated stop-start operation will not necessarily result in a measureable reduction in the quantity of solar energy collected, excessive pump running time can be accompanied by a very low overall efficiency simply because stored energy may be dissipated during periods of negative temperature difference.

It seems likely that in a typical domestic solar water heating system in the UK the number of hours of pump operation will be between 800 and 1800 per year, and that the number of pump starts should not exceed 4000 per year even in a draindown system. A much lower number of pump starts may be expected in systems in which the collector has high thermal mass.

Part of the difficulty of giving more precise estimates is that what constitutes optimum control may itself be the subject of further development. For example, some designers still contend that the aim should be to collect the maximum amount of solar energy whilst others recognise that in economic terms it may not be worthwhile operating the pump many times in a day if only a small gain results. However, a switch-on differential of between 3.5 and 7°C, combined with a switch-off differential of between 0.5 and 2.5°C is still considered to be sound although a differential as small as 0.5°C would require that the control system be known to be sufficiently stable to preclude drifting to an even lower (or negative) value. Nominal settings of 5°C and 1.5°C appear to be good rules of thumb.

Overall thermal performance

Whilst realisation of good annual performance from a solar heating system does not preclude the existence of major faults that could lead to premature component failure, it can provide an assurance of return on investment. However, without the use of automatic and expensive heat metering equipment there is often no way of determining performance to any meaningful degree of accuracy.

If electric auxiliary heating is used it is possible, using only a kilowatt-hour meter and a totalising water meter to obtain during good weather a reliable indication of the reduction in auxiliary energy consumed per unit of hot water demand, provided that feed and delivery temperatures remain substantially constant. To avoid errors due to change in average storage temperature readings may be taken at daily or longer intervals. However, in wintertime the solar contribution may be less than the uncertainty in system heat losses.

If a gas boiler is used for water heating only, assessment of the solar contribution without the aid of complicated equipment may still be possible, provided that the boiler has its own gas meter. Results from systems using other fuels may be subject to greater uncertainty.

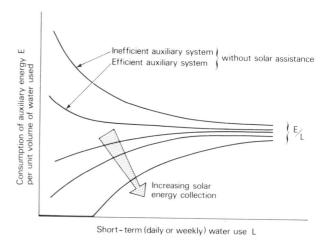

Fig 7 Characteristics of water heating systems showing poor use of auxiliary energy at low water demand. The greatest reduction in E/L occurs when collection of solar energy is sufficient to prevent operation of an inefficient auxiliary system.

In assessing overall performance the relevant quantity is the reduction in auxiliary energy consumed. However, calculations of the reduction per unit of water demand can highlight the efficiency of the auxiliary system.

Figure 7 shows the type of results that could be expected if the auxiliary system was inefficient under part-load operation. With a high water use any solar energy collected may displace a similar quantity of auxiliary fuel. However, at low use decreased efficiency of the auxiliary system (perhaps due to poor control) may cause a sharp rise in E/L but during periods of high solar gain, and depending upon the system design, all the (small) water heating requirement could be satisfied.

To assess the energy saving it is obviously necessary to compare any given value of E/L with its equivalent value without a solar contribution.

Further reading
Building Research Establishment
WOZNIAK, SJ. Solar heating systems for the UK: design, installation and economic aspects. BRE Report. HMSO, 1979; £6

Digest 205. Domestic water heating by solar energy

British Standards Institutiton
BS 5534 Code of practice for slating and tiling
BS 5918:1980 Code of practice for solar heating systems for domestic hot water

Domestic water heating by solar energy

Although in the UK a solar system can only augment a conventional domestic water heater, there is increasing interest in the use of solar energy and a number of firms are now marketing equipment. This digest describes briefly how solar water heating systems work and draws attention to potential problems which can be avoided in design; however, development is still at an early stage and there is little experience on which to base estimates of long-term performance and economics of solar systems.

Physical principles

A typical collector module is shown in Fig 1. Short wavelength solar radiation incident on the panel is transmitted through the glass and is absorbed on the black surface of the collector plate, raising the temperature of both the plate and any fluid circulating through the water channels. Most of the long wavelength radiation emitted by the plate when warm is retained within the assembly because glass transmits such radiation badly. Some heat is, however, lost in this way and some by conduction through the insulation behind the plate. Hence the operating efficiency of a solar panel decreases as the plate temperature rises.

System design

A simple system using natural circulation is shown in outline in Figure 2. As the temperature of the water in the panel rises, its density decreases thus establishing a circulation and the water in the cylinder is progressively heated. For efficient performance however, the vertical distance between the top of the panel and the bottom of the cylinder should be at least 300 mm and, particularly if the collector is mounted on a roof, this may not be convenient to arrange. It is therefore more usual for a small electric circulating pump to be incorporated in the circuit; this enables the storage tank to be placed in any convenient location although it should be as close as possible to the collector to minimise both heat losses and pumping costs. The pump should be controlled by a circuit which senses the temperature difference between the water in the collector and the cylinder; water will then only be circulated when useful heat may be gained.

Natural circulation, however, has the advantage of simplicity in design and fewer maintenance problems than a pumped system. Circulation occurs only when solar input is sufficient to heat the water in the panel to a temperature greater than the water in the cylinder and, provided the bottom of the cylinder is at least 600 mm above the top of the panel, there should be no reverse flow when there is no solar input.

Double glazing improves the heat retention properties of the unit but about twice as much of the incident radiation is reflected and absorbed before reaching the collector plate and the net benefit is marginal in a domestic water heating installation in the UK. Double glazing is indeed disadvantageous when the average water temperature is low, when heating a swimming pool for example. The collector plate is usually of steel, copper or aluminium construction with the water channels formed by pressing from sheet or with welded tubes. Non-metallic collectors have been used; their profiles must be different from that shown

Fig 1 Typical solar water heating panel

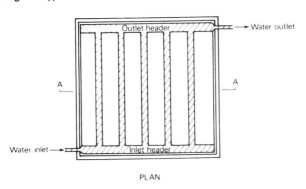

PLAN

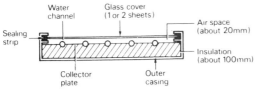

CROSS SECTION A – A

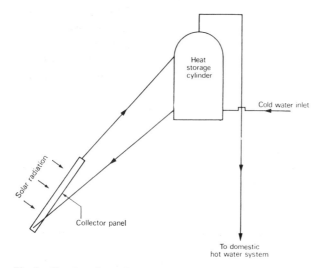

Fig 2 Simple solar collection system

in Fig 1 because the thermal conductivity of plastics is much less than that of metals.

Freezing may occur in the collector in winter if a 'direct' system such as that shown in Figure 2 is used. This can be avoided by replacing the heat storage cylinder with an 'indirect' cylinder of conventional design; anti-freeze and corrosion inhibitors may then be added to the water that circulates through the collector.

Whilst Figure 2 shows the simplest means of collecting solar energy, a system offered as a complete package is likely to be more complex; a typical layout is shown in Fig 3. When the temperature at the outlet of the panels exceeds that of the bottom of the solar cylinder by more than a preset amount (usually 2–3°C), the circulating pump is switched on by the control unit and the water in the solar cylinder is heated until insufficient temperature difference is detected between points A and B. The water passing into the conventional cylinder is thus warm and less heat has to be supplied by conventional means to raise its temperature to the desired value, probably about 55°C. A correctly-designed solar system will even provide water on a few days in summer at the required tap temperature and no further heating will be required.

Heating panels Ideally they should face the noon sun but their exact orientation is not critical, any convenient direction in the SE–SW quadrant being satisfactory; shading by adjacent buildings or trees should be avoided if possible. The panels should slope at between 20° and 60° to the horizontal but, again, the exact angle of inclination is not a critical factor. A normal domestic installation will require 4 to 6 m² of panel area or about 1 m² for every 50 litres of daily hot water demand. The total panel area is the most important factor in determining the heat collected annually.

The water circulation rate should be in the range 35 to 70 litres per hour for every m² of panel and the flow should be equal through each panel.

Solar cylinder A conventional indirect cylinder of about 200 litres capacity will be suitable for a domestic installation with about 4 m² of panel; the cylinder and all connecting piping should be well insulated. Cylinders are now available with two indirect coils, the lower for solar-heated water and the upper for connection to a conventional boiler. These are convenient if space is limited since only one cylinder is required.

Expansion volume As in a domestic central heating system, provision must be made for expansion of the water. This may take the form of a header tank at the highest point in the system, or a diaphragm expansion volume may be used. The latter is normally the easier to accommodate when panels are roof mounted and, for a domestic system, would need a volume of two to five litres capacity depending on the water capacity of the panels. It is advisable to incorporate a 'deadleg' between the expansion volume and the solar circuit to reduce the temperature of the water in contact with the diaphragm.

One-way valve The temperature of the panels will often fall below that of the solar cylinder at night and reverse circulation, which will cool the cylinder, can take place if a one-way valve is not fitted. If it is situated at other than the lowest point in the system, a drain-cock should be fitted immediately above it.

Air vent As in a domestic central heating system, an air vent is required at the highest point in the system to release air-locks during filling and pressurising. An automatic airvent, normally float-operated, will obviate the need to purge air from the system during its first months of operation.

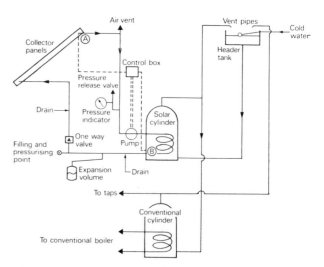

Fig 3 Pumped, indirect solar water heating system

Control unit These are now available complete with the necessary temperature detectors, which must be installed so that the water temperature, and not the ambient temperature, is sensed.

Two other components, not shown in Figure 3, may be considered desirable.

Maximum temperature controller The temperature in the solar cylinder may rise above a safe level if no water is drawn off in heat-wave conditions. A small fan-cooled heat exchanger can be fitted in the solar circuit, controlled by a temperature detector, to ensure that the temperature in the solar cylinder is never excessively high.

Automatic make-up unit (for sealed systems) Some fluid may excape from the system as a result of over-heating or minor leaks; this unit enables the interval between inspections to be increased.

Corrosion

The use of dissimilar metals in a plumbing system can cause corrosion. In a solar system, the main risk occurs when aluminium panels are used with copper tube; pitting corrosion of the panels can take place even in the absence of physical contact of the two metals. Precautions which can be taken include the use of corrosion inhibiter in the water circulating through the panels but it may be preferable to use a sealed circuit filled with distilled water and suitable anti-freeze. The long-term effectiveness of such precautions is, however, not yet reliably established and systems with aluminium panels should be regularly examined for leaks. Steel panels can be used with more confidence in indirect systems because of the experience gained in domestic central heating systems. Copper panels are, of course, completely compatible with copper tube.

Freezing

In an indirect system, such as that shown in Figure 3, anti-freeze (of a type approved by the local water authority) can be added to the water which circulates through the panels. Both direct and indirect systems can be designed in which the panels drain whenever the pump is switched off but this is not normal practice because the fresh water continually being circulated through the panels can form scale and impair the efficiency of the panels. Special anti-freeze solutions (to BS 3150) are available for use with aluminium but their service life is limited to between two and five years after which time the solution should be renewed. The use of a heat transfer oil is an attractive answer to problems of both freezing and boiling but information on this is lacking at present.

Boiling

The fluid in the system may boil if failure occurs in the pump or control unit or if no water is drawn off for a long period in summer. As more efficient panels are developed, this risk will increase. A pressure valve is a necessary safety precaution in a sealed system and may be conveniently combined with a pressure indicator to check that there are no leaks in the system. The outlet of the valve should be connected via an atmospheric break to a suitable drain point or container. In an 'open' system, where a header tank is used, no pressure release valve need be fitted.

Installation

The prime requirements when panels are mounted on an existing pitched roof are clearly that they should remain fixed under all conditions and that the roof should remain weathertight. Because of the many differences in construction of both panels and roofs, it is impossible to give detailed fixing techniques but some important considerations can be mentioned. If the panel is to be mounted on top of the roof covering, the roof must remain structurally safe with regard to the fairly considerable extra weight. In this situation, panels with aluminium casings might suffer corrosion from contact with new concrete roof tiles and the panels are at risk in high winds unless very securely fixed. The weight of the panels will be less of a problem if tiling is removed and the panel is fixed either on top of, or between, the rafters. This will also reduce the risk of condensation between panel and tiling causing corrosion attack but it creates problems of maintaining weathertightness. Careful attention must be paid to weatherproofing, the panels being treated as if they were skylights and flashed into the roof. In new houses it might be a cheaper alternative to build the panel assembly from its component parts and cover it with patent glazing. By this means, it might be possible to arrange for accessibility from within the roof space for maintenance although this is difficult with lower-pitched roofs. It will usually be easier to make the construction weathertight (at least at the bottom edge) if the panels are positioned in the lower part of the roof; this will also aid maintenance, especially glass cleaning which becomes more important with lower-pitched roofs because of the greater risk of dirt building up on the surface. Fitting a panel on top of the tiling in the lower part of the roof may introduce problems of rain water overshooting the gutter but a small upstand at the bottom of the panel may prevent this.

Legal requirements

There are at present no specific legislative controls over solar heating systems as such, but any installation must comply with the Building Regulations, Water Bye-laws and planning or other relevant controls. The responsibility for administering and interpreting the Building Regulations rests with the local authorities and it is necessary to contact the appropriate council at as early a stage as possible before starting work.

On the planning side, which is quite separate and distinct from control under the Building Regulations and Water Bye-laws, permission might also be required from the local authority for an installation if, for example, it affected the external appearance of a building. The local planning authority would be able to advise on particular cases.

The Building Regulation and planning controls do not contain all the statutory requirements which may have to be complied with when a building is erected, altered or extended; again the appropriate local authority would be able to advise.

Performance

In the United Kingdom about 3.5 GJ* of solar radiation are incident in an average year on each m² of south-facing roof, obviously with far more during summer than winter (see Figures 4 and 5) and with rather more to the west of the country. A domestic solar water heating system with 4 m² of panel area may be expected to operate at an annual efficiency of about 35 per cent and so will supply about 5GJ

(1400 kW hours or 48 therms) of heat over the year; this is 40 per cent of the domestic hot water requirements of the average household. With 6 m² of collectors, about 6.5 GJ will be obtained. Against this must be set about 0.5 GJ of electricity used annually by the pump. The useful heat supplied is not proportional to the area of panels because an increase in panel area will lead to the system operating on average at a higher temperature and therefore at a lower collection efficiency. Any heating system will require regular maintenance and the cost of this work will have to be considered in an economic assessment.

* 1 Gigajoule = approximately 278 kW hours or 9.5 therms.

Further reading
An appraisal of solar water heating in the UK; R G Courtney; BRE Current Paper CP 7/76
Solar energy utilisation in the UK: current research and future prospects; R G Courtney; BRE Current Paper CP 64/76
Energy consumption and conservation in Buildings; BRE Digest 191
Reliability and performance of solar collector systems; BRE Digest 254.

Figs 4 and 5 Global solar radiation; average daily totals for June and December in kWh/m² (1kWh = 3.6 MJ)

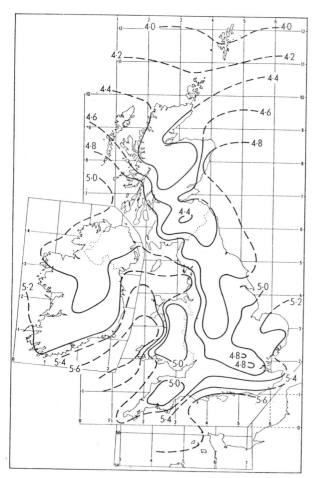
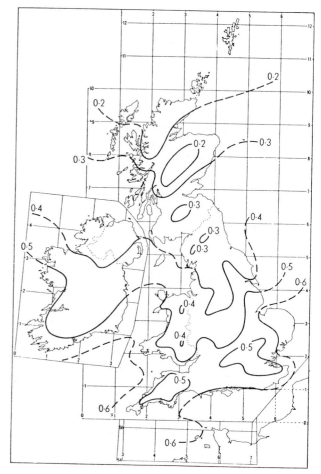

Heat pumps for domestic use

Whilst the UK sales of heat pumps are at present small, they are expected to grow steadily, especially in areas where natural gas is not available, in the next few years as their energy and cost-saving possibilities become widely known, and as the price of energy increases.

This digest explains some of the factors to be considered in a domestic heat pump installation, and points out some of the pitfalls, for the benefit of building designers, specifiers and users not previously acquainted with heat pumps. It is concerned primarily with pumps which use the outdoor ambient air as their heat source and which supply their output as hot water; however, most of the digest is also applicable to machines with warm-air output, and some of it to those with earth or water heat-sources.

Basic principles

The heat pumps at present commercially available for domestic use all operate on the compression cycle using electric drive. They extract energy from a low-temperature source using thermodynamic principles similar to those of a refrigerator except that the useful output is on the 'hot' side rather than the 'cold'. The main transfer of energy is provided by the latent heat of vaporisation and condensation of a refrigerant (usually Freon) which is pumped around a sealed circuit (Fig 1). It leaves the compressor as a hot vapour at high pressure and passes into the condenser through which is circulating the medium (air or water) from the heating system. The vapour, being at a higher temperature than the heating medium, gives up latent heat to it and in doing so condenses to a liquid. It then passes through a capillary or expansion valve, in which its pressure and temperature drop, into the evaporator, over which is flowing the energy source (eg the outside air). The refrigerant is now colder than the source and so there is a transfer of heat to the refrigerant causing it to vaporise. Now as a low pressure gas it is returned to the compressor for the cycle to begin again.

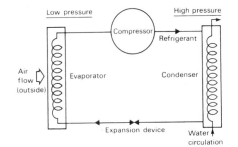

A refrigerant is chosen which will condense and evaporate at temperatures related to those of the heating medium return and the source.

Fig 1 The most basic air-to-water heat pump circuit. Commercial machines may incorporate additional heat exchangers, refrigerant/lubricant reservoirs, control and safety devices etc.

The advantage of a heat pump is that the output energy available for heating is greater than the energy needed to drive it (the difference having been extracted from the source).

The ratio of output energy to drive power is known as the *Coefficient of Performance* (COP): defined as

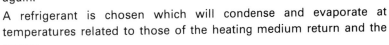

$$\frac{\text{Total useful heat output}}{\text{Total electric power input}}$$

To estimate the performance and economics of a heat pump installation, the upper term should *exclude* any losses (eg from external pipework) and the lower one should *include* the power consumed by internal ancillaries such as circulating pumps and fans, crankcase heaters etc.

The COP varies as the source and output temperatures change: the smaller the difference between them, the higher the COP. Thus, to estimate the performance of a heat pump over a whole heating season, a *seasonal* COP is adopted. This can be calculated approximately from known heat pump performances and meteorological data, but is better taken from the monitored performance of an actual installation, as the effects of part-load cycling, which may tend to reduce the COP below its full-load steady-state values, are difficult to calculate. However, as a rough guide, the seasonal COP is unlikely to be less than the rated value at a source temperature of 0°C; figures of 2.0 to 2.5 are currently being realised.

Sizing and boosting

For new dwellings, heat loss calculations will probably be done by the designer; where a heat pump is fitted to an existing house, with or without an existing central heating system, similar calculations are necessary. As the cost per kilowatt of additional output of a heat pump is relatively high, it makes economic sense to base the calculations on as low-loss a house as can reasonably be achieved; so weatherstripping, reduction of unnecessary adventitious ventilation, radiator shields, improved wall and roof insulation where practicable, should all be assumed to have been done before the heat pump is installed.

As outdoor temperature falls, the heat loss from a building (kept at a constant indoor temperature) rises, and the maximum available output from an air-source heat pump falls. The balance point is the outside temperature at which loss equals output plus adventitious gains (see Fig 2). By selection of a suitable size of heat pump, this is usually at air temperatures of 0°C to 5°C. At the higher balance points there will be a substantial auxiliary or 'boost' heat requirement on cold days. This could be met, for example, by leaving in place an existing boiler which would only be fired when the heat pump was unable to cope unaided, or by accepting that in such circumstances the living-room fire was lit, and its radiator turned off. Where the only boost envisaged is from direct electric-resistance heating, a lower balance-point is needed so that the effective coefficient of performance of the installation is not uneconomically low.

Alternatively a heat pump can itself be regarded as an auxiliary form of heating, capable of providing the full requirement during spring and autumn only. This is particularly so for water-source machines, which may be unable to operate in very frosty conditions.

The choice of tariff for an electrically-driven heat pump also needs consideration. If a dwelling is likely to be heated intermittently it may consume so large a proportion of its electricity at full rate that the 'off-peak' tariffs (which increase the full-rate price) may not be justified. On the other hand, particularly where substantial thermal storage can

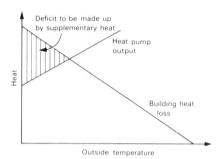

Fig 2 Variation of the space heating load of a building and the output of an outside air source heat pump as a function of temperature.

Fig 3 The outdoor unit of a 'split' heat pump.

be provided (eg heavyweight house construction and large hot-water cylinders) the tariffs with low off-peak should be chosen. Extensive thermal storage with off-peak topping up could provide the 'boost' heating in cold spells, but the economic implications of such systems are not yet clear. It must be remembered that 'off-peak' times also tend to be those of lowest air temperature, so the heat pump's performance will be somewhat reduced.

Output temperature

The hot water output of a heat pump is typically at 45-55°C, whereas for a domestic boiler it is at 65-75°C; some heat pumps incorporate a separate or 'superheat' circuit to provide part of the output at 60°C for domestic hot water.

Where a heat pump directly replaces a boiler, the lower temperature will mean a reduced heat output, at full load, from the existing radiators, perhaps by as much as one-half. However, this may not be a serious problem: existing heating systems almost always have their radiators oversized relative to the design heat loss of the rooms and, as discussed earlier, steps to reduce heat losses (below the original design values) should have had priority over the change to a heat pump. A careful check will, in most cases, show that the existing radiators (perhaps with increased flowrate or modified for top entry and bottom return) will still provide sufficient heating, although the ratio of convective to radiant output will have increased. Where it is clear that the existing unit would no longer be adequate, a change to a larger radiator or one with an extended heating-surface, or to a fan-convector, will be necessary. The radiant component of the heating will be reduced, and the occupants may notice this change close to the radiator; this in practice can sometimes lead to disappointment where the local radiant effect has been especially valued. In new buildings, low-temperature emitters can be used and heat pumps are particularly suited to underfloor heating systems because of the large effective surface areas.

If the heat pump is to be used in conjunction with a fossil-fuel boiler, the problems of reduced heat emission can be avoided. However, a heat pump cannot efficiently deliver heat much above 55°C and this may be too low for direct connection to boilers burning sulphur-laden fuels. The two appliances therefore become alternatives and valving arrangements should isolate the heat pump from the hot-water circuit when the boiler is operated.

Fig 4 The indoor unit of a 'split' air-to-water heat pump, with its cover removed.

Split/unitary heat pumps

Air-source heat pumps have to pass substantial volumes ($500m^3/kWh$ or more) of external air through their evaporators and so the evaporator housing is usually situated outdoors. The remainder of the heat pump can be installed either indoors or out. Indoors will mean a so called 'split' system, as there are two separate cased units which have to be joined by refrigerant piping as well as electrical wiring; the pipework necessarily has to be done on-site. The unitary machine houses all its components in a single outdoor casing, which must then be connected to the heating system of the house as well as to the electricity supply, and for convenience, an indoor control panel.

Each type of system therefore requires pipes, some of which will be hot, running from outdoor unit to house; obviously these pipes should be kept as short as possible and well insulated. In the case of unitary systems, it may be necessary to drain the pipes if the heating is to be turned off during freezing weather. In the case of the split system, the pipes carry refrigerant. Their installation requires the highest standards of care and cleanliness to ensure that no dirt, moisture or scale enters the refrigerant circuit. If it does it will eventually reach either the compressor or one of the valves (even if filters are fitted) or cause corrosion. It must be emphasised that the installation of such piping should only be done by persons properly trained in the correct techniques (such as dry-nitrogen purging during brazing) and lies beyond the craft training of a normal plumber.

Small unitary air-to-air heat pumps, requiring only a hole through a wall, and an electrical connection, may be suitable for DIY installation, but all other types need skilled plumbing and the attention of an expert to commission them.

Fig 5   A unitary air-to-water heat pump (7.5 kW output) installed outdoors. Note the frost beginning to form on the evaporator fins (air temperature 6.5°C, 95 per cent RH)

Defrosting

The evaporator coils of an air-source heat pump have to be colder than the ambient air; this causes condensation on the fins. In certain climatic conditions, common in British winters, this condensate will freeze on the fins so that the evaporator gradually becomes coated with ice and its efficiency thereby reduced. Heat pumps therefore incorporate a defrosting system, which periodically removes the ice.

The user must understand the need for defrosting and to be aware (eg by inspecting the evaporator coils in cold, damp weather) of its efficacy. Malfunction of the defrosting arrangements is one of the commonest faults and inadequate defrosting can lead to ice blockage; less conspicuously, excessive or unnecessary defrosting is a waste of energy.

Siting of external unit

It has already been mentioned that the unit needs to be close to the dwelling to keep pipe runs short. The best location must be decided for each individual case, but the following points need to be borne in mind:

Air stream The evaporator fan will induce and expel a large volume of air, forming a very noticeable air current in its vicinity. The outgoing air will be some degrees cooler than ambient, and should not be discharged in a direction (eg across a side passageway) where people need to walk through it. Many machines discharge their air vertically to avoid this problem but they should not be installed below a window opening.

Weather and drifting Outdoor units are made with casings or special housings providing adequate protection against the weather although special precautions might be necessary near the sea. However, care needs to be taken to ensure that the air intake cannot be blocked by fallen leaves or driven snow. If this cannot be guaranteed, units must be sited so that any blockage can be quickly spotted and removed.

Condensate diposal Condensate from the evaporator has to be drained away and the casing usually incorporates channels to collect it and lead it to an outlet tube. Some machines have to be installed at a slight tilt to encourage the flow of condensate. Although the volume produced is not normally large, it is sufficient to require proper provision for its disposal. When frosting/defrosting cycles are occurring, the whole of the condensate for a cycle will be discharged in a short time (3-4 minutes) and the drain must be adequate to accept it. The possibility of this condensate itself freezing must also be considered.

Noise The noise made by evaporator fans and other outdoor components is, in the quietest machines, unobjectionable, but some can be annoying to a neighbouring house, particularly when bedroom windows are open. Acoustic screens can reduce evaporator fan noise by 5dB or so, but they are cumbersome and expensive and it is certainly best to site a heat pump in a position where any noise it does make is directed away from other dwellings. The compressor noise from a unitary machine is usually masked by the fan noise but in a split machine the compressor will be indoors, where it may emit as much noise as a large freezer. As with many mechanical devices, the noise levels can rise as the equipment ages so that an installation which is only just acceptable when new may become unacceptable after a year or two.

Solar assistance Some installations make use of extra benefits from solar energy, for example by drawing the evaporator air from the roof space, which will be heated by sunshine, or through some form of solar collector. In these installations, the type of assistance will determine the evaporator location.

Testing on start-up

Compared with boiler systems, heat pumps are more complex and their behaviour is much more closely related to outdoor atmospheric conditions. It is unlikely therefore that a single short running test will 'prove' all the functions of a heat pump, particularly if its installation is completed during the summer. It is possible in some cases to simulate a winter condition by partially blocking the air supply to the evaporator, and where a machine has a micro-electronic control a fairly complete diagnostic check can be made. Individual manufacturers have developed certain checking procedures appropriate to their machines.

However, it should be realised that only the experience of winter weather, with its varying combinations of temperature and humidity, can provide a full check on all aspects of a heat pump's performance, and an installer should be expected to carry out a return checking visit during the first spell of severe weather following a heat pump's installation. As this should include the observation of one or more complete defrosting cycles, it is unlikely to involve less than one full day, although two or more adjacent installations could be checked during the same period.

Fall-off

The performance of a heat pump can decline significantly due to the loss of refrigerant or a partial pipe or valve blockage (or simply to fouling of heat-exchanger surfaces) without any outward sign to the householder. This is especially so in installations where electric-resistance 'boost' is automatically called in by the thermostatic controls: the next electricity bill may be the first indication that something is amiss. It is important, therefore, that the householder should have some means of judging whether the heat pump's performance is up to standard. A simple temperature difference check may be sufficient, or machines with micro-electronic controls can be programmed to perform their own regular checks, and show a warning light if a fault develops.

Economics

It is not at present possible to make general statements about the economics of domestic heat pumps, except that it would be unusual to find circumstances in which an electrically-driven heat pump was competitive with a gas-fired boiler at 1981 gas and electricity prices. The running cost of such a heat pump is already lower than that of oil-fired and direct electric systems but the high capital cost of the installation means that economic calculations are necessary which allow for the different importance of capital and operating costs to different users.

To obtain a comparative assessment for a particular installation, the following data are necessary:

House
Design heat loss
Seasonal total heat loss
Annual hot water consumption (if supplied by the heat pump)

Heat Pump
Capital cost
Installation cost
Expected life
Expected maintenance cost
Expected seasonal COP
Electricity tariffs

Oil Fired Boiler
Capital cost
Installation cost
Expected life
Expected mainentance cost
Expected thermal efficiency (or take as 65-70 per cent)
Oil cost

Off-peak electric storage heating
Capital cost
Installation cost
Electricity tariffs

It is conventionally assumed that, of the heat emitted by storage heaters (in total, 100 per cent of electricity consumed) only 75 per cent supplies heat usefully available when it is needed.

Fig 6 Indoor and outdoor views of a 2 kW air-to-air heat pump designed for single-room heating and installed in a trial house.

Specification

A prospective purchaser of a heat pump will need, and can reasonably expect, the following information:

Performance Output in kW, at air temperatures of about 0°C and 6°C.

Output at −6°C and 15°C will also be useful as the extremes under which the machine might run. (Some heat pumps can be overloaded at high outdoor temperatures and may include a cut-out to prevent this).

The output may additionally be quoted at different heating system flow temperatures (say 40°C and 60°C). An estimate of the *seasonal* coefficient of performance during a typical UK heating season:

$$\frac{\text{Total useful heat output}}{\text{Total electric power input}}$$

Consumption Power consumed in kW (including fan and pump power) under the running conditions above. Nature of supply (phase, hertz, volts) and maximum starting current. Size of isolator and supply cable required.

Source Approximate volume of air handled through evaporator. Fan rating (kW). Cross-sectional area of air inlet/outlet (if relevant). Pipe sizes for earth or water sources.

Output Temperature of hot water and central-heating supplies (if separate). Connecting pipe sizes. Designed flow rates and pressure drops. Circulating pump rating. For air-output machines, air flow, temperature, and duct sizes.

Control Control arrangements for heat pump. Other controls, eg room thermostats, outdoor temperature sensor, thermostatic radiator valves (these may not necessarily be the same controls as supplied for boiler fed systems).

Boost Rating of electric-resistance boosters if fitted, and type of control. Other boosters, or control interfacing into existing (eg boiler) system.

Size	Indoor and outdoor units. Weight, with and without packaging.
Installation	Diagrams showing positions of connections, access covers, controls etc, with any recommendations to facilitate maintenance access. Maximum and recommended interconnecting pipe lengths for split systems. Diagram of weather cover (if separate). Details of condensate discharge piping.
Noise	At various distances (up to 20m) and directions for outdoor units; at 1m for indoor units.
Refrigerant	Type and standard charge weight.
Defrosting	Means of defrosting and of controlling defrost cycles. Arrangements, if any, for calling-in boost heaters during defrosting.
Price	Making clear any additional costs and including a rough estimate of typical installation cost, and of optional accessories.
Installer	Explanation of whether manufacturer undertakes installation or lists and trains approved installers.
Warranty	A clear statement of what warranty is provided over and above the purchaser's legal rights, and the apportionment of liability between manufacturer, seller and installer.
Maintenance	An indication of how much annual maintenance might reasonably be expected.

Fig 7 A communal heat pump. The small building on the right houses an air-to-water heat pump, design output 70 kW, to heat a row of 12 houses. The horizontal duct carries the water flow and return mains.

Further reading *which includes some discussion of further types of heat pump now under development*

FREUND, P; LEACH, S J; & SEYMOUR-WALKER, K J. Heat Pumps for use in Buildings. BRE Current Paper 19/76.

FREUND, P. The Application of Heat Pumps in Buildings in the UK. Proc CIBS Symposium on Energy, Services & Buildings, 1980.

HEAP, R D. Heat Pumps. E & FN Spon, 1979.

REAY, D A & MACMICHAEL, D B A. Heat Pumps, Design and Applications. Pergamon Press, 1979.

Energy Conservation: a study of energy consumption in buildings and possible means of saving energy in housing. BRE Current Paper 56/75.

Energy consumption and conservation in buildings. BRE Digest 191.

Ventilation requirements

The air in an enclosed space is likely to contain contaminants which may be unpleasant or even harmful to the occupants or which may cause deterioration of the fabric. This digest discusses fresh air requirements and tolerable levels of contamination from various sources and explains the calculation of dilution rates. It is concerned mainly with ventilation during the heating season. In summer, the rates required will generally be higher than those derived from the information given here because of the need to reduce temperatures in non-air-conditioned buildings.

Clean air

It is conventional to compare the quality of air within a space with 'fresh air' and it is important therefore to define this as a standard. Table 1 shows the major constituents of the atmosphere at ground level in open country. Outside air may of course be polluted by contaminants released into the atmosphere from industrial processes and the burning of fossil fuels for heating. In urban areas substantial local pollution may be created by road traffic, industrial premises and heating plants. Care must be taken, therefore, in any particular circumstance to take account of variation from the standard constitution of air shown in Table 1.

Table 1 Composition of dry atmosphere

Constituent	Percent by volume
Nitrogen	78·08
Oxygen	20.94
Carbon dioxide	0.03
Argon and other gases	0·95

Principles of dilution

Figure 1 shows a space of volume V ventilated by a supply of air at a rate Q. The general equation which describes the concentration c of a particular contaminant within the space at time t is:

$$c = \left[\frac{Qc_i + q}{Q + q}\right]\left[1 - e^{\frac{-(Q + q)t}{V}}\right] + c_o e^{\frac{-(Q + q)t}{V}} \quad \cdots\cdots (1)$$

where: c is the concentration of contaminant at time t
  c_o is the concentration of contaminant when $t = 0$
  c_i is the concentration of contaminant in the incoming air
  Q is the volume flow rate of ventilating air
  q is the total volume flow rate of a particular contaminant from any sources within the space

(q Q V and t can be in any self-consistent system of units)

After a long time, the concentration reaches a steady or equilibrium value, c_e, given by:

$$c_e = \left[\frac{Qc_i + q}{Q + q}\right] \quad \cdots\cdots (2)$$

If c_i and c_o are zero, ie the outside air is uncontaminated and the space contains no contaminants initially, equation (1) simplifies to:

$$c = \frac{q}{Q + q}\left[1 - e^{-\left(\frac{Q + q}{q}\right)\left(\frac{qt}{V}\right)}\right] \quad \cdots\cdots (3)$$

This equation is the basis of Fig 2, which may be used to calculate the concentration at time t for given values of Q and q. The equilibrium concentration is given by:

$$c_e = \frac{q}{(Q + q)} \quad \cdots\cdots (4)$$

Using equation (4), or equation (2) if the incoming air contains the contaminant, it is possible, given a limiting value for c_e and input rate q, to calculate the minimum required ventilation flow rate Q.

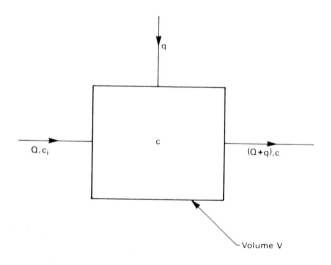

Fig 1 Contaminant entering a room of volume V at a rate q with fresh air ventilation Q

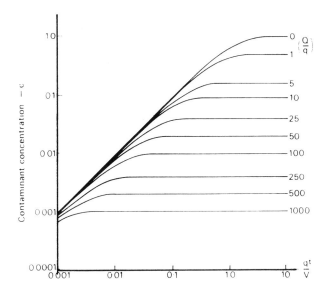

Fig 2 Variation of gas concentration c with t and ventilation rate Q for gas leakage rate q

Two particular points arise from the equations: the equilibrium value is independent of the initial concentration of contaminant within the space and the volume of the space affects only the rate at which equilibrium concentration is reached and not the equilibrium value itself.

The equations assume good mixing of the contaminant and the air within the space. However, this may not necessarily take place, particularly if there is a considerable difference in density between air and the contaminant and, as a result, a stable layer of contaminant may form. This can occur with heavy vapours such as petrol and liquefied petroleum gases or light gases such as methane, the principal constituent of natural gas. Under these conditions, special care must be taken with the position and design of ventilation openings [1] to minimise the risk of unexpectedly high concentrations.

Contaminants

There are many possible contaminants and each will be associated with a limiting value of concentration either to prevent harm to persons inhaling them, to prevent the formation of an explosive mixture or to prevent deterioration of the fabric by biological or chemical action. The most common are given here, against their main sources.

Physiological CO_2, H_2O, body odour
Combustion CO_2, H_2O, SO_2 (from fully-burnt fuels) CO, CH_4, petrol vapour (from partially or unburnt fuels)
Tobacco smoking Odour, CO, irritants
Household activities H_2O, odours

The input rates of some of these contaminants can be defined with some certainty in relation to their source and are listed in Table 2. For others, particularly in relation to leakage of unburnt fuels, an estimate will have to be made from the prevailing circumstances.

Limiting values of common contaminants

Using the following limiting values, and those in Table 3, together with input rates from Table 2, the required flow rates of fresh air can be calculated for any situation. Limiting values for less common contaminants can be found in ref [2].

Table 2 Rates of production of common contaminants

Combustion

Fuel	Contaminant		
	Carbon dioxide *l/s per kW*	**Water vapour** *g/h per kW*	**Sulphur dioxide** *l/s per kW*
Natural gas	0·027	156	—
Kerosine	0·034	96	$8·9 \times 10^{-6}$
LPG	0.033	130	—

Physiological

Activity (adult)	Contaminant	
	Carbon dioxide *l/s per person*	**Water vapour** *g/h per person*
Resting	0·004	30
Light work	0·006–0·013	40
Moderate work	0·013–0·020	40
Heavy work	0·020–0·026	—
Very heavy work	0·026–0·032	—

Tobacco smoking

Carbon monoxide 0·08 litres/cigarette

Household activities *24 h average*
Water vapour
g/day

Cooking	3000
Bathing	1000
Dish washing	1000
Clothes washing	500
Clothes drying	5000

Carbon dioxide Up to four per cent has been found to be quite acceptable in inspired air but 0·5 per cent is the generally accepted limit. The amount of carbon dioxide in the supply air for combustion can affect burner performance and may, if too high, cause incomplete combustion and consequent excessive production of carbon monoxide. Again, the accepted limit is 0·5 per cent.

Carbon monoxide Carbon monoxide is a toxic gas in even small concentrations and the threshold limit value* is set at 50 ppm. Higher levels are tolerable for shorter exposure times. The limits of flammability (the range over which combustion is possible) are 12 to 75 per cent.

Sulphur dioxide The currently accepted threshold limit value is 5 ppm.

Water vapour Digest 110[3] indicates methods for reducing the risk of and designing to avoid both interstitial and superficial condensation. The starting point for these calculations, once internal and external dry bulb temperatures have been stipulated, is the moisture content of the internal air. This, therefore,

---

* Threshold limit value is a time-weighted concentration for an average length working day over a 40-hour working week; see also ref (2).

Table 3 Limiting values of common contaminants

Contaminant	Limiting concentrations	
	Toxicity %	Flammability %
Carbon dioxide	0·5	–
Carbon monoxide	0·005	12.0–75.0
Sulphur dioxide	0.0005	–
Methane	30	5·0–15·0
Propane	30	2.0– 9.5
Butane	30	1.5– 8.5
Acetylene	30	2.5–82.0
Hydrogen	30	4.0–74.0
Petrol	0·10	1·4– 7·6

produces the main limiting value for the concentrations of water vapour for use in ventilation calculations. Other limits on water vapour content may be expressed in terms of relative humidity: this can vary over a wide range although levels below 30 per cent or above 70 per cent may cause discomfort and levels above 70 per cent may encourage the growth of moulds.

Fuel gases Fuel gases such as methane (natural gas) are generally non-toxic but in concentrations above about 30 per cent symptoms of anoxaemia can be apparent. The limits of flammability for some fuel gases are given in Table 3.

Petrol Petrol vapour, which can occur from spillage, is toxic in concentrations of only 0·1 per cent. It is also extremely flammable with flammability limits in the range 1·4 to 7·6 per cent.

Odours
Odours present a particular problem as they consist of a large number of constituent chemical components generally present in only small concentrations whose proportions are likely to vary. Attempts to define and measure odours chemically have generally been unsuccessful; in the case of tobacco smoke and body odours in particular, it has been found necessary to measure directly the air flow rates required to ensure a satisfactory air quality based upon the number of cigarettes being smoked or persons present. In general, tobacco odour dominates and masks body odour; a further complication is that with nearly all odours the human olfactory mechanism rapidly adapts and the perceived odour intensity drops rapidly from an initial value on entering a contaminated space to a lower, fairly steady level after a matter of minutes.

Body odour The fresh air supply necessary to maintain body odour at a satisfactory level depends upon standards of personal hygiene and differs between children and adults. Figures 3(a) and 3(b) show the required flow rates for school children and adults of average socio-economic status.[4] Two points should be noted. Firstly, the flow rate per person depends upon the density of occupation (the reason for this is not clear, but may be related to the rate of chemical breakdown of some of the constituents of body odour). Secondly, due to adaptation, very much lower flow rates are required if the level of odour is assessed by an occupant of the space rather than an observer newly entered from outside.

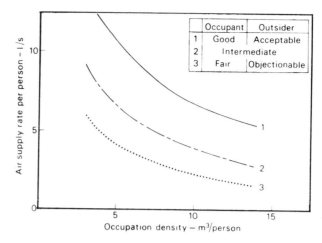

Fig 3(a)   Air supply rate for odour removal—school children

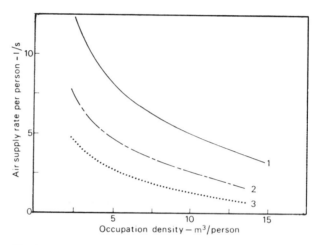

Fig 3(b)   Air supply rate for odour removal—adults

Tobacco smoke Apart from carbon monoxide production the smoking of tobacco can produce an undesirable odour, particularly to non-smokers, and because of certain of its constituents, in particular acrolein, may produce irritation to the eyes and nasal passages. Research has shown that larger flow rates are necessary to combat the former and this will be used as the basis for deriving fresh air requirements.

A summary [5] of available research results indicates a considerable variation in recommended flow rates. In the absence of more definitive information, a value of 20 m³ per cigarette smoked appears to be a reasonable compromise. To translate this into an air supply rate requires a knowledge of the number of smokers present and the rate of smoking. The average smoker consumes 1·3 cigarettes per hour: this requires a fresh air rate of 26 m³/h or 7 l/s per smoker. As about 50 per cent of the adult population smoke, an allowance can be made for this in the design ventilation rate of spaces which are relatively heavily-populated, eg open-plan offices, which may have a lower required flow rate than cellular offices [5]. It also follows that if the smoking rate is expected to be more than 1·3 cigarettes per hour, appropriate corrections will need to be made.

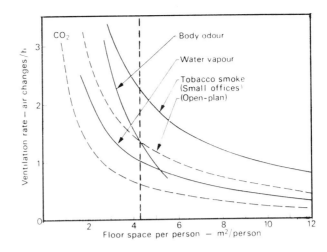

Fig 4 Ventilation requirements for offices
*vertical dotted line shows lower limit as defined by
Offices and Shops and Railway Premises Act (assuming
ceiling height of 2·7m)*

Total requirements

If the purpose and occupancy levels of a space can be defined then the foregoing sections enable a total ventilation requirement to be calculated. In most common cases satisfying the contaminant with the highest required ventilation flow rate will usually mean that others are also satisfied, ie individual flow rates are not usually additive. As an example, the requirements for given occupancy levels have been constructed for a typical office and are shown in Fig 4. For convenience of interpretation, they are presented in terms of air change rate for a given area of floor space per person. This requires the assumption of a floor to ceiling height, which for this example has been taken as 2·7m. Two lines are presented for tobacco smoke. For small offices it is assumed that air must be provided for the situation in which all occupants smoke, whereas for open-plan offices some allowance is made for the probability that only a proportion of the occupants are smokers.

In many situations, and particularly in dwellings, input rates depend greatly on the pattern of occupation and habits which are much less easy to define than the example of the office given here. In these cases, the accurate definition of required air flow rate may have to await the results of behavioural studies.

References
1 Ventilation in relation to toxic and flammable gases in buildings; SJ Leach and DP Bloomfield; BRE Current Paper CP36/74
2 Chartered Institution of Building Services Engineers Guide, 1970, **Book B**; Section B2
3 Condensation; BRE Digest 110; HMSO
4 Ventilation requirements; CP Yaglou, BC Riley and DJ Coggins; Trans ASHVE, 1936, 42, p133
5 Ventilation requirements for smokers; GW Brundrett; Electricity Council Research Centre; ECRC/M870; Dec 1975

Principles of natural ventilation

Unless filtration is used, a supply of fresh air is needed in any habitable building to control the level of contaminants present; a method of determining the quantity of air required is given in Digest 206. A properly-designed mechanical ventilation system should be able to provide this quantity where and when it is required but has the disadvantages of initial capital cost and running and maintenance costs. The alternative, which is virtually without cost but suffers from the variability of meteorological conditions, is to use the natural movement of air through the building due to wind and to temperature difference. This digest discusses the mechanisms which govern natural ventilation and illustrates them with formulae for simple cases.

Meteorological factors

Wind

The wind is turbulent and its mean speed varies with height. The vertical profiles of wind velocity and the turbulence characteristics vary with the stability of the atmosphere and the roughness of terrain over which the wind is passing. Local topographical features such as hills and valleys can also affect wind profiles. All that is needed here is an outline knowledge of the variation of wind speed with height and a simple formula[1] can be used. For different types of terrain this describes the wind speed variation as a power-law profile:

$$\frac{U}{U_m} = Kz^a \qquad \ldots\ldots\ldots(1)$$

The wind speed (U_m) is measured at a large number of sites in the UK by the Meteorological Office, and is quoted for an equivalent height of 10 m, in open countryside. Using equation (1) it is possible to relate the wind speed at any other height and for any of the types of terrain to the wind speed U_m. The appropriate conversion factors are given in Table 1.

Definition of terms used

a	Exponent relating wind speed to height (allowing for terrain)	
A	Area of opening	m^2
A_b	Equivalent area for bouyancy-driven ventilation	m^2
A_w	Equivalent area for wind-driven ventilation	m^2
d	Width of crack or similar opening	m
g	Gravitational constant	m/s^2
H	Vertical distance between two openings	m
h	Height of opening	m
J	Function relating to window opening angle ϕ	
K	Coefficient relating wind speed to height (allowing for terrain)	
k	Leakage coefficient	
L	Length of crack or similar opening	m
n	Exponent for flow through small openings	
p	Pressure	Pa
p_o	Reference static pressure	Pa
Δp	Pressure difference	Pa
Q	Volume flow rate	m^3/s
U	Wind speed	m/s
U_m	Meteorological wind speed at height equivalent to 10m	m/s
U_{50}	Value of U_m which is exceeded for 50 per cent of the time	m/s
U_r	Reference wind speed measured at a height equal to that of the building in the free wind	m/s
z	Height	m
θ	Absolute temperature	°K
θ_i	Mean absolute temperature within building	°K
θ_o	Absolute ambient temperature	°K
$\bar{\theta}$	Mean value of θ_i and θ_o	°K
$\Delta\theta$	Difference between mean internal and external air temperatures	°C
ϵ	Ration of area of upper to lower opening	
ν	Kinematic viscosity	m^2/s
ρ	Density	kg/m^3
ϕ	Angle of window opening	
C_d	Discharge coefficient	
C_p	Pressure coefficient $\left[\frac{p - p_o}{\frac{1}{2}\rho U_r^2}\right]$	
Re	Reynolds number $\frac{d}{\nu}\sqrt{\frac{2\Delta p}{\rho}}$	

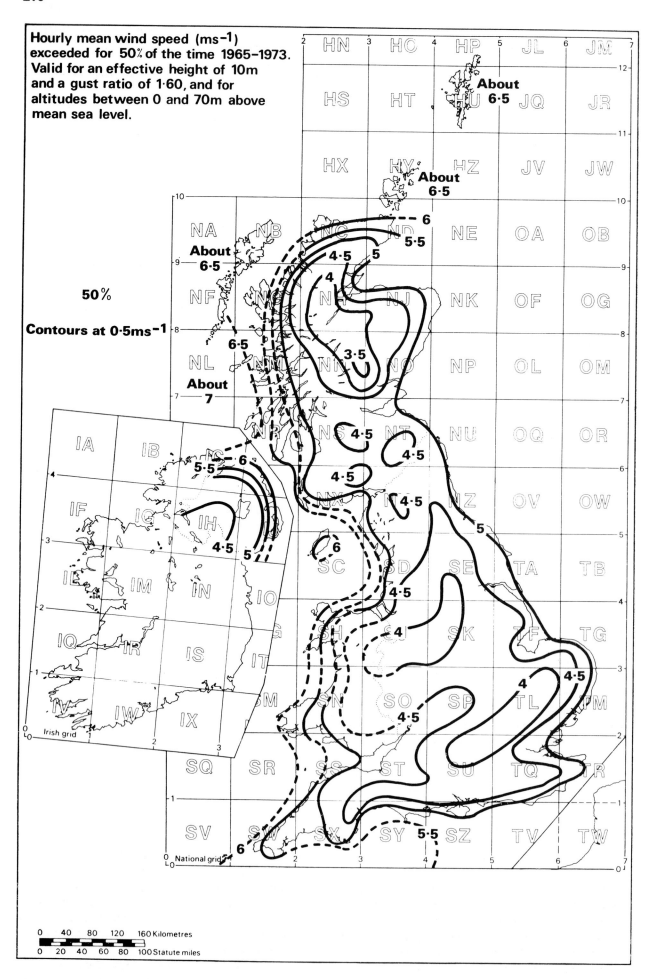

Hourly mean wind speed (ms⁻¹) exceeded for 50% of the time 1965–1973. Valid for an effective height of 10m and a gust ratio of 1·60, and for altitudes between 0 and 70m above mean sea level.

50%

Contours at 0·5ms⁻¹

Irish grid

National grid

0   40   80   120   160 Kilometres
0   20   40   60   80   100 Statute miles

Fig 1 Contours of U_{50} for the United Kingdom

Data on mean wind speed has been condensed[2] to provide a description of the cumulative frequency of wind speed which is exceeded for 50 per cent of the time, U_{50}. Using Fig 1 and the data given in Table 2, the meteorological wind speed U_m exceeded for any chosen proportion of the time can be found for any site in the UK. It is then possible, using the data from Table 1, to determine the wind speed for a particular height and type of terrain exceeded for any given proportion of time. It is assumed that the cumulative frequency distribution is independent of wind direction, which varies considerably at most sites in the UK. The predominant directions may be determined from wind 'rose' maps [3].

Ambient atmospheric air temperature

Ambient air temperature varies during each day and from day to day, but may be characterised by monthly mean and a monthly mean diurnal variation for any particular site. Table 3 gives the monthly mean temperatures for five sites; further data can be obtained from ref 4 and 5. Daily mean variations for Heathrow are given in ref 3 together with standard deviations associated with these means.

Flow characteristics of openings in buildings

A building may be regarded as a series of discrete 'cells' connected by air flow paths. Usually these cells will be rooms or circulation spaces, although floor, roof and wall voids might also need to be considered. Not all such cells will be inter-connected, and some may be joined by more than one flow path. The nature of these air flow paths will vary considerably from large openings such as doors and windows to very small cracks in components. When a difference in pressure is applied across an opening, a flow of air will take place through the opening. The magnitude of this flow depends upon the dimensions, shape and the Reynolds number. Using dimensional analysis to summarise this relationship, the flow rate, Q, is given by

$$Q = A.F(Re, \text{geometry of opening})\sqrt{\frac{2\Delta p}{\rho}} \quad \ldots \ldots (2)$$

The Reynolds number, Re, is defined for convenience in terms of pressure, as follows,

$$Re = \frac{D}{\nu}\sqrt{\frac{2\Delta p}{\rho}} \quad \ldots \ldots \ldots (3)$$

where D is a length scale appropriate to the cross-section of the opening, eg the diameter for a circular opening. For long, narrow openings, such as cracks, it is more convenient and conventional to replace A by d.L in equation (2) and D by d in equation (3). For openings with a typical dimension (ie that used in equation (3) in the calculation of Re) greater than about 10mm, which will include airbricks as well as

open windows and doors, the function F may be regarded as a constant, and is usually referred to as the discharge coefficient C_d. Thus,

$$Q = A.C_d\sqrt{\frac{2\Delta p}{\rho}} \quad \ldots \ldots \ldots (4)$$

It has become conventional to give C_d a value equal to that for a sharp-edged opening, which at high Reynolds numbers is 0·61, and to refer to the area so defined for any particular opening as the 'equivalent' area. This will be close to the geometric area for openings such as windows and doors, but may be larger in the case of openings such as those in air bricks which are long in the flow direction in comparison with their width. Table 4 gives experimentally-determined values of equivalent area for various types of purpose-made openings.

Table 1 Factors for determining mean wind speed at different heights and for different types of terrain from Meteorological Office wind speed U_m measured at 10m in open country

Terrain	K	a
Open flat country	0·68	0·17
Country with scattered windbreaks	0·52	0·20
Urban	0·35	0·25
City	0·21	0·33

Table 2 Values of the ratio of mean wind speed exceeded for a given percentage of time to the 50 per cent mean wind speed U_{50} (from ref 2)

	Location	
Percentage	Exposed coastal	Sheltered inland
80	0·56	0·46
75	0·64	0·56
70	0·71	0·65
60	0·86	0·83
50	1·00	1·00
40	1·15	1·18
30	1·33	1·39
25	1·42	1·51
20	1·54	1·66
15	1·70	1·80
10	1·84	2·03

Table 3 Mean monthly temperatures (°C) for five sites in the United Kingdom 1941–1970 (from ref 4)

	Aberdeen	Aldergrove	Manchester	Kew	Scilly Isles
January	2·5	3·5	3·3	4·2	7·7
February	2·7	3·8	3·7	4·5	7·3
March	4·5	5·7	5·7	6·6	8·5
April	6·8	7·9	8·3	9·5	9·9
May	9·0	10·4	11·3	12·6	11·9
June	12·1	13·3	14·3	15·9	14·4
July	13·7	14·4	15·7	17·5	16·0
August	13·3	14·3	15·5	17·1	16·3
September	11·9	12·7	13·7	14·9	15·1
October	9·3	10·1	10·5	11·6	12·9
November	5·3	6·4	6·5	7·5	10·2
December	3·7	4·6	4·3	5·3	8·7
Annual	7·9	8·9	9·4	10·6	11·6

For small openings, such as cracks around closed windows and doors, the form of the function F is much more complicated. Figure 2 shows the results determined experimentally for a range of typical metal window cracks. For high values of Re, F approaches a constant value and an equation of the form of (4) applies; for very low values, F is proportional to Re and the flow rate will be proportional to Δp. However, the expected operating region under normal conditions is as shown in Fig 2. This leads to a variation of flow rate with Δp expressed in the form

$$Q = L.k.(\Delta p)^n \quad \dots\dots\dots (5)$$

where $0.6 < n < 0.7$ and k is a constant for which typical values are given in Table 5.

Pressures generated at building surfaces

The effect of wind

It has been found that, for a particular wind direction, the pattern of air flow around a building is comparatively independent of wind speed, provided that the building has sharp corners. The surface pressure will vary with the wind speed squared whilst all other conditions, including wind direction, remain constant; in consequence the pressure, p, generated by the wind at a point on the surface may be defined in terms of a single coefficient, C_p, as follows:

$$C_p = (p - p_o)/\tfrac{1}{2}\rho U^2_r \quad \dots\dots\dots (6)$$

Once the distribution of C_p at the surface has been determined for a single wind-speed and a particular wind direction (probably from a scale wind-tunnel test), the pressure may be computed for any other wind speed. U_r is conventionally taken as the wind speed measured in the free wind at a height equal to that of the building. Pressures averaged over the surface for simple building shapes are given in Digest 119. For buildings which stand alone or are relatively much higher than surrounding buildings and obstructions, the difference in mean pressure coefficient between windward and leeward faces will typically be equal to 1.0. For buildings in sheltered situations, such as those shown in Fig 3[6], a difference in mean coefficient of the order of 0.1 can be expected.

The effect of temperature difference

Air density varies approximately as the inverse of absolute temperature. The weight of two vertical columns of air of different temperatures separated from each other by a vertical surface will differ and a pressure difference will be applied across the intervening surface. Thus, if the air temperature within a building is higher than that outside, pressure differences will create an air flow through openings in the intervening fabric.

Table 4 Equivalent areas of ventilation openings

	Overall size mm	Equivalent area mm²
Air brick, terra cotta, square holes	225 × 75	1 400
Air brick, terra cotta, square holes	225 × 150	4 300
Air brick, terra cotta, square holes	225 × 225	6 400
Air brick, terra cotta, louvres	225 × 150	2 000
Air brick, terra cotta, louvres	225 × 225	4 300
Air brick, cast iron, square holes	225 × 75	7 200
Air brick, cast iron, square holes	225 × 150	12 700
Air brick, cast iron, square holes	225 × 225	19 600
Air brick, cast iron, louvres	225 × 75	3 100
Air brick, cast iron, louvres	225 × 150	11 300
Air brick, cast iron, louvres	225 × 225	19 200
Typical internal louvres grille	225 × 75	2 400
Typical internal louvres grille	225 × 150	7 200
Typical internal louvres grille	225 × 225	10 700

Table 5 Values of k for windows (in l/s per metre of crack length for $\Delta p = 1$ Pa)

Window type	Value of k	
	Average	Range
Sliding	0.08	0.02 – 0.30
Pivoted	0.21	0.06 – 0.80
Pivoted (weather-stripped)	0.08	0.005 – 0.20

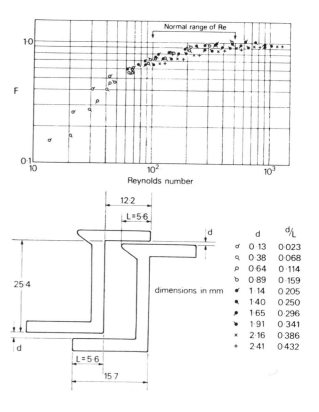

Fig 2 Flow of air through window cracks

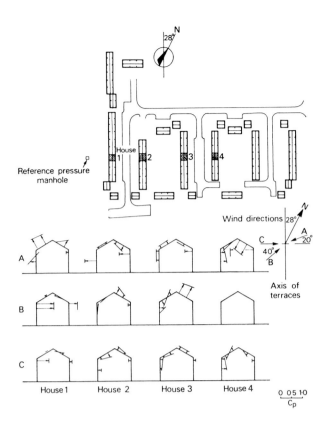

Fig 3 Effect of shelter on surface pressure coefficients

The general characteristics of natural ventilation can, however, be demonstrated by considering some simple cases. Figure 4 shows a simple, two-dimensional building; internal divisions are ignored and the building consists of a single cell with openings as shown. These will be considered to be large, and therefore flow through them is governed by equation (4). Table 6 shows schematically the approximate airflow pattern and gives the formulae from which the ventilation flow rate Q can be determined.

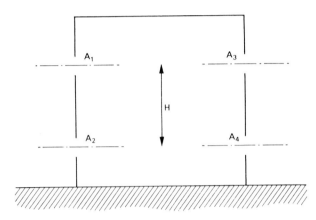

Fig 4 Arrangement of openings in simple buildings

The determination of natural ventilation rates

The airflow through a building and the ventilation rates of rooms within the building can be determined, for a given design wind speed and direction if the following are known:

(i) the position and flow characteristics of all openings;

(ii) the detailed surface mean pressure coefficient distribution for the wind direction under consideration;

(iii) the internal and external air temperatures.

However, it is difficult to obtain a solution in all but the simplest cases because of the large number of non-linear simultaneous solutions which require solution, and the only practicable method is to use a digital computer. A number of computer programs are under development and are at a stage when they are being compared with full-scale measurements to test their validity.

Such programs are only as accurate as the data from (i), (ii), and (iii) and it is very rare that these are known in detail for existing buildings, let alone those at the design stage. A comprehensive series of wind-tunnel tests may give the information required under (ii), but recent work shows that it is far from easy to predict the positions, let alone the flow characteristics, of all of the openings.

Wind effect only Due to the difference in mean pressure between windward and leeward faces, air flows in through the openings A_1 and A_2 and out through A_3 and A_4. A_w is the overall effective area of the four openings; it can be seen, therefore, that openings in parallel can be added together arithmetically whilst those in series must be obtained by adding the inverse of the squares. It can also be noted that ventilation rate is proportional both to wind speed and to the square root of applied pressure difference. Thus, a range of ΔC_p from 0·1 to 1·0 (ie sheltered to exposed) gives only an approximately 1 :3 difference in ventilation rate at the same reference wind speed.

Temperature difference only In this case air flows in through the lower openings A_2 and A_4 and out through A_1 and A_3. The equivalent area is now A_b. From the formula it can be seen that ventilation rate is proportional both to the square root of the temperature difference and to the square root of the vertical distance between openings.

Combined effect of wind and temperature For a fixed wind speed with small temperature differences the flow is similar to that for wind only, but as the temperature difference increases, the inflow of air at upper openings due to wind is reduced and outflow is increased; at lower openings the reverse occurs. Depending upon the relative values of the opening areas a point is reached when the flows are reversed at the upper windward opening, and as the temperature difference is further increased the flow approaches that for temperature difference only. A reasonable approximation of the combined flow rate can be made by taking the flow rates calculated for both conditions separately and taking the larger to apply to the combined case. For the case in Fig 4, this leads to an expression of $\frac{U}{\sqrt{\Delta\theta}}$, given in Table 6, which determines whether temperature or wind will dominate. The form of this expression indicates that taller, more sheltered buildings will have ventilation rates independant of wind speed for a large part of the colder months.

Other mechanisms

Single-sided ventilation

Wind only In summer, the ventilation rates needed to assist in maintaining comfortable internal conditions are at least an order of magnitude larger than those required in winter. These large rates can generally be obtained by cross-ventilation, except in the circumstance when large openings are available on one external wall only, eg in a school classroom or an office in which doors to any internal corridor are closed for reasons of privacy or noise. In these situations, the cross ventilation would be small since the small area of the internal openings would be the dominant factor. In fact, considerable exchange of air can take place through the openings in the external wall because of turbulent diffusion, by outward-opening lights interacting with the local airstream to give an exchange of air between inside and outside and, if there is more than one window, by pressure differences between the windows causing flows into the room.

The formula shown in Table 7 represents a minimum rate; this may be larger for certain wind directions and certain types of opening windows.

Temperature difference only. It is clear that the mechanism for temperature-driven ventilation can apply in the 'single-sided' case with a number of openings at different heights within the room. When an equilibrium is reached, the outflow equals the incoming mass flow and the level at which the pressure difference across the dividing surface is fixed. This is the 'neutral level' and can be used as the reference height from which the flow rates through each of the openings can be calculated and hence the total ventilation flow rate determined. Table 7 shows a common example of two openings, eg a vertical sliding window. The formula is given in terms of A, which is the total open area and ε.

Another common case is the single plane opening. Air flows in at the lower part of the opening and out at the upper part. Table 7 shows the flow pattern and the simple formula which applies to it. Figure 5

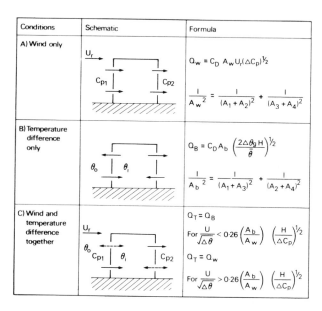

Table 6 Cross-ventilation of simple buildings

Conditions	Schematic	Formula
A) Wind only		$Q_w = C_D A_w U_r (\Delta C_p)^{1/2}$ $\frac{1}{A_w^{2}} = \frac{1}{(A_1+A_2)^2} + \frac{1}{(A_3+A_4)^2}$
B) Temperature difference only		$Q_B = C_D A_b \left(\frac{2\Delta\theta_g H}{\theta}\right)^{1/2}$ $\frac{1}{A_b^{2}} = \frac{1}{(A_1+A_3)^2} + \frac{1}{(A_2+A_4)^2}$
C) Wind and temperature difference together		$Q_T = Q_B$ For $\frac{U}{\sqrt{\Delta\theta}} < 0.26 \left(\frac{A_b}{A_w}\right)\left(\frac{H}{\Delta C_p}\right)^{1/2}$ $Q_T = Q_w$ For $\frac{U}{\sqrt{\Delta\theta}} > 0.26 \left(\frac{A_b}{A_w}\right)\left(\frac{H}{\Delta C_p}\right)^{1/2}$

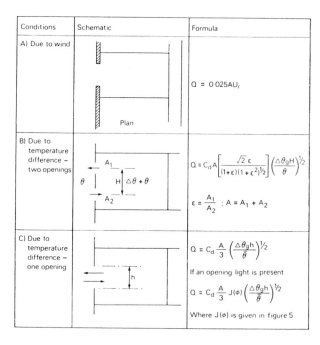

Table 7 Spaces with openings on one wall only

Conditions	Schematic	Formula
A) Due to wind	Plan	$Q = 0.025 A U_r$
B) Due to temperature difference – two openings		$Q = C_d A \left[\frac{\sqrt{2}\,\varepsilon}{(1+\varepsilon)(1+\varepsilon^2)^{1/2}}\right]\left(\frac{\Delta\theta_g H}{\theta}\right)^{1/2}$ $\varepsilon = \frac{A_1}{A_2}$; $A = A_1 + A_2$
C) Due to temperature difference – one opening		$Q = C_d \frac{A}{3}\left(\frac{\Delta\theta_g h}{\theta}\right)^{1/2}$ If an opening light is present $Q = C_d \frac{A}{3} J(\phi)\left(\frac{\Delta\theta_g h}{\theta}\right)^{1/2}$ Where $J(\phi)$ is given in figure 5

shows how the presence of an outward opening side-mounted casement or a centre-privoted window modify the flow rate as a function of opening angle.

Given a fixed area of opening light, the largest rate of ventilation is obtained, in the case of single opening, by making it tall and narrow, and for more than one opening by separating them by as large a vertical distance as possible. Increasing the angle of opening for side-mounted casement and centre-pivoted windows has little effect beyond an angle of approximately 50°.

Combined effect of wind and temperature As in the case of cross-ventilation, the ventilation rate due to both effects acting together can be taken as the larger of the two individual values.

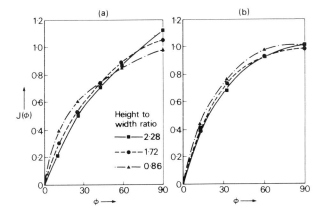

Fig 5 Variation of J (ϕ) with angle of opening ϕ for
(a) side-mounted casement windows
(b) centre-pivoted windows

Pressure fluctuation

The pressures generated by wind at the surface of a building fluctuate. This is due to the turbulent nature of the wind and to the interaction of the building and the wind which creates regions of flow separation and a wake. The use of mean pressures in the preceding section is therefore technically incorrect, but the error is small unless the difference between mean pressures is small. This can be due to shelter or to the configuration of the building relative to the wind direction. Considering, for example, a terraced house with the wind parallel to the terrace, the mean pressures on each face would be expected to be approximately equal, giving rise to a zero or very low ventilation rate if the formula in Table 6 is used. In practice, instantaneous pressure differences between the two sides of the house can be quite large and will give a flow into the house, alternately from each side. As far as the house is concerned, however, the ventilation rate is not dependent on the direction of flow and a higher than expected rate is achieved. At present, there is limited information concerning this mechanism, but the available experimental results indicate that, all other factors being equal, the ventilation rate can be approximated by giving a value for ΔC_p of 0·2 in the formula in Table 6.

Measurement of ventilation rates

Under natural conditions, there are many paths for the air to enter and leave a room or building and so it is not possible to use conventional anemometric techniques to measure volume flow rates. Instead, methods based on a tracer gas are generally used. The gas can be considered as an artifical contaminant and the equations for variation of contaminant concentration given in Digest 206 apply. Two methods can be used.

The continuous flow method A tracer gas is introduced into the space at a known rate and the measurement of the equilibrium concentration gives the volume flow rate at which air is leaving the space.

The decay method This is the more commonly used, in which a limited quantity of gas is introduced into the space and, provided good mixing occurs, the concentration within the space decays exponentially with time. From this, the ventilation rate can be determined. A number of tracer gases are used, their requirements being that they should be stable, non-toxic, not react with other materials within the space and that their concentration can be measured easily using suitable instruments. The most commonly used tracer gases and their methods of detection are:

Nitrous oxide	Infra-red gas analysis
Helium	Katharometer
Hydrogen	Katharometer
Carbon dioxide	Infra-red gas analysis
Krypton-85	Geiger-Muller Tube

References and further reading

1 Davenport AG; 1963 Proceedings of the conference on wind effects on buildings and structures, Vol 1, 1965, HMSO
2 Caton PGF; Maps of hourly mean wind speed over the United Kingdom 1965–1973, Meteorological Office, Climatology Memorandum, August 1976
3 Institute of Heating and Ventilating Engineers Guide, Book A, 1970
4 Maps of mean and extreme temperature over the United Kingdom 1941–1970, Meteorological Office, Climatology Memorandum No 73, August 1975
5 The climate of the British Isles; ed Chandler TJ and Gregory S, Longman, London 1976
6 The measurement of wind pressures on two-storey houses at Aylesbury; BRE Current Paper CP 70/74.

BRE Digests

119 Assessment of wind loads
141 Airflow around tall buildings
206 Ventilation requirements.

Ventilation of internal bathrooms and WC's in dwellings

The ventilation of internal bathrooms and WC's requires effective substitutes for openable windows. Natural and mechanical systems of ventilation can be designed for single dwellings or a number of dwellings, and are discussed here under the headings of individual and common-duct systems. The major part of the digest is concerned with mechanical extract ventilation by vertical common-duct systems.

Natural ventilation

On the windward side of a building, the outside air pressure is normally higher than the inside pressure; on the leeward side it is normally lower. Air will move from the higher to the lower pressure zones through any apertures in the walls. The higher the wind speed, the greater the pressure difference and therefore the rate of air change.

Air is also moved by temperature difference. Air warmed within a building will tend to rise and to escape through high-level outlets; it is replaced by cooler air entering at low level. The greater the temperature difference, the faster will be the rate of air flow. This type of movement is described as 'stack effect'.

Natural ventilation in buildings depends on wind pressure, on the stack effect, or on both, and duct systems can ventilate internal rooms by these natural forces without a fan. If properly designed, for some limited applications such as individual systems serving low-rise buildings, they can perform adequately. Although such systems may contravene British regulations and byelaws, they have been allowed and are discussed here because they could be the subject of waivers.

Individual systems

Examples of systems of natural ventilation for individual dwellings employing one or two separate horizontal or vertical ducts, or a combination of horizontal with vertical ducts, are shown in Figs 1a, b, c. Because there is a risk of these systems operating in reverse, replacement air should be drawn from the outside by an inlet duct (Fig 1a) rather than from an adjoining room or lobby (Fig 1b).

There is no connection *between* dwellings but in buildings of more than four floors, the space requirements for individual vertical ducting become excessive and wind speeds are often too high for trouble-free operation, especially of horizontal systems.

Common-duct systems

Common-duct systems for natural ventilation could effect a saving in the space needed for ducting but are not recommended because of the risk of air flow between rooms in different dwellings.

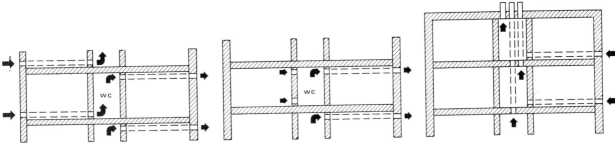

Fig 1a (Section) Horizontal system with inlet and outlet ducts

Fig 1b (Section) Horizontal system with outlet duct but no inlet duct (replacement air enters from adjoining lobby)

Fig 1c (Section) System with combination of vertical outlet ducts and horizontal inlet ducts

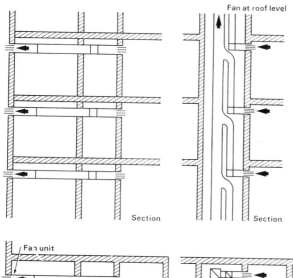

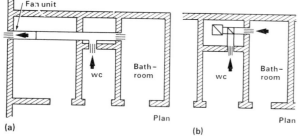

Fig 2 (Sections above, plans below) **(a)** individual horizontal ducts **(b)** common-duct with vertical shunts

Mechanical ventilation

The risks of variable or reverse air flow associated with natural ventilation systems, and their unsuitability for tall buildings, have led to the general use of mechanical ventilation in the UK. Basic types of mechanical extract system are illustrated in Fig 2.

Individual systems

Individual mechanical systems require a single duct, either vertical or horizontal, connecting the internal room to the outside air; an extract fan installed in the duct operates continuously or intermittently. There is no connection between dwellings. Such systems are specially suited to converted buildings and to owner-occupied dwellings in which the responsibility for running and maintaining the system lies with the occupier. Most local authorities and landlords prefer one or two large fans external to the dwellings, as in a common-duct system, whereas individual systems in a large building need numerous small fans and outlet points, often on external façades.

Intermittent operation may be allowed and the following notes are a guide to reasonable design. The fan should operate while the compartment is occupied and for at least 20 minutes thereafter. It should extract during any single operation at least 20 m^3 of air from a WC or from a bathroom with no WC, or 40 m^3 from a bathroom with WC. The air speed in the duct should not exceed 3·5 m/s. Adequate provision must be made for the entry of replacement air. A spare fan or motor, to take over in the event of breakdown, is *not* necessary.

Individual systems should also conform to the recommendations given under the following headings on pages 2 and 4:

Ventilation requirements	Section 1(b)
Noise	Section 2(f)
Flow measurement and testing	Section 2(g)
Entrance lobby and replacement air	Section 4

Common-duct systems

Most buildings with internal bathrooms have common-duct mechanical extract systems operating continuously. Horizontal branches or vertical shunts link the internal rooms of each dwelling with the common duct. Air is extracted through a grille from each room and replacement air flows into the rooms through any gaps round the doors or through grilles in corridor walls.

The notes that follow conform generally, though not in every detail, with:

The Building Regulations 1972
The Building Standards (Scotland) (Consolidation) Regulations 1971
Greater London Council Byelaws
BS CP 352:1958 *Mechanical ventilation and air-conditioning in buildings*
BS CP 3: Code of basic data for the design of buildings: Chapter IV *Precautions against fire*
BS CP 413:1973 *Ducts for building services*

1 Ventilation requirements

(a) The minimum air extract rate from a WC or from a bathroom with no WC is 20 m^3/h; from a bathroom with WC, it is 40 m^3/h.

(b) Extracted air should discharge to the outside air and the system should be separate from any other ventilating plant.

The ventilation requirement is expressed in terms of volume of air to be extracted rather than air changes per hour, because this can deal with rooms of different sizes. Consideration of flow in these terms simplifies testing and the specification of standard duct sizes; it meets statutory requirements for all practical purposes.

2 The system

(a) **Design air extract rates** should exceed the minimum rates stated in 1(a) by about 20 per cent, to allow for variation after balancing.

(b) **Shunt and common main ducts.** Inlets from rooms should be connected to the common main duct through a vertical shunt duct at least 1 m long; this should terminate at its lower end with an inlet piece inserted through the service duct wall from the internal room. The air speed in a shunt duct with smooth sides should not exceed 3·5 m/s, or in a main duct 7·5 m/s; higher velocities may lead to noise and cause a nuisance.

A shunt duct system in which air extracted from an internal room is passed vertically upwards (Fig 2b) is preferred to a system with horizontal branches because it is more compact in layout, offers better sound attenuation between dwellings and is less likely to allow carry-over of smoke between dwellings in the event of a fire. Because of noise transmission, flow variation and fire risk, shunt ducts from dwellings on the same floor level should not be connected to the same vertical main duct.

(c) **Extract grilles, balancing devices and dampers.** An extract grille should be fitted to each ductwork inlet piece; it should be sub-divided into no more than six equal parts. The pressure loss through a grille should be at least 25 N/m² at the minimum allowable air flow rate, so as to limit the flow variation due to external pressure changes. As an adjustable grille is closed, the pressure drop increases, air speed increases, and at some point noise will occur. The designer should ensure that the system can be balanced and will operate satisfactorily before this point is reached. 'Balancing' means adjusting the various resistances to air flow in the system so as to obtain the required flow conditions throughout. A system may be prebalanced, when resistances are set by the contractor before the ductwork is installed, or site-balanced after installation.

The air-flows into a system from various floor levels should all be approximately equal. The balancing of air-flows into a common main duct, if necessary, is best done by using an extract grille adjustable at the face, or a fixed circular orifice plate within the shunt duct. The area of the orifice should be at least one quarter that of the shunt. Main duct flows can be balanced by dampers at the heads of the vertical main ducts.

There is no statutory upper limit to the air extract rate but it is suggested that the recommended design rate should not be exceeded by more than 20 per cent; too high a rate can waste heat during the heating season. Air extract rates should, therefore, be within the following limits:

WC, or bathroom with no WC	20–28 m³/h
Bathroom with WC	40–56 m³/h

In the past, blockage of balancing devices within shunt ducts by accumulated dust and dirt has been a major cause of deteriorating performance. There should be no adjustable damper, balancing device or other adjustable flow restricter within the vertical duct-work, nor should any such device be fitted immediately behind a fixed extract grille. If blockage occurs at the grille face, it can be seen and easily cleared away. Access points should be provided to allow ducts to be swept. Dampers at the tops of main ducts are a potential source of noise because of the high air velocities through them. They are best positioned away from the uppermost dwelling, eg at points A in Fig 3.

(d) **Fans.** Fans should be capable of extracting the design total flow against the resistance imposed by the duct system and extract grilles. The fan static pressure should be at least 125 N/m² for buildings up to 18 m high and at least 185 N/m² for higher buildings, but it may be necessary to increase this to counteract wind pressures. If the loss of pressure through the ducting is less than the recommended fan static pressure, the fan will extract more than the design total air flow. This may be reduced, if desired, by fitting a damper at the fan outlet or inlet.

With sufficient fan power and in-built resistance to air flow, an extract system can be made largely immune to external changes in air pressure—mainly the effects of wind and of doors opening—which would otherwise cause fluctuations in flow.

Duplication of fans and motors to provide alternative power in the event of failure is a requirement of the GLC byelaws; the Building Standards (Scotland) (Consolidation) Regulations 1971 require duplication of the motor if the system serves more than one house. If duplicate fans are permanently fitted to a system, the change-over damper or dampers, whether manual or automatic, should be so designed that the air pressure within the system assists in holding them in the correct position. The fan unit should be regularly serviced to the manufacturer's specification.

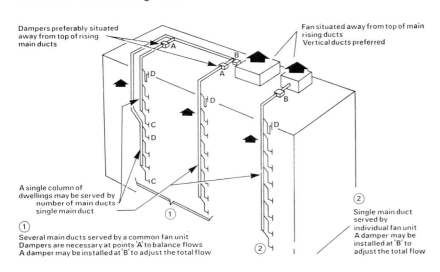

Dampers preferably situated away from top of rising main ducts

Fan situated away from top of main rising ducts
Vertical ducts preferred

A single column of dwellings may be served by number of main ducts single main duct

① Several main ducts served by a common fan unit
Dampers are necessary at points 'A' to balance flows
A damper may be installed at 'B' to adjust the total flow

② Single main duct served by individual fan unit
A damper may be installed at 'B' to adjust the total flow

Fig 3 Typical vertical common-duct systems

(e) **Ducting.** Primary factors in selecting a material for ducting are the expected life, fire risk, cost, availability and weight. The system should be capable of easy assembly and have permanently air-tight joints.

Ductwork is usually enclosed in service ducts and, therefore, inaccessible; it should last without maintenance for as long as the building itself. The traditional ducting material, galvanised steel, is suspect from this standpoint; alternatives with an acceptable life expectancy are asbestos-cement, aluminium, and unplasticised PVC.

Vertical ductwork is a potential route for fire spread between dwellings or compartments of a building and whilst it is usually recommended that ventilation ductwork should be non-combustible, unplasticised pvc systems, carefully designed, have been used successfully. In any case, the materials for both ductwork and insulation should be carefully selected to ensure that fire and smoke spread through the system is reduced as far as practicable.

To avoid air leakage into the ductwork requires careful jointing. Circular ducting with spigot and socket joints is preferred and the materials mentioned above are available in this form. Spirally-wound aluminium pipes require care in installation and probably specialist skill. The jointing of asbestos-cement should prove satisfactory if done to the manufacturer's specification but in small service ducts it might be difficult to make the joints. A leak-tight system is easily constructed with PVC soil pipes and fittings.

(f) **Noise.** Noise from the system should not exceed 35 dB(A) in any room intended for habitation, or 40 dB(A) in any other room.

The fan is a potential source of nuisance from noise and attention must be paid to its inherent noise level, its siting and mounting. Noise may be transmitted through the ductwork or through the building structure to habitable rooms. Structure-borne noise can be reduced by carefully siting the fan and by using anti-vibration mountings. Transmission through the ductwork is usually less troublesome but fans should be located as far from the heads of rising ducts as is practicable (*see* Fig 3).

(g) **Flow measurement and testing.** The system should be checked, after commissioning, for air flow, using a hooded vane anemometer (Fig 4) of diameter not less than 100 mm; the local authority should do this. Testing with smoke pellets is not satisfactory. As a basis for testing, a diagram of the ductwork layout (similar to Fig 3) is required; air-flow rates should be measured at extract points at the top and bottom of each vertical main (points C and D on Fig 3) and at several other points.

There is no simple, reliable test for duct leakage that can be recommended.

3 Fire precautions

Ventilation ductwork must comply with the relevant requirements of Part E of the Building Regulations and should, in most cases, be contained within a service duct, the walls of which have a fire resistance similar to that required of the surrounding structural elements. Inspection or access doors and frames should have similar fire resistance. Recommended practices are described in CP 413 *Ducts for building services.*

Fire and smoke spread via the protected shaft should be limited by the provision of fire dampers and fire stopping. The latter has ancillary advantages —providing a means of fixing the ductwork and helping to increase the sound insulation between dwellings. Digest 158 describes honeycomb fire dampers which are suitable for use in some ventilation ducts.

4 Entrance lobby and replacement air

Internal WC's and bathrooms should be entered from an entrance lobby. Replacement air should be drawn from this lobby, not from external air.

Fig 4 Hooded vane anemometer

Energy conservation in artificial lighting

The rising cost of electrical power is an incentive to consider ways of reducing the consumption of the lighting installation, certainly in large buildings and possibly in the home, if this can be done without lowering standards; in new buildings it is important to plan for the optimisation of energy use for lighting to achieve the desired visual standards.

Lighting requirements are essentially subjective; there is a large range of conditions over which the eye peforms satisfactorily, and there is equally a large range of variation among individuals as to what constitutes satisfactory conditions. Enough experience now exists, however, to indicate the way in which both performance of difficult visual tasks and satisfaction vary with quantity of light in terms of the average response of a large population and of the spread of individual responses about this mean. The effect of age on seeing is also well-known, as is the effect of brightness contrast on the resulting discomfort glare experienced by the occupants of a room.

Since energy consumed in any system is the product of power rate and time (watts and hours), reduction of either or both of these can reduce consumption. This digest first considers making the most use of the power delivered to the light sources, both in terms of conversion into light and of efficiency in providing optimum conditions for seeing the task; it then deals with measures leading to shorter periods of operation of the light sources. The digest then discusses the effects of these measures on savings in energy and the cost implications of adopting them.

Lighting uses about four per cent of the UK's primary energy and of this 92 per cent is associated with buildings. As a proportion of the electrical energy generated, however, lighting accounts for some 15 per cent, and in a large, modern air-conditioned building, about half the annual consumption is accounted for directly by the lighting, with a further contribution by the lighting to the refrigeration load. By contrast, domestic lighting and appliances account for only six per cent of the total primary energy used, most of the consumption being shared between space and water heating and cooking. Here, but more particularly in commercial and industrial buildings without mechanical cooling, lighting can to some extent reduce the heating load because all its power is eventually degraded into heat.

Standards of lighting generally recognised in the UK and widely adopted are those recommended by the IES Code*. The illuminances recommended for various seeing tasks are neither minima nor optima; the Limiting Glare Indices, which limit the possibilities of discomfort glare, are, however, maxima.

Since it is clearly meaningless to be able to state a minimum acceptable illuminance for a given task, it must be left to individuals to decide what reduction of standards they wish to accept or impose, and what reduction of satisfaction, working accuracy and productivity can be accepted as a result. But a more meaningful approach is to consider how recommended standards can be met with less consumption of energy.

*IES Code for Interior Lighting 1977 (obtainable from CIBS Lighting Division).

Optimum use of power

The following recommendations apply equally to existing buildings and to the design of installations for new buildings. Most of them apply to dwellings as well as to non-domestic buildings, although the choice of sources is more limited for the former. If the recommendations are followed, it may be possible to reduce the electrical loading, or at least to obtain better lighting for the same loading.

Use light sources which have the highest 'efficacy' (the ratio of light output in lumens to the power in watts consumed by the circuit).

Fluorescent lamps are available in wattages and colours suitable for most commercial and domestic interiors and provide up to five times as much light for the same power consumption as ordinary incandescent lamps. Care has to be taken however over the choice of the colour and colour rendering of the lamp for the purpose required and it must be borne in mind that the stated wattage of the lamp does not include the consumption of the necessary gear for starting and controlling the discharge: this can amount to 20 per cent of the power delivered to the lamp. The introduction of solid-state electronic ballasts could, however, improve this efficiency greatly.

High pressure mercury and sodium discharge lamps are available up to thirty times more powerful than the largest fluorescent lamps, but their colour characteristics are different again from those of the familiar incandescent lamps. These two characteristics make them more suitable for industrial interiors where they can be mounted at a high level although the lower wattages, (more particularly the mercury lamp with halide additive) have been used successfully in shops and offices.

Discharge lamps last four to seven times as long as general service incandescent filament lamps (although some 'double-life' incandescent lamps are available with a slightly lower output than normal). Although they cost much more, the need for less frequent replacement means that discharge lamps are more suitable for mounting in locations where access is difficult.

High pressure discharge lamps have a disadvantage in use in situations where interruptions of supply may occur, because they take from one to twenty minutes to cool down and restrike, according to the type of circuit used. Consequently, if any danger from black-out due to a power failure exists in a building, it is essential that emergency lighting is provided whatever the main light source.

Use luminaires with as high as possible a light output ratio (efficiency) consistent with their function.

The highest light output efficiency does not necessarily result in the best illumination; a bare lamp luminaire is inefficient in directing light on to the working plane. A reflector round a lamp to concentrate the light below is more efficient but will probably not produce a satisfactory working environment without additional lighting. As a general guide, luminaires with prismatic control suspended below a ceiling perform their function more efficiently than those distributing their light by diffusion or those recessed into ceilings or soffits. It is important to make sure that the luminaires comply with discomfort glare requirements.

Attempts to improve illuminance on the working plane or to reduce power loading by lowering the mounting height of the luminaires, may result in patchy lighting and loss of light reflected from the ceiling. Upward light is not wasted, for it reduces the contrast of the luminaire with its background and thus reduces the discomfort glare effect; it improves the appearance of the interior by avoiding a 'dark tunnel' effect; it also provides an indirect component to the lighting to soften shadows.

Provide the necessary illuminance at the task or in the task areas by local or localised 'Task lighting' and provide the general lighting of the interior for circulation, visual appearance, background to task areas, etc, by 'Ambient lighting' at a lower illuminance.

The value of a system of 'Task/ambient lighting' or 'Task/building lighting' will depend very much on the extent and pattern of the distribution of tasks around the interior and the frequency with which these change. Such an arrangement is frequently used in the home, where table lamps or floor standards provide the light required for reading or sewing while centre-lights or wall lights provide the background.

The aim of such lighting is to direct and maintain attention to the work by giving it a higher luminance than the background, which should be less bright and capable of resting the eyes when looking up. Too dark a background to the work area will produce a harsh and uncomfortable contrast, so the general lighting must not provide too low a luminance. A designed working plane illuminance of one-third of the task illuminance should be the minimum elsewhere in the room.

Systems of task-plus-ambient lighting are not suitable for all interiors; for example, they are unsuitable where provision must be made for the same level of visual task to be performed anywhere in the interior at any time. Even where the location of tasks can be strictly defined, arrangements must be possible for luminaires to be mounted close to the task on desk bench or machine, or else to be suspended from the ceiling, wall or overhead equipment. These luminaires can generally be equipped with lamps of lower power than those in general lighting luminaires and less of them may be required where the task areas are well separated in the interior. Whatever the arrangement, the luminaire requires both an electrical supply to feed it and also space in which it can be fitted. There is responsibility also on the users to avoid maltreatment and a need for frequent maintenance.

A further advantage of task lighting is that it permits the arrangement of incident light in a way which will maximise the contrast of the task. As an example, the most common task in an office is reading printed or written material where visibility depends on the contrast between the ink or pencil mark and the surrounding paper. This contrast can be changed by changing the direction of the light. In an interior lit by an array of luminaires mounted on the ceiling, it is inevitable that the light from some luminaires will be reflected in the direct line of sight of the observer, so that shininess of ink or paper will produce lower visual contrast (reflected glare). Local, lighting can be obliquely set so that task illumination is not in the plane of the observer's eye and the contrast of the task may, therefore, be appreciably improved.

Calculations indicate that a given illuminance provided by oblique local lighting should produce the same visibility of written or printed matter as general lighting at a somewhat higher illuminance.

Keep existing luminaires, lamps and room surfaces clean by increasing the frequency of cleaning.

In a new installation, this can enable the required illuminance to be maintained with fewer sources or less power. In an old installation, improved maintenance (including the replacement of fluorescent and high pressure discharge lamps at intervals not longer than their nominal life) will provide more light for the same consumption of energy. Whether it is advisable to reduce the total number of light sources in an existing installation to take advantage of a higher efficiency resulting from improved maintenance will depend on whether this can be done without any noticeable reduction in uniformity of illuminance on the working areas. Any local reduction in illuminance will obviously be less acceptable at a working point than in a circulation area.

Reducing unnecessary use

It is a matter of common observation that lights are often fully on in parts of buildings when no, or very few, people are in occupation and also when daylight is providing a high illuminance over at least some part of the working area. This over-use arises in different ways but most frequently by not switching off rather than by switching on unnecessarily. However, if too large an area of lighting is controlled by one switch the requirements for light by one individual may lead to large numbers of luminaires being switched on when only one or two are really required. Such a situation might arise from working in a place which is particularly poorly daylit or from working in a large room when no one else is present.

Manual Controls

Controls should at least permit individual rows of luminaires parallel to window walls to be controlled separately, and control systems (both mechanical and electronic) have been installed in some buildings which permit individual luminaires in a large installation to be switched by the occupants most affected. Switches should be as near as possible to the luminaires which they control, and one system which has been effective uses cord-operated ceiling switches adjacent to each luminaire. A technically feasible system, but one with which there is little experience yet, has electronic controls (ultrasonic or infra-red) placed on occupants' desks to give them control of one or more luminaires; a master control of this type would avoid any necessity for wiring to switches on walls.

Time Controls

If the occupation of a building effectively ceases at a fixed hour every working day, it may be worth installing a time control so that most of the lighting is switched off soon after this time. Arrangements may need to be made, however, for individuals working late to override part or all of the switching with subsequent automatic switching off. The building cleaning routine may also need special arrangements; sequential control of lighting may be appropriate when a cleaning gang move from floor to floor. Arrangements must be made however, to ensure that no-one ever has to enter an unlighted space or to be in a space where all the lighting is out of their control.

Photo-electric Controls

Failure to switch off lights in areas receiving sufficient daylight is another major cause of energy waste. This can occur when the lights are switched on, say at the beginning of the day when daylight alone is insufficient, and remain on when the daylight later provides more than the illuminance to which the artificial lighting was designed. Photo-electric control can ensure that the lighting cannot be turned on or remain on when the daylight provides the required illuminance by itself. In interiors where there is a large range of daylight factors, eg a fairly deep interior with two or more rows of luminaires running parallel with the window wall (or walls), it may be advantageous to use a separate controller for each row.

On-off control

An on-off switch controlled by the level of daylight produces a sudden change of illuminance on the working plane of roughly two to one if it is set to switch off the artificial lighting when daylight alone could provide the same illuminance. There is considerable evidence that the occupants of a room find it unsatisfactory if large areas of lighting are controlled in this way, although, it appears to be more acceptable if, say, the outside row of luminaires close to a wall with windows admitting a reasonable amount of daylight are controlled in this way. This is mainly because switching will be infrequent.

Top-up control

Equipment is available to control the light output of fluorescent lamps so as to top-up the daylight when it fails to reach the design level of the artificial lighting by itself. With this system, the artificial lighting is not fully on unless daylight falls to a negligible level. As daylight increases, the output of the lamps falls to keep the illuminance provided by the combination of the two sources constant until, when daylight alone is adequate, the lamps are switched off completely. Conversely, as daylight falls below the illuminance which the artificial lighting could provide, the lamps are switched on at an almost imperceptibly low output which increases progressively to maximum as the daylight illuminance falls towards zero. Clearly such a system will use less energy than one which switches the lighting on fully for the whole time that the daylight is below the design illuminance, but more saving can be made if some positive action is needed by the occupants to initiate the switching-on action of the controller.

Energy savings

Change of light source

The improvements in efficiency may be summed up by expressing the relative efficacies (taking gear losses into account) as follows.

Lamp	Relative Efficacy
General Service	
Incandescent filament	0 83 – 1.5 (100W lamp = 1)
'Deluxe' fluorescent	1.7 – 3.75
High efficiency fluorescent	3.75 – 5.4
HP Mercury	3.75 – 5.8
HP Sodium	5.0 – 9.0

The above figures cover the range of lamps commonly used, as the efficacy varies with the wattage loading.

Luminaire light output ratio (LOR)

A recessed opal diffuser luminaire can have a light output ratio of 40 percent, while a recessed one with a prismatic diffuser can have an LOR of 48 percent. If mounted below the ceiling, the LOR can increase to 75 percent, an improvement of light emitted of 87 percent and 56 percent respectively.

Task/ambient lighting

The reduction of installed lighting power achieved by providing task illuminance in conjunction with lower ambient illuminance will depend very greatly on the density of occupation of the space. One office with a rather low density of 15 sq. metres per person achieved a reduction of 44 percent in installed lighting load by using 20 Watt fluorescent lamps in local lights at each side of the desks and in adjustable drawing board lamps. This however, may represent somewhat higher than average savings in relation to the normal density of office occupation.

In the example quoted, measurements of contrast rendering indicated that although the new installation provided only 80 percent of the horizontal illuminance on the task which the previous installation produced, there should have been a net improvement in task visibility.

Manual switching

Any reduction in energy use resulting from improved accessibility or flexibility in switching will clearly be dependant on the patterns of activity in the space. In the installation referred to in the previous paragraph, the fact that several of the office staff had a great deal of outside work and consequently their desk lights were not turned on when they were absent led to a total energy saving over a year's operation of nearly 83 percent of the energy used by the original installation. On the other hand, on one floor of a new office building where ceiling pull switches were installed to operate individual luminaires in a large open office, most luminaires tended to be left on the whole time the room was occupied. On another floor of the same building, however, with the same switching arrangement, but a different arrangement of working groups and desk locations, about one-third of the luminaires were usually off.

In a series of random visits involved in a survey of 50 offices, it was found that despite the 'switch it off' campaign in progress at the time, a potential saving of around 11 per cent of the power in use could have been made by switching off the lights which were not required at the time. Increased facility of operation or clarity of control panel identification could well have helped to convert some of this potential into an actual saving. Rearrangement of the switching to improve flexibility of control could, moreover, have doubled the potential saving. The survey included all types of office space, including cellular. For multi-occupant spaces, much larger savings can be achieved.

Time control

At least one survey has shown that the energy consumed in an office building can be much greater (by up to 30 percent) than can be accounted for by the full lighting load operating for the normal working day. However, the extent to which savings can be achieved by time control of the lighting depends on the extent of late occupation, the cleaning routine and the security patrol arrangements. In a school study, it was clear that the lights were not finally turned off until some time between 22.00 and 23.00 hrs, presumably when the caretaker made his final rounds, although adult classes ended at 21.30. Although this use accounted for less than 0.5 per cent of the lighting energy consumed, 90 to 95 per cent of the lighting remained on over the lunch-hour even in the summer, accounting for some nine per cent of the total use, and some of this could also be controlled by a time switch. There is evidence, moreover, that once having been switched off, the lighting is less likely to be switched back on manually on return after lunch.

Photo-electric control

The savings achievable by substituting photo-electric control for normal manual switching depend partly on the amount of daylight entering the space and partly on what use the occupants made of the original manual switching arrangements but trial installations in offices and schools showed savings of around 30 percent of lighting energy.

Luminaire maintenance

Typically the light output of a luminaire may fall to about 75 percent of the initial light output due to soiling during the first six months use and to about 70 percent over a further six months; thus the penalty for doubling the length of the cleaning cycle might be a ten per cent additional loss of light. A similar loss may be incurred by lengthening the period of lamp replacement to 1200 hours of running from 7000 hours for a fluorescent lamp or to 9000 hours from 7000 hours for a mercury halide lamp.

Increasing the reflectances of room surfaces by redecoration can have an important effect on the illuminance on the working plane. If a room with ceiling reflectance 50 percent, wall reflectance 30 percent, and floor reflectance 10 percent is redecorated so that the reflectances are increased to 70, 50 and 30 percent respectively, the illuminance from a diffusing luminaire may be increased by 20 percent.

Costs and savings

The cost of most of the measures discussed is small in relation to the energy saved, even as additions or replacement in an old building. In a new building some of the improvements in manual control can be cheaper than installing the conventional wiring runs for wall switches. Cost effectiveness analysis has been applied to some of the measures making some reasonable assumptions about circumstances, and high on the scale of internal rate of return comes the simple automatic on-off control of lighting for areas with generous amounts of day-lighting in new office buildings; rather lower is the conversion to task/ambient lighting, followed by the replacement of incandescent tungsten lamps with fluorescent lamps.

The improved life and efficacy of fluorescent lamps compared with incandescent lamps has the effect that the cost of one lumen-hour of light from the former is about one third of that from the latter, in spite of the higher cost of the lamps. There is, however, a commitment to the extra capital cost of the control gear and of more expensive luminaires.

A further halving of the cost of light can be achieved by changing to high pressure sodium discharge lamps, but very little further reduction is possible by changing to high pressure mercury lamps (either halide or fluorescent). The advantage of these high pressure discharge lamps is that they are available in higher wattages and therefore higher total light outputs, so fewer luminaires are needed provided the mounting is sufficiently high to give the required evenness in illuminance over the working area.

Even at the present stage of development, photo electric dimming control could be cost effective in many new buildings. Relative energy costs would need to increase significantly however, or equipment costs fall considerably, before it is likely to be cost-effective to refit existing buildings. A course which would allow the possibility of easy installation at an appropriate later date would be the installation of an extra conductor wire when wiring new buildings.

Further reading

Predicting artificial lighting use — a method based upon observed patterns of behaviour. D R G Hunt, Lighting Res + Tech 12 (1) 1980.

Other BRE Digests
138 Operating costs of services in office buildings
191 Energy consumption and conservation in buildings
256 Office lighting for good visual task conditions

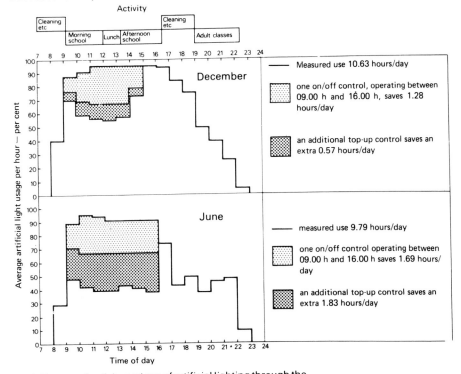

Fig 1 Pattern of activity and use of artificial lighting through the day in a deep-plan secondary school. Possible savings by using automatic controls are shown by the shaded areas.

Lighting controls and daylight use

In a non-domestic building, electric lighting is essential for a pleasant and productive working environment. It is also a major contributor to the building's energy cost; indeed, for many offices it is the largest single consumer of primary energy. The use of automatic lighting controls is an important option in both new and existing buildings and complements other options to reduce energy costs from lighting.

Waste in lighting energy occurs mainly in two ways: the use of full artificial lighting when daylight is sufficient to meet part, or even all, of the lighting requirements and lighting being maintained when occupants are absent. Behavioural studies at BRE have established that much of this waste is a result of traditional switching arrangements for lighting: a single or multiple on/off switch panel situated by the entrance to the space.

This digest discusses automatic lighting controls and gives guidance on the types of control best suited for particular types of installation. It shows how energy savings can be predicted and compared with traditional manual switching and suggests alternatives to the traditional approach. A decision chart guides the specifier or designer by classifying the space in question according to its use pattern. This classification leads to a ranked assessment of possible automatic control strategies.

The digest provides a method for predicting energy savings and assesses the other potential benefits from lighting controls; it also relates the provision of energy conscious control facilities to general lighting quality considerations.

Automatic lighting control in lighting design

Good design of artificial lighting aims to provide visual satisfaction within the lit space and, where appropriate, a visual environment that enables visual tasks to be performed efficiently and comfortably (see Digest 226). Although the main benefit and prime reason for recent interest in lighting controls has been the saving of electrical energy, it should be remembered that provision of more localised controls to enable occupants to exercise discretion over the lighting of their particular work areas can significantly increase user satisfaction.

However, it is reasonable to ask how the provision of controls to encourage economic use of electric lighting can relate to more general considerations for the provision of appropriate visual conditions. Although a gross oversimplification (see the CIBS Interior Lighting Code), these conditions tend to be characterised by the lighting level (illuminance) provided for the task to be carried out and the uniformity of illuminance to be provided throughout the space. The illuminances recommended in the Code are neither maxima nor minima but represent good current practice; however, it must be said that the preference and performance studies which form part of the back up to the recommendations show very large variations between people and conditions and have rarely been carried out in situations which benefit from daylight.

In general, the illuminance and uniformity recommendations in the Code have been developed for night-time conditions; during the day, the presence of windows will impose a daylight illuminance that can easily be 25 times greater in an area close to the window wall than in another area a few metres into the room, even without direct sunlight. The fall-off in illuminance is a smooth function of the distance from the window; in such circumstances, the visual system tends to exhibit brightness constancy such that the parts of the room which are some distance from the window are not perceived as being relatively deprived of light. There is a need for greater stringency in the recommendations for uniformity for night-time conditions because the variation in brightness over small distances can be greater than the gradual variations associated with daylight. These greater variations are more likely to cause a breakdown in brightness constancy, and may lead to distraction or discomfort.

The control systems discussed under *Selection of control strategy* enable greater advantage to be taken of available daylight than do traditional switching arrangements: by implication their main use will be during daylight hours, when the illuminance and uniformity criteria are less meaningful. For night-time conditions, the controls should not prevent occupants creating visually satisfying conditions by using more electric lighting than might be needed (at face value) for their immediate task area. The same is true of 'core areas' (area remote from windows such as the interiors of deep-plan places, where the daylight contribution to working illuminance is negligible). During the daytime all electric lighting in the core area may be required to balance the brightness of windows seen in the distance; at night the recommended illuminance ratios between the task area and surroundings will be desirable to provide a satisfactory appearance.

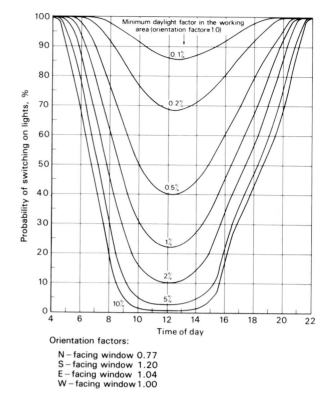

Orientation factors:
    N – facing window 0.77
    S – facing window 1.20
    E – facing window 1.04
    W – facing window 1.00

Fig 1 Switch ON probabilities

Estimating savings in electricity

Estimation of savings requires both a prediction of consumption with controls and an estimate of use under existing conditions (for existing installations) or of use with traditional switching arrangements (for new installations).

Lighting use under traditional manual control

The basis for estimating use of lighting under traditional manual control is given in Fig 1, derived from BRE behavioural studies[1][2]. It gives an estimate of the probability (averaged over a year) of electric lighting being switched on at the start of a period of occupation as a function of time of day and the available daylight, characterised by the 'minimum daylight factor in the working area'.

The daylight factor at a given position is the ratio of daylight illuminance at that point to the horizontal illuminance simultaneously experienced outside under a completely unobstructed sky of known brightness distribution. It varies from building to building, depending on the sizes and position of windows in the space, the transmission characteristics and cleanliness of the window glass and the reflectances of the surfaces of the space. Digests 41 and 42 give guidance on how the daylight factor can be calculated for a given space. Minimum calculated daylight factors in buildings designed to benefit from natural lighting during the day range from 0.1 to 2 per cent. Daylight factors are traditionally based on calculations using a particular distribution of sky brightness (the CIE sky); they should be modified according to the factors in Fig 1 to account more accurately for the orientation of windows.

In estimating use it should be assumed that full loads are used and that lighting will not be turned off until the space becomes completely empty.

Thus, from a knowledge of the likely occupation pattern and daylight distribution in a space, prediction can be made of the proportion of the working year that lighting will be used.

Example

A space has an orientation-corrected minimum daylight factor of 0.5 per cent, and the working day is from 0800 to 1800. For how many hours each year will the lighting be used?

From Fig 1, the probability of switching on is approx 75 per cent. For a continuously occupied space (not necessarily full) lighting will remain on once switched on, until the space becomes completely empty at the end of the working period. Therefore, lighting use will be for 75 per cent of the 'working year':
ie 0.75 × 10 × 250 (working days) = 1875 hours.

For an intermittently occupied space, a profile is required of the times that the space is empty and switching probabilities obtained for the start of each occupation period; these are then summed for the working year after weighting with the lengths of each period.

Lighting use under alternative controls

Time switching: automatic switching to a predetermined timetable.

Localised switching: switches provided throughout the space rather than concentrated at the entrance.

Daylight linking: automatic control of lighting by photoelectric sensing of daylight levels.

Occupancy linking: automatic switching by sensing presence of occupants.

Time switching If switching is controlled on and off, the estimated use is derived directly from the proposed schedule. If switching on is by demand but switching off is time-controlled, Fig 1 can be used. The probabilities for switching on after automatic switch off (at lunch-time for example) are calculated along the same lines as before and overall use computed from these probabilities (weighted by appropriate periods from the time switching schedule).

Localised switching Figure 1 can be used but switching probabilities need to be obtained for each zone (controlled by separate switch). Overall use is then obtained by weighting these probabilities by part loads in each zone and summing for the complete installation. If occupancy is variable or intermittent (see *Occupancy type*), further weighting is carried out according to assumptions about occupancy.

Daylight linking by photelectric on/off switching Figure 2 shows the percentage of a working year (assumed to be 0900–1730 hr daily) that a photoelectrically controlled lighting installation would be switched off as a function of the design illuminance of the electric lighting and daylight factor (orientation corrected). Departures from the standard day of up to one hour either way at each end of the day have little effect. The daylight factor should be calculated for the depth from the window wall at which the controlled lighting is situated and the predictions assume that the control will be calibrated to switch at the design level required. Consumption is simply obtained from the proportion of the working year that lights will be on multiplied by the lighting load controlled. For multizone control, a calculation is required for each zone.

Daylight linking by photoelectric dimming (top-up) Figure 3 shows the percentage of the working year (again assuming 0900–1730 hr daily) for which the equivalent full load would be off using a photoelectrically controlled dimming system. This takes into account periods during which output from the lighting is less than maximum — hence the term 'equivalent full load'. The curves are for different design illuminances as functions of orientation-corrected daylight factor. In constructing the curves, an assumption has been made concerning the energy consumption of the special ballasts required for dimming. The assumption is based on measured performance of a dimming system and can be assumed to apply to well designed systems. Calculation of consumption is the same as under *Photoelectric on/off switching.*

Occupancy linking As for localised switching, an assumption must be made about the expected occupancy pattern of the given space; for automatic on and off occupancy switching, an estimate of consumption follows directly from that assumption. For automatic off only, with local demand on, the calculation of consumption needs to take into account probabilities of switching on (Fig 1) following an automatic off, according to the assumed occupancy pattern.

A saving in energy used for lighting may lead to savings associated with air conditioning or, conversely, an increase in energy required for heating. It is outside the scope of this digest to examine this interplay in detail but it should be noted that, provided appropriate controls are present, overall energy efficiency will be greatest when lighting is not used extravagantly to offset heating requirements.

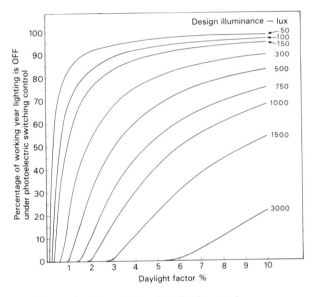

Fig 2 Photoelectric switching (ON/OFF) control
Standard year:
0900 — 1730 BST, April to October inclusive

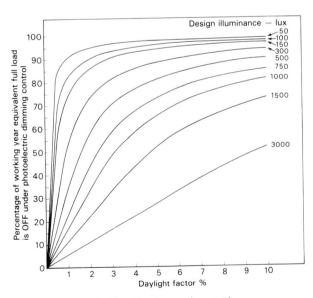

Fig 3 Photoelectric dimming (top-up) control
Standard year:
0900 — 1730 BST, April to October inclusive

DECISION CHART — SELECTION OF CONTROL STRATEGY

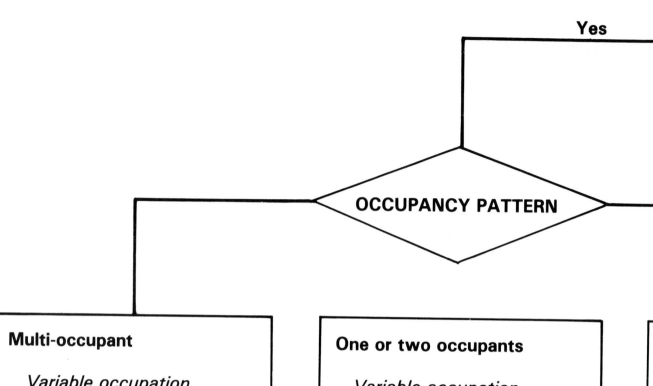

Yes

OCCUPANCY PATTERN

Multi-occupant

Variable occupation
- ●●● Time switching
- ●● Localised switches
- ● Photoelectric
  daylight linking
- ● Occupancy linking

Intermittent scheduled occupation
- ●●● Time switching
- ● Localised switches
- ● Photoelectric
  daylight linking
- ● Occupancy linking

Full occupation
- ●●● Time switching
- ●●● Photoelectric
  daylight linking
- ●● Localised switches

One or two occupants

Variable occupation
- ●●● Localised switches
- ●● Occupancy linking
- ● Time switching
- ● Photoelectric
  daylight linking

Full occupation
- ●●● Localised switches
- ●● Photoelectric
  daylight linking
- ● Time switching

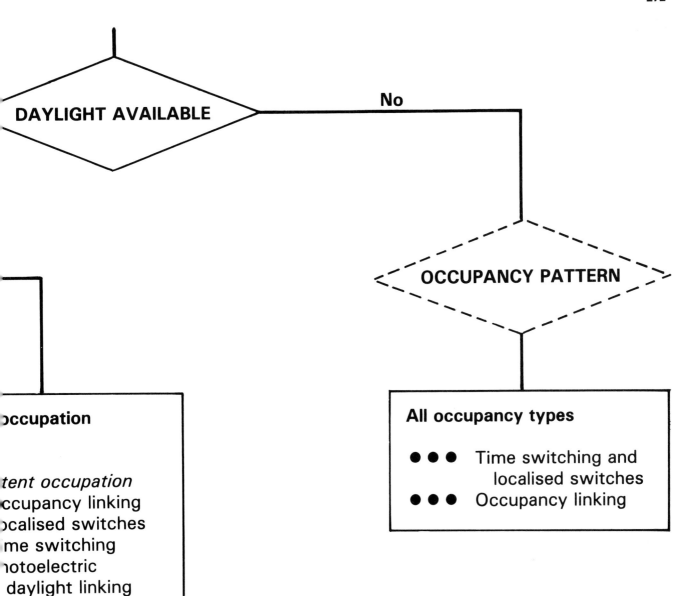

DAYLIGHT AVAILABLE

No

OCCUPANCY PATTERN

occupation

tent occupation
ccupancy linking
ocalised switches
me switching
hotoelectric
daylight linking

All occupancy types

● ● ● Time switching and
        localised switches
● ● ● Occupancy linking

Key

● ● ● Definitely recommended
        to produce savings

● ●   Could be expected to
        provide economies but rate
        of return on investment
        would not be as high

●   Needs consideration; might
        depend on a detailed
        examination of the installation

Selection of control strategy

The control strategies available are summarised in the decision chart in order of probable energy saving for each occupation pattern. The following paragraphs supplement the chart.

Daylight

If sufficient daylight is available to meet lighting requirements for significant parts of the working day, energy savings can be considerable. BRE studies have shown that the probability of switching on artificial lighting on entering a space correlates closely with the daylight availability at the time but switching off rarely occurs until the last occupant has left. The control strategies shown in the chart aim to invite the switching decision to be remade at times when daylight availability will have improved (time switching) or aim to place the switch in a location where the occupants' perception of daylight adequacy will be more relevant to their needs than for a switch location at the entrance to the space (localised switching).

For many types of installation such provisions will be adequate. However, further savings can be achieved by using automatic sensing of daylight levels (photo-electric daylight linking) or occupancy (occupancy linking). The use of these options depends on the type of occupation. For spaces with negligible daylighting, a combination of time switching and localised switches will cover most situations although care must be taken to ensure that 'timed off' control does not produce dangerous blackout conditions. For installations with sparse and intermittent occupancy, such as large store rooms and warehouses, localised (distributed) switching will eliminate the need for 'blanket lighting' of the whole space; occupancy detector control will also be a major option.

Occupancy pattern

After daylight, the most significant factor in the use of lighting under traditional control is the occupancy pattern. For example, a multiperson working area, which may appear well daylit, will have much higher running hours for its electric lighting than a series of cellular spaces with equivalent daylighting. As already explained, switching on occurs at the start of occupation if the adequacy of daylight is judged as insufficient, but switching off occurs only when the space becomes empty. In a multi-occupant office this might not be until the end of the working day, whereas a cellular space could be vacated two or three times during the day with consequent opportunities for the returning occupant to reassess the need for artificial lighting.

Occupancy type

The description of different types of occupation pattern can be achieved in a number of different ways; for example, it can be related to the type of activity in the spaces to be described. For the purposes of prescribing lighting controls, a broad description which essentially relates to a frequency of entering and leaving the space is sufficient. Some examples for the general headings may be useful:

Variable occupation: engineer/architect design office, where occupants are frequently on site or consulting colleagues in other parts of the building; research laboratory where time is divided between laboratory and office.

Intermittent scheduled occupation: school classroom with defined timetable; committee room used by a series of different occupants at predetermined times; sports hall.

Full occupation: clerical office, occupants largely 'tied' to desks during working day; factory space, occupants at machines or work benches.

Intermittent occupation: storeroom; warehouse space; installation which does not represent the user's main working area and which is visited occasionally during the working day.

Clearly these descriptions overlap. For example, it may be difficult to decide when 'intermittent' becomes 'variable'. The design should normally lean towards a solution which leaves occupants with maximum flexibility.

Hardware for the selected control strategy

Time switches

Available hardware includes the well-tried and tested multi-position, electro-mechanical time switch, and various solid state alternatives that have been developed more recently. Time control can represent an important element of a building energy management system.

For small installations (below say 2kW) the time switch can be used to actually switch the lighting load but more often than not it provides time signals for operating relays or contactors, which control power to the lighting circuits.

Time switching necessarily implies that the timed signals are transmitted to the controlled elements via some communication channel. This can be the mains supply itself, with the 'signal' merely an interruption of the mains supply. If the time switch is remote (or centralised) and override facilities are required (for example to enable localised switching for occupants) some other communication channel may be necessary to enable such override and it may be desirable to allow different switching patterns for different parts of the lighting installation. Low-voltage wiring systems can be used for this purpose. Recently, mains-borne signalling using microelectronic coding techniques have become available.

A further alternative using the mains wiring involves the use of latching relays at the liminaires or luminaire switch panels, so that when a mains interrupt pulse of short duration (about 1 sec) is generated by a time switch, the relays latch off even when mains supply is restored. Override or local control involves resetting the relay to the on position using conventional switch hardware, such as a rocker switch or pull cord.

Localised switches

Convenient localised switching can be accomplished merely by providing more 'mains' switch positions than has become normal practice. With due regard for safety requirements, switches should operate on lighting in the immediate vicinity and wherever possible the switching arrangement should reflect the profile of penetration of daylight. So, for an installation consisting of rows of fluorescent lighting parallel to a window wall, there should at least be as many switches as individual rows. Economies will result from (a) having the switches for each row placed at approximately the same distance from the window wall as the lighting itself and (b) having a further breakdown into groups of luminaires within rows, with switches close to their area of influence.

Alternatives to wall-mounted mains switches include low-voltage switching, use of luminaire mounted pull cords and even remote ('wireless') switches using infra red or ultrasonic transmitting and receiving devices similar to those commonly used for controlling TV or 'hi-fi'.

Photoelectric daylight linking

Photoelectric switches (on/off) Two basic forms of automatic photoelectric switching control can be used to link electric lighting use to daylight availability. The cheaper method is to switch the lights by a photocell, mounted externally or facing out of a window to sense daylight only (open loop control). This is similar to photoelectric street lighting control, except that calibration is required in situ because the daylight level for switching depends on the particular characteristics of the building. For example, a given daylight illuminance at the sensor can result in a variety of internal illuminances depending on window size, furniture layout, decorations etc. The use of an external sensor is not suitable where there are complex shadows across the facade. The alternative approach has the sensor mounted in the area to be controlled to sense both daylight and artificial light (closed loop control). In this case, a switch on level and switch off level need to be set so that activation of the electric lighting does not immediately cause switching off. For either type of photoelectric switch, the device should allow a delay to be set so that after a switching action has occurred no further action can take place until after the set delay. This minimises the problem of rapid switching caused, for example, by fast-moving clouds. Photoelectric on/off switching causes sudden and noticeable changes in lighting level and complaints from occupants about distraction have been reported. For this reason, it is recommended only for working areas close to a window wall, where the frequency of switching will be least. Successful installations which make use of multi-level switching in multi-lamp luminaires for a large working area exist, but clearly require careful planning and their complexity will result in higher costs.

Photoelectric dimming ('top-up') Unlike switching, 'top-up' control is unobtrusive and ensures that at all times the sum of daylight and electric lighting reaches a given minimum (the design level). This is achieved by photoelectrically sensing the total light in the controlled area and automatically adjusting electric light output to 'top-up' to the set level. If daylight alone is adequate electric lighting is dimmed to extinction. The energy saving potential of 'top-up' control is greater than for photoelectric switching and the mode of control likely to be more acceptable to occupants. However, although savings will be greater, costs are higher because of the more complex control electronics and special lamp ballasts required.

Lamp type restrictions Photoelectric switching can be applied to a wide range of lamp types; for high intensity sources special ballasts may be required to minimise restrike times. Photoelectric dimming is most satisfactorily applied to fluorescent lamps, although this is not yet possible with the recently developed smaller diameter tubes. Although dimming of incandescent lamps presents no problem, the light output/power characteristic is such that energy savings are unlikely to be achieved cost effectively. (In practice, such lamps are unlikely to be used when energy efficiency is a major concern.) Dimming of some types of high intensity lamp is possible although there is little experience of its use in the UK. Doubts have been raised concerning effects on lamp life and, for the present, the technique is not recommended for the high intensity lamps.

Occupancy linking

The use of controls which sense presence or absence of occupants is a recent development in lighting. The techniques involved have been used for some time for security and burglar alarm systems but application to lighting controls has hitherto been prohibitively expensive.

Several techniques are currently being used for sensing: ultrasonics (detecting frequency shifts caused by the Doppler effect resulting from reflections from moving objects), infra red pyrometry (detecting heat pattern changes caused by movement), and acoustics (detecting activity generated noise).

The commerically available devices are generally designed to switch on as well as off and some include parallel photoelectric on/off control.

Overall systems

This digest has briefly reviewed the available options for control under the headings given in the decision chart. There are a number of guidelines that should be considered when selecting a system.

The use of lighting controls to promote energy efficency results from:

(a) the importance of relating lighting use to occupancy patterns.

(b) the abili' 'o take much greater advantage of available daylight than is otherwise likely.

With reference to the decision chart, overall occupancy patterns should be reflected in centralised (automatic) time switching with lunchtime switch off an important element. For appropriate installations, if no other measures are taken, significant savings will accrue from the substantially lower probability of occupants switching on lighting after lunch when there is more daylight.

In parallel with timed switching, distributed switching, rationally related to daylight penetration and broken down into as small a switching unit as possible (a single luminaire if possible) will further enhance the use of daylight and encourage lighting use related to individual occupancy patterns, preferences and needs.

Depending on the nature of the work carried out by occupants, the type of space and the particular occupancy pattern of the space, savings will also be possible by making use of photoelectric control or occupancy detector control. Where distributed switching within a space is not possible, control by time, photocell or occupancy may need to switch on as well as off. However, in general it is recommended that such automatic control should only be in the OFF sense, and that switching ON should be by occupant demand using convenient localised means. It should be stressed that such a strategy is likely to prove acceptable for the occupants only if the means to override the automatic element of the control is convenient to use.

Finally, although in general the use of controls is to be encouraged, it would be wrong not to point out that their satisfactory operation depends on a positive commitment to their commissioning. Some manufacturers have given obvious thought to the inherent problems of commisioning and some offer a commissioning service. All too often, however, instructions leave much to be desired and a proper specification of commissioning procedure should be called for.

References and further reading

(1) HUNT, D R G. The use of artificial lighting in relation to daylight levels and occupancy. Building and Environment, 1979, 14, 21–33.

(2) HUNT, D R G. Predicting lighting use – a behavioural approach. Lighting Research and technoloy, 1980, 12 (1).

For a fuller description of the application of information gained in behavioural studies of lighting use to guidance on controls see:
CRISP, V H C and HENDERSON, G. The energy management of artificial lighting use. Lighting Research & Technology, 1982, 14 (4).

For more comprehensive treatment of savings associated with photoelectric control see:
HUNT, D R G. Improved daylight data for predicting energy savings from photoelectric controls. Lighting Research and Technology, 1979, 11, (1).

Case studies:
CRISP, V H C and URE, J W. The energy implications of flexible lighting controls. Proc IEE Conf Effective use of electricity in buildings; London, 1980.

CRISP, V H C. Photoelectric control of lighting — case studies. Proc CICC Conf Experience of energy conservation in buildings; Nottingham, 1980.
CRISP, V H C. Lighting controls to save energy. International Lighting Review (to be published).

BRE Digests
41 Estimating daylight in buildings: Part 1.
42 Estimating daylight in buildings: Part 2.
226 Thermal, visual and acoustic requirements in buildings.
232 Energy conservation in artificial lighting.
256 Office lighting for good visual task conditions.

Lighting design recommendations
CIBS Code for Interior Lighting.

Office lighting for good visual task conditions

At present, most lighting installations are designed simply to give a specified average illuminance on a horizontal working plane, although sometimes predictions are made of the level of discomfort glare to check that it is within recommended limits. In many cases no other design work is done. To ensure good visual task conditions in the office it is important that other aspects of the lighting are considered. By doing so, a more efficient working environment will result with less likelihood of problems of visual distraction or fatigue and the potential for more efficient energy use.

Office lighting is designed primarily to enable visual tasks to be performed by the occupants; it should, therefore, be designed to make the task as visible as possible. Bright reflections in the task will reduce its visibility and may cause discomfort. This digest considers the causes of these reflections for common office tasks such as written and printed material on paper and visual display units associated with word processors and other computer operations. The use of Contrast Rendering Factor (CRF) to quantify the effect of reflections is explained and guidance is given on acceptable levels of CRF and methods of calculation and measurement. Suggestions on design to avoid veiling reflections in offices are made.

The human eye sees the details of a visual task by discriminating between the darker and lighter parts of it. For example, this printing is visible because the letters are considerably darker than the paper on which they are printed. This difference in brightness of the visual task (the task contrast) can be expressed quantitatively as:

$$C = \frac{L_b - L_t}{L_b}$$

where L_b = luminance (brightness) of background and
L_t = luminance (brightness) of task.

In general, high contrast visual tasks are easier to see than those with lower contrast.

The contrast of a visual task depends on the intrinsic reflectance properties of the task and on the way in which it is lit. If the task material is completely matt, incident light is reflected equally in all directions, therefore the direction of incident light is unimportant. However, very few visual tasks are composed of materials which are truly matt and if

Terms used in this digest:

Visual task:	Conventionally, those details and objects that must be seen for the performance of a given activity, including the immediate background of the details or objects.
Task contrast:	The difference in brightness between the detail and the background of the visual task divided by the brightness of the background. In general, the higher the contrast, the greater the task's visibility.
Veiling reflection:	A bright defocussed image reflected in the visual task; for example an image of luminaire or a window. The effect usually is to reduce the task contrast and hence its visibility.

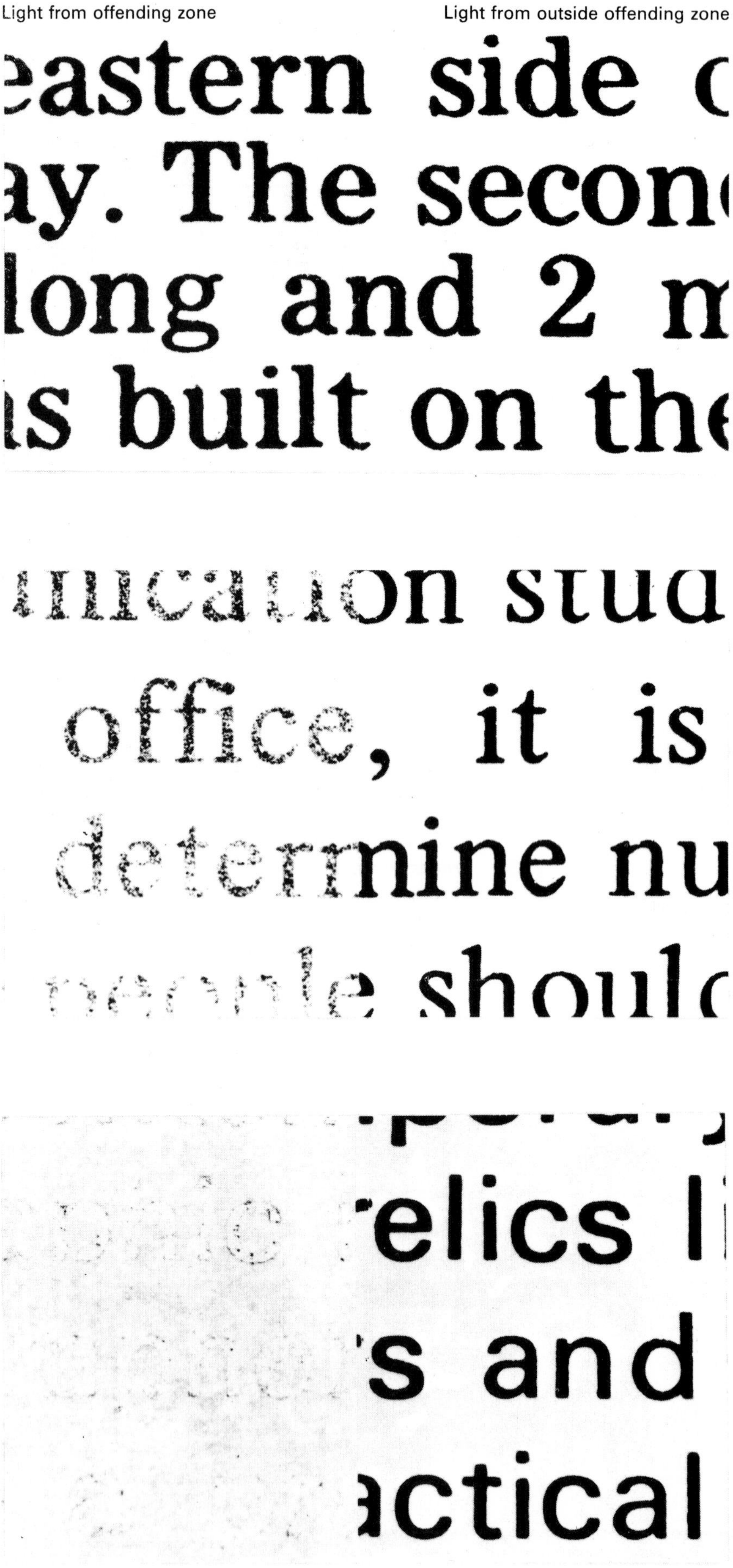

Light from offending zone   Light from outside offending zone

Matt ink on matt paper

eastern side o
ay. The secon
long and 2 m
s built on the

Semi-glossy ink on matt paper

ilication stua
office, it is
determine nu
nernle shoulc

Glossy ink on glossy paper

elics l
s and
actical

Fig 1 Veiling reflections are most commonly seen in glossy magazines but the effect is present to some degree in all reading matter under most conventional lighting installations.

the surfaces of these materials produce a specular, or mirror-like, component of reflection, defocussed images of bright sources such as luminaires are seen reflected in them. These bright images produce a veiling effect reducing the task contrast and hence its visibility (see Fig 1). The incident light direction is therefore crucial to the observed task contrast. This is most apparent with very glossy materials but can also be demonstrated to some extent using this Digest, with the page lit from the front at an angle of incidence equal to the viewing angle (see Fig 2).

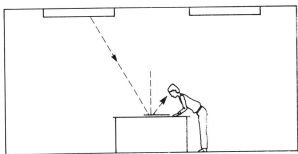

Fig 2 Viewing situation: angle of incidence = angle of reflection.

For a visual task with specular materials occupying a certain area (eg a page on a desk) there will be a set of incident directions from which the light will produce an image of the light source on some part of the task area. These incident directions can be projected on to the ceiling, where they form an area called the 'offending zone'. Any bright luminaires situated within the offending zone produce mirror-like 'veiling reflections' in the task. As about 85 per cent of horizontal office tasks are viewed at angles between 0° and 40° to the vertical, these angles have been used to produce the offending zone shown in Figure 3. A simple way to find the offending zone for a particular situation is to replace the task with a mirror of the same size: the area of the room surface seen in the mirror from the viewing position comprises the offending zone.

Contrast Rendering Factor

Visual tasks with materials of different specularity show different contrast variations as the direction of light falling on the task changes. For example, a glossy visual task may have a high contrast at one position and a low contrast due to veiling reflections at another position, while a matt visual task may have the same medium contrast at both places. A given value of visual task contrast therefore gives insufficient information about the effects of the lighting. To reduce this ambiguity, the contrast of the task can be measured under a reference condition of completely diffuse unpolarised incident light. The ratio of the visual task contrast under the lighting being studied to its contrast under reference lighting – the Contrast Rendering Factor (CRF) – is a relative measure of the ability of the lighting to produce high contrast and hence good visibility. If, in the example above, at a particular point in a room a glossy visual task has a high contrast and a matt visual task has a medium contrast and under reference lighting the glossy visual task again has a high contrast and the matt visual task has a medium contrast, the CRF is high at that point in the room for both tasks. But if at another point the glossy visual task has a low contrast, its CRF is also low at that point indicating poor visibility.

The reference lighting condition is chosen because it is relatively easy to reproduce, not because it gives the highest possible contrast for the visual task. Hence CRF may have values greater or less than unity depending whether the lighting being studied produces a visual task contrast better or worse than the reference lighting. In general, a high CRF indicates good visual task conditions which will allow good task performance.

The effect of illuminance

The human visual system becomes more sensitive to small differences in brightness (ie contrast) as the overall brightness increases and so visual tasks with contrasts usually encountered in offices become more visible at higher luminances. However, at the illuminances commonly used, this increase in visibility because of increased illuminance is relatively small for most tasks. Greater increases in visibility can be produced by increasing the visual task contrast. One way of doing this is to increase the CRF at a fixed illuminance. In principle, if CRF is increased, the same visibility can be obtained at a lower illuminance, enabling a reduction in energy consumption. However, insufficient is known about the detailed relationship between visibility and performance of visual tasks to enable the trade-off to be performed and further research is being carried out to provide design guidance.

Visual Comfort

Veiling reflections not only affect task performance by reducing the contrast of visual tasks, they also give rise to feelings of discomfort and increased task difficulty. Indeed, veiling reflections have been shown to produce discomfort before they are bad enough to cause a measurable decrease in task performance. A high CRF should therefore be sought for comfortable working conditions.

Recommended level of CRF for offices

Although the complete avoidance of veiling reflections will lead to good task visibility and comfortable working conditions, this is not usually possible. It is therefore necessary to know to what extent some veiling reflections can occur before either task performance decreases appreciably or discomfort causes complaints, ie the minimum acceptable value of CRF.

Lighting recommendations in Great Britain are mainly taken from the IES Code for Interior Lighting published by the Illuminating Engineering Society (now the Lighting Division of the Chartered Institution of Building Services). The 1977 edition of the Code advocates the avoidance of veiling reflections but gives no guide as to what may be acceptable. A more recent publication, the Illuminating Engineering Society of North America's Lighting Handbook 1981, gives only similar general recommendations.

However, research has shown that for office tasks discomfort occurs as CRF decreases before there is any appreciable performance drop. Comfort is therefore the more critical design factor. Prolonged discomfort may also lead to long-term performance loss, although this has yet to be demonstrated. Studies of the acceptability of veiling reflections have shown that, regardless of initial visual task contrast, weak veiling reflections are subjectively unimportant for written tasks on matt or semi-matt paper and it has been recommended that a CRF of 0.7 should be used as a standard for offices. For illustrations and very glossy paper, CRF does not seem to be a suitable measure for predicting subjective responses to specular reflections since contrast reversal may occur (where task detail becomes brighter than the background), producing high contrast but considerable discomfort owing to veiling reflections. Even so, situations where CRF is high for the more matt tasks will tend to give good visual conditions for glossy tasks.

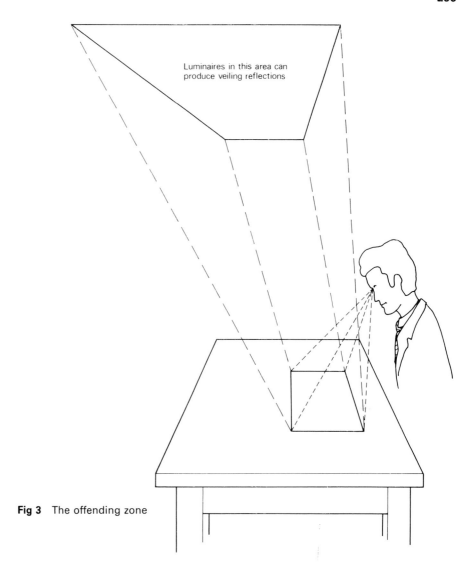

Luminaires in this area can produce veiling reflections

Fig 3 The offending zone

Calculation of CRF

The calculation of CRF is not easy because both direct and inter-reflected light must be considered. If the calculation is to be carried out with any reasonable degree of accuracy at a number of points within a space, a computer program is required. This is often the simplest method for determining a complete picture of the variation of CRF in an interior and the only one for installations at the design stage. A number of computer programs have been written and their predictions compared with measurements for existing installations. Some of these programs are available from commercial computer bureaux, others are used by lighting manufacturers for their own lighting designs.

Great care must be taken in the use of these programs, attention being paid particularly to the data used for the calculations. To calculate CRF it is necessary to have a very detailed knowledge of the reflection properties of the task as well as a complete picture of the direction and intensity of all the light incident on the task. These have been measured for a very few tasks and the method of measurement used is important. Calculations are therefore usually done for one of these known tasks and it is important to consider which task should be used.

The calculational complexity required to obtain accurate results means that the computer programs are all relatively large, often need considerable computation time, and so are expensive. They can, however, provide considerable detailed information, which is useful for comparing different lighting installations, especially at the design stage. They can also take into account changes in decor, eg room surface reflectances and furniture re-arangements.

Field measurement of CRF

The most fundamental visual method of measurement of CRF is with a visibility meter. This is only satisfactory for specialised research work and even then presents considerable problems. The use of a telephoto-meter to measure the luminance contrasts of a visual task is considerably easier and may be justified in some cases, although the equipment required is expensive and has to be handled carefully.

An instrument has been developed in Denmark which automatically compares the luminances of standard black and white tiles at a given viewing angle under a particular lighting condition and electronically computes the CRF. It is generally available, although rather expensive, and provides a very simple method of measuring CRF.

All the instruments mentioned are of a specialised nature and might be regarded as prohibitively expensive. However, a high correlation between CRF and a pair of measurements using a simple illuminance meter has been obtained*. Since CRF is strongly dependent on the proportion of the light incident on the task which comes from the offending zone, this method uses an illuminance meter tilted at 25° to the horizontal with a shield over the photocell so that only light within a cone 15° each side of the specular angle is measured. The ratio of the difference between this measurement of the light from the offending zone and the horizontal illuminance to the horizontal illuminance on the task was used to form regression equations for predicting CRF for pencil, pen and dry transfer tasks. These values were shown to correlate well with the CRF measured with a telephotometer. This simple measurement of illuminances will be of sufficient accuracy for many cases, and would certainly differentiate between positions with high and low CRF.

Design for high CRF

Whilst CRF is determined by a number of variables, some general guidelines for good CRF design can be drawn and are discussed in sequence moving away from the visual task, rather than in order of importance.

Visual tasks

Low CRF is caused by specular reflection in the task. If all visual tasks were completely matt, these reflections would not occur and the visual task contrast would remain the same irrespective of the incident light direction, giving a CRF of unity in all cases. Visual tasks which approach this ideal are available, eg matt printing on matt paper, and some types of photo-copying: their use should be encouraged.

Luminaire position

In most offices it is not possible to use only matt visual tasks and so care must be taken to avoid relatively high luminances in the offending zone (usually created by the presence of luminaires within it). This can be accomplished by the use of a luminous ceiling but these are relatively inefficient and can have other drawbacks: for example the appearance is not always suitable.

In some situations it is possible to arrange for a particular viewing direction to be used. The use of ceiling-mounted luminaires in rows parallel to the direction of view will produce high CRF values for all positions and viewing angles between the rows: only positions directly under each row will have low CRF. It is, therefore, desirable to separate the rows as much as possible since this gives larger working areas where high CRF values occur. A luminaire with a wide light output

*BOYCE P R. The Contrast Rendering Factor & Office Lighting. ECRC/R1133, Electricity Council Research Centre (1978).

distribution (such as a bat-wing distribution) is particularly useful in this case since it allows a wider separation of rows than has been common in the past.

One advantage of using rows of luminaires is that there are easily identifiable areas where will be no luminaire in the offending zone for defined viewing directions. This advantage is reduced if the luminaires are arranged in other ways, for example a chequer-board pattern.

If daylight from side windows can be used, desks should be positioned at right angles to the windows for high CRF values. In an installation using both daylight and artificial lighting, the luminaire rows should therefore be parallel to the window wall.

In many cases the direction of view cannot be controlled. If the working positions and directions of view are known, the positioning of luminaires can avoid the offending zone. If, as is more often the case, working positions are unknown, the luminaires should be arranged on the ceiling leaving as many large areas as possible without luminaires, so that these areas will be low luminance offending zones. Care must then be taken to avoid a luminaire in the offending zone when arranging the working position.

An alternative to using general ceiling-mounted lighting is to use local lighting. Luminaires should not be placed at the back of the desk but at the sides. This ensures they will usually be outside the offending zone.

Luminaire characteristics

Luminaire size A bright luminaire in the offending zone gives a low CRF; however, if the luminaire is small but with higher luminance (with, for example, high-pressure mercury or metal halide lamp), bigger areas of ceiling can be left clear than if larger fluorescent luminaires are used. This can allow more flexibility in working positions and give larger areas of high CRF, although they have to be balanced against the decrease in CRF at the fewer bad positions as the luminaire size is decreased (and the luminance increased).

Number of luminaires An alternative way of reducing the ceiling area occupied by bright luminaires is to reduce the number of luminaires used. For a given design illuminance, fewer luminaires will be required if both lamps and luminaires are as efficient as possible. An efficient lamp of suitable colour properties should be used together with an efficient luminaire, not only to reduce costs and energy consumption, but also to help to give high CRF. A wide light output distribution will also allow luminaires to be spaced at greater distances, leaving larger areas of ceiling and so increasing the number of places where working positions may be sited without a bright luminaire appearing in the offending zone.

Light output distribution This is of secondary importance to task position relative to luminaire and task specularity but a number of points do need to be considered. Polarising luminaires do not produce any great improvement in CRF and are generally less efficient. Different light output distributions usually produce improvements at some positions with disadvantages at others but bat-wing distributions allow wider spacing of luminaires. In most cases the choice of luminaire is likely to be more influenced by its utilisation factor and the discomfort glare it produces than by its effect on CRF.

Room surfaces

Since the CRF is affected by the proportion of light incident on the task from within the offending zone, it may be possible to increase the proportion of light from outside the offending zone and so raise the CRF. This can be done simply by increasing the reflectances of the room surfaces. If there is a luminaire in the offending zone the CRF will still be low but with high room surface reflectances the CRF may be raised to a more acceptable value.

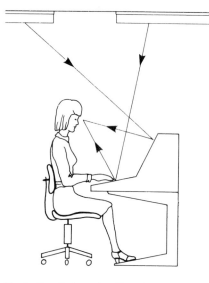

Fig 4 Prediction of veiling reflections.

Visual display units

So far, discussion has been·concerned mainly with flat, horizontal visual tasks. A rather different type of task which is becoming increasingly common in offices is the VDU, consisting usually of a near vertical screen and a typewriter keyboard. Reflections in either the screen or the keys can cause problems (see Fig 4).

Reflections in the horizontal keys can be avoided by using the design methods outlined above and problems are less likely if the keys have a matt finish and are easily cleaned so that the greasy specular film that builds up can be readily removed.

Veiling reflections in the screen can both reduce the contrast (and the visibility of the display) and be distracting if they occur outside the immediate task area. These reflections can be avoided either by eliminating high luminances (usually caused by luminaires or windows) from the room or ensuring that any high luminances are not reflected towards the operator. Bright reflections of luminaires can be avoided either by eliminating the luminaires altogether and using indirect lighting or using low luminance luminaires with a narrow downward light distribution and a maximum cut-off angle of 55° from the downward vertical, such as that provided by matt black or specular louvres. Alternatively the VDU may be positioned so that bright luminaires are not reflected towards the operator. In practice this is often not easy because the screens of many VDUs are curved and a wide range of viewing angles can be used. Best results should be obtained if the VDU is placed so that the operator's line of sight is parallel to the luminaires and to the windows.

Bright reflections of windows can be avoided by using blinds or curtains. Venetian blinds or louvres are less effective than roller blinds because, when partially open, the slats and louvres can reflect a distracting striped pattern on the screen.

There is no single, simple solution that can be applied to all interiors to eliminate veiling reflections, ie to give high CRF's. The activity to be carried out will have a strong influence. Conflicts may occur between CRF requirements and those, for example, for glare or energy consumption. However, the avoidance of veiling reflections must be considered in all interiors where detailed visual tasks are performed. The final lighting design will be a balance of all the individual requirements tailored to the particular application.

Further reading
BOYCE P R & SLATER A I. The Application of CRF to Office Lighting Design. Lighting Research & Technology *13*(3) 65–69 (1981).
IES Code for Interior Lighting 1977. Illuminating Engineering Society, London. (Now Lighting Division, Chartered Institution of Building Services).
Technical Memorandum 6: Lighting for Visual Display Units, Chartered Inst Building Services, London 1981.
IES Lighting Handbook 1981. Illuminating Engineering Soc of North America.
An Analytic Model for Describing the Influence of Lighting Parameters upon Visual Performance Publication 19/2 of Commission Internationale de L'Eclairage, Paris (1981).
BRE Digest 226 Thermal, visual and acoustic requirements in buildings
BRE Digest 232 Energy conservation in artificial lighting

Index

Volume numbers shown in italic type